JOHN CATT'S

# Which London School? & the South-East

# 2018/19

29th Edition
Editor: Jonathan Barnes

JOHN
CATT
EDUCATIONAL
LIMITED

Published in 2018 by
John Catt Educational Ltd,
12 Deben Mill Business Centre,
Woodbridge, Suffolk IP12 1BL UK
Tel: 01394 389850    Fax: 01394 386893
Email: enquiries@johncatt.com
Website: www.johncatt.com
© 2018 John Catt Educational Ltd

The photograph on page 51 © Paul Riddle

Designed and typeset by John Catt Educational Limited

**A CIP catalogue record for this book is available from the
British Library.**

ISBN: 978 1 911 382 51 5

**Contacts**
Editor
Jonathan Barnes

Advertising & School Profiles
Tel: +44 (0) 1394 389850
Email: sales@johncatt.com

Distribution/Book Sales
Tel: +44 (0) 1394 389863
Email: booksales@johncatt.com

# Contents

# London is your classroom

**Jonathan Taylor, Collegiate Head of North Bridge House, explains why the advantages of going to school in and around London go well beyond academic results**

London is a wonderful, cosmopolitan city. For children fortunate enough to be educated in and around the capital, the diversity of culture, business and character offer fresh, exciting experiences every day.

Where else can students spend the morning at the Chemistry Bar in the Science Museum's Wonderlab, an afternoon's work experience with international business leaders in the City, play a sporting fixture with local rivals after school, and enjoy an evening performance of *Tosca* in the West End?

London's rich culture and heritage act as an extension of the classroom; they enable teaching well beyond the boundaries of the school. The city is home to some of the world's top museums, galleries and music venues, all within easy reach using public transport. Its streets are awash with famous landmarks, beautiful parks and open spaces, enriching children's learning on a daily basis.

London is big but it is also local – it is a series of villages, all of which have their own unique resources. On North Bridge House's doorstep in Canonbury, for example, is the prestigious Estorick Collection of Modern Italian Art. Through our partnership, our students visit regularly and develop a deep understanding of the artwork. They pose questions to spark debate about what they see, feel and hear. This in-depth, regular experience wouldn't be achievable without being just round the corner from the gallery.

But London is more than a cultural and scientific hub, it is also an enormous generator of talent and opportunity. To compete in the highly competitive international job market, school leavers will need 'global skills'. At North Bridge House we understand that means students have to learn how to think for themselves and to deliver creative and innovative solutions to problems. One of the easiest ways to achieve this is through direct experience of innovative business, which fortunately London has in abundance. It is home to many blue-chip companies with headquarters in the city. Schools are ideally placed to forge partnerships so that their students gain first hand understanding of the skills and qualifications they will need as future leaders.

North Bridge House's World of Work programme, for instance, has developed partnerships with London businesses spanning all major industry sectors including creative, high tech, engineering, legal, medical and finance to help prepare our students for their future careers. A Canonbury student introduced to EY via this programme, currently studying Economics at University of York, is now an official student Brand Ambassador for the multinational professional services firm headquartered in London.

As a global crossroads, cultural diversity is at London's very core. Around 37 per cent of the capital's population have moved to the city from a different country (2011 Census, ONS). Daily exposure to the realities of the globalised world in which we live – from commuting on public transport, to urban noise and bustle, to the multicultural makeup of London society – equips children with global skills and resilience they need to adapt to the wider world when they finish their education.

We are committed to helping all North Bridge House students develop a global mindset, which owing to our campus' cosmopolitan environment, begins for new students on day one. Students support local community groups and causes close to our school campuses and celebrate diversity within our student population and other schools in the community.

> Where else can students spend the morning at the Chemistry Bar in the Science Museum's Wonderlab, an afternoon's work experience with international business leaders in the City, play a sporting fixture with local rivals after school, and enjoy an evening performance of *Tosca* in the West End?

London's independent schools are internationally famed for their academic prestige and often noted for their character-building expertise. This concentration of excellence means parents not only have a wide range of choice, it also means schools have excellent opportunities for collaboration on sporting fixtures, musical performances, teacher training and development too. Collaboration naturally drives healthy competition, keeping everyone – students, staff and even parents – on top of their game.

The world's brightest and best teachers flock to London. With an ambitious, curious student population and exciting career advancement options, schools can retain and develop teaching staff of the highest calibre. The Institute of Education (IOE) at University College London, is a fantastic training resource, nurturing some of the best international teaching talent using innovative methods that benefit the capital's children first hand. At North Bridge House, we are fortunate to work with IOE students and regularly employ its graduates. The sheer number of high calibre academic and education research institutions in the city also gives London schools a broad choice of partnerships, training and development. North Bridge House hosts debates in association with the *Times Educational Supplement* for teachers in the UK and around the world. We extend our partnerships to engage with parents and local community groups across the four North Bridge House Schools, running evenings with expert academic speakers covering hot topics such as child development, mental health, neuroscience and sleep research.

As we navigate unclear waters post-Brexit, London's independent schools continue go from strength to strength, and the city continues to provide endless resources to enhance the curriculum we teach in the classroom.

Samuel Johnson said to Boswell in *Journal of a Tour to the Hebrides* (1785) "By seeing London, I have seen as much of life as the world can show". Being educated in this great city is a unique privilege and one that our children should be rightly proud to experience.

*For more information about North Bridge House Schools, see page 63*

# How to use this guide

## Are you looking for...

### Help and advice?

If so, take a look at our editorial section (pages 5-40). Here you will find articles written by experts in their field covering issues you may well come across when choosing a school for your child.

### A school or college in a certain geographical area?

Then you need to go to page D101 to find the directory page reference to a particular area. We suggest that you look first in the directory for basic information about all the schools in each region, complete with contact details, so that you will be better informed about the choices available to you. From this section you will be directed to more detailed information in the profile section, where this is available.

### A certain type of school or college in a particular area?

Look in the directories for the area you want (again, you can find the directory page reference on D101). Underneath each school listed you will find icons that denote different types of schools or qualifications that they offer. You can find a key to these icons on the following page; this key is repeated at the front of each section of the directory.

## Schools featured in this guidebook are also profiled on its accompanying website: www.whichlondonschool.co.uk and www.schoolsearch.co.uk

School profiles include embedded Twitter feed and YouTube/Vimeo video, direct links to email, website and social media. Users can search by region, county, or postcode; and by age, gender and day/boarding.

**A specific school or college?**

If you know the name of the school or college but are unsure of its location, simply go to the index at the back of the guide where you will find all the schools listed alphabetically. You will find that some page numbers are prefixed with the letter D, this denotes that the school appears in the directory section. Schools with page numbers not prefixed by the letter D are those that have chosen to include a fuller school profile, which will provide you with much more extensive information.

**Maps?**

See pp 42, 77 and 90 for maps of London, Greater London, and the South-East. There are also maps within the directory sections on D103 (Central London), D127 (Greater London) and D135 (South-East).

**More information on relevant educational organisations and examinations?**

Look in the examinations and qualifications section and the useful organisations section, both located towards the back of the guide.

---

## Key to directory

County            ————————— **Wherefordshire**

Name of school or college   ————————— **College Academy**

Indicates that this school has a profile   ————————— *For further details see p. 12*

Address and contact number   ——————— Which Street, Whosville, Wherefordshire AB12 3CD

**Tel:** 01000 000000

Head's name   ————————— **Head Master:** Dr A Person

School type   ————————— **Type:** Coeducational day & boarding

Age range   ————————— **Age range:** 11–18

Number of pupils. B = boys G = girls   ————————— **No. of pupils:** 660 B330 G330

Fees per annum.
Day = fees for day pupils.   ————————— **Fees:** Day £11,000 WB £16,000 FB £20,000
WB = fees for weekly boarders.
FB = fees for full boarders.

(ii)(A)(£)(✎)(16)

---

## Key to directory icons (abridged)

**Key to symbols:**
- Boys' school
- Coeducational school
- Girls' school
- International school

**Schools offering:**
- (A) A levels
- Boarding accommodation
- (£) Bursaries
- (16) Entrance at 16+

- (IB) International Baccalaureate
- Learning support
- (16) Tutorial/sixth form college
- Vocational qualifications

# The benefits of 'urban boarding'

**John Taylor, Assistant Principal (Boarding) at DLD College London, gives an insight into why pupils choose to board while studying in their hometown**

UK Boarding schools and colleges are often the most sought-after institutions in the worldwide education system. Despite the traditional heritage often associated with them, many have now moved with the times to offer 21st century facilities, education and pastoral care. Not only do these schools and colleges attract international students but local domestic students are now starting to seek the benefits of a residential education, *ie* boarding.

Urban boarders, those opting to board whilst attending a school or college in their hometown or local city, are welcomed with a range of opportunities that they may not encounter if they were to make a daily commute for their education whilst living at home.

When studying and residing at a school or college, particularly an institute that attracts a large international profile, students have the valuable opportunity to connect with others from various different places around the world, something which they may not do if they were to attend a day school. Learning about other cultures and

nationalities can not only educate the students about different faiths and practices, but it can also help them to learn more about themselves.

Speaking to our students, Adam Moyler, a domestic boarder, described the international cohort at the college as one of the "key benefits of boarding in his home city." He added, "I opted for the residential choice with the understanding that I have the freedom to go home at weekends to see my friends and family, however since moving I now find myself spending increasingly more time at the college on weekends due to the bond I have created with my peers. I spend my time mixing with a close friendship group all of differing nationalities and other boarders at the college, something which I find to be just like a family."

Often associated with providing the best possible schooling, boarding can offer academic consistency. Remaining on the same site allows the student to continue their learning in a single environment rather than having

Urban boarding is a way for the student to immerse themselves into their own experience where the learning never stops. Being in an educational environment means that even when they're outside the classroom they are still fostering key life-skills that they wouldn't learn when at home.

to adapt to a different surrounding during the transition from school hours to evening time.

Urban boarding is a way for the student to immerse themselves into their own experience where the learning never stops. Being in an educational environment means that even when they're outside the classroom they are still fostering key life-skills that they wouldn't learn when at home. Living away from the comforts and support of family enables the student to deal with day-to-day organisational skills. Preparing them for the challenges of life, boarding sets them up to learn the crucial aspects of independence in a supportive, yet safe and nurturing setting.

The flexibility of urban boarding for domestic students allows for the challenges that are met with parental separation. Students have the option to see their family at weekends, school holidays and occasionally in the evening, avoiding those difficult goodbyes and bouts of homesickness.

Calming the nerves of students (and their parents!) are houseparents, carrying a primary role of pastoral care; they are the first port of call for students. It is paramount that houseparents get to know the students in their care so they feel able to come and talk whenever they are having difficulties. When speaking to Adam he described the relationship with his houseparent as a big help when living away from home, commenting "I have settled into boarding easily knowing that I have someone to talk to when any problems arise, or when they don't."

Many boarding schools run activities for boarders to enjoy, and so that they can have the best experience possible. This may include special occasions such as Christmas celebrations, Burns Night and Chinese New Year

events. They often also run boarders' trips at weekends to different places in and around the area, as well as holding in-house activities and events to encourage students out of their rooms to socialise and get to know one another. At DLD College London, in the evenings and at weekends the College's atrium is transformed into a social space with movies, music, sofas and rugs, games, quiz nights, competitions, table tennis and a whole range of other activities. Boarders' trips are also run most weekends to all kinds of places in and around London.

Boarding in the centre of the city places students directly on the doorstep of a large variety of opportunities to be entertained, educated and enlightened – London is our classroom.

A thriving co-curricular programme is an addition to college boarding that enables the student to take advantage of the newly found time that they have. When speaking with Adam he found that, "since boarding at the college as opposed to commuting, I now have time to participate in the weekly boxing club sessions rather than needing to rush back home in time to complete homework." Motivating and inspiring students to participate in such activities and giving them the opportunities to do so contribute to the encouragement of an active and healthy lifestyle. Yoga is also made available to the students to help relieve stress and increase mental health.

Investing in boarding, despite perhaps not needing to due to the feasibility of attending a local day school or college, allows for complete investment in the student's educational journey – greater efficiency leads to a greater academic result.

*To find out more about DLD College London see page 48*

# £5m target for school's bursary campaign

## Social mobility takes precedence at Kingston Grammar School

Kingston Grammar School has recently unveiled further plans to keep social mobility at the top of the independent education agenda by announcing that it has raised bursary funds of over £3.5 million in the last 12 months, taking its endowed funds to over £4 million with the aim of reaching the £5 million mark before 2020.

The KGS Bursary Fund Campaign will generate a vital source of annual income to provide financial assistance to those who most need and can benefit from it. In the last five years alone, the School has awarded over £2 million in bursaries to 164 students, averaging 33 children each year.

With the number of bursary applications increasing year on year, KGS aims to raise further funds so that even more children can receive an education that will shape their future lives and enable them to achieve their full potential.

Head Master Stephen Lehec says: "Part of the School's founding ideals is to support those with the greatest potential to make a positive difference in the world but who need our support to achieve this. We are deeply committed to making childhood aspirations a reality. As a leading HMC co-educational independent day school, we are doing our utmost to facilitate genuine social mobility where it's needed most by reaching out to our local communities. We are committed to not only fulfilling but exceeding our role to promote this. Our bursary programme plays an important role but, of course, is not unique. We have also developed links with local primary and secondary schools. This year will see the introduction of our own, fully accredited teacher training courses at Kingston Grammar School, which have been trialled as part of the HMC teacher training programme over the last three years."

We are committed to ensuring that as many highly able children as possible receive the chance of an outstanding education, regardless of their family's financial situation. Our aim is to identify and admit those students who show the greatest potential to benefit from not only the excellent academic education that Kingston Grammar School delivers, but also the ethos and wider opportunities offered.

He adds: "An education at Kingston Grammar School is a truly life-changing experience. We give our young people the valuable skills and knowledge they need to prepare for a successful adult life and embark on their journey to achieving great things in the future including the will and ability to give back to others and make our world a better place in the future. This is one of the reasons that our alumni have been so supportive of this current campaign – they are giving back to help others achieve. They understand that our motto of Work Well and Be Happy is something that can be imparted, shared and realised beyond their time at the School.

"We are committed to ensuring that as many highly able children as possible receive the chance of an outstanding education, regardless of their family's financial situation. Our aim is to identify and admit those students who show the greatest potential to benefit from not only the excellent academic education that Kingston Grammar School delivers, but also the ethos and wider opportunities offered. In 2017/18 alone, KGS, together with

contributions from the KGS Foundation, is supporting 33 students totalling £486,011 for the year. The KGS Bursary Fund provides assistance to those who need it most, but we always have far more applications than we can support but we want to support more.

"In raising these funds, we can also play our part, along with the rest of the independent education sector, in trying to keep fee increases to a sensible level that is more in line with, if not below, inflation, and make an education at a great independent school an affordable reality for more families. It is well known that school fees have been spiralling well above what most families can afford and this campaign is part of a wider body of work across the sector to address this issue."

Chris Carnegy (Old Kingstonian (OK) 1980) works in media and broadcasting and is a Foundation Ambassador and supporter of the KGS Bursary Fund. "There aren't many experiences that can change the course of your life in quite the way that your school days can. Kingston Grammar School gave me so many opportunities, including outside the classroom, which broadened my horizons and helped me find my way ahead. For me it seemed natural to want to help someone else have the same life chances. Part of the beauty of the KGS Bursary Fund is that you'll only ever be able to imagine the potential it might unleash."

KGS alumnus Derek Finlay (OK 1950) created the RD Finlay Bursary Fund as part of the KGS Endowment, with the aim of enabling numerous young men and women to enjoy the full benefits of a seven-year education at KGS, regardless of their parents' income.

Being the recipient of KGS bursary support himself had a profound impact on Alexander McLean (OK 2003), founder of the African Prisons Project: "The fruit of planting a seed which allows a child to gain a good education will be borne in your lifetime and for generations to come. This gift will never leave the recipient and will affect untold others through them."

*For more information about Kingston Grammar School see page 84*

# Technology and transforming the classroom – are we at the start of a revolution in education?

**Will Williams, Senior and Academic Deputy Head at Pangbourne College, discusses the benefits of implementing technology in classrooms, how to maintain the school's ethos when doing so, and the challenges faced**

The use of technology in schools has been approached with trepidation by many teachers, viewing it as a potential disruption to the classroom and a complication in their own planning. With technological advancements having a growing influence on every aspect of our lives though, this perception is changing as rapidly as the technology itself.

In 20 years, we've gone from chalkboards to the possibility of using virtual reality in the classroom, and we could now be entering a truly revolutionary phase in education.

Whilst the desire is increasing, the implementation is not straightforward, and no parent wants their child to be a guinea pig when it comes to schooling. There are myriad potential solutions for both students and teachers, but the solutions chosen have to be appropriate to the school and its values.

One of the main restrictions of any school is time. A rigorous academic schedule teamed with a packed extra-curricular programme leaves very little room for manoeuvre, and commitment to societies and sports should never come at the expense of academic progress.

Chosen well, there are opportunities to ease workload for staff, enhance formative reporting and monitor behaviour more effectively. For pupils we can help them reflect on and develop their own learning, engaging them with subjects in new and exciting ways.

At Pangbourne, we have been aiming to encourage meta-cognition, whereby students consider more carefully what they do and do not know and take greater control of their own learning. This is an area which can see positive results with the aid of new technologies. By the end of 2016, Ofcom reported that 41 per cent of 5 – 15 year olds own a smartphone, and this increases to over 90 per cent for 16 – 24 year olds. Turning these devices into educational tools is a logical step, and now we can select the best means to do it.

We have found that using apps such as Kahoot!, which creates homework challenges and quizzes for any chosen subject, adds a competitive edge to learning and revision and the assessment is done by the app, freeing up time for the teacher. Kahoot! also offers a progress checker which allows students to compete 'against themselves' by testing against their previous results which are logged – this is incredibly beneficial for GCSEs and A-Levels now, given the change to linear exams which require students to pull together knowledge over two years of learning.

Use of video with an interactive element is another area within which we can look to engage students and better utilise the resources at our disposal. The programme Edpuzzle allows teachers to annotate online video and link to relevant content and questions which will be the next step in the lesson.

The content can be something more advanced for students who have assimilated the initial information well, or something on a similar level which allows them to absorb the content in their own time in a different manner. This means teachers can curate various resources to accommodate all levels of learning. With the proven impact of interleaving content from previous learning with the current focus, the such tech applications are supporting new research into *how pupils learn*. As with Kahoot!, the results data is available both pupil-by-pupil, and question-by-question, making individual and class assessment possible in a fraction of the time it would normally take.

Encouraging this level of independence provides a perfect platform for a higher education. As students progress through school, encouraging self-reflection on their own learning and development puts students in the best possible situation for sixth form and university stages. This well-rounded approach and independent work ethic corresponds with the values of our particular school, where we encourage strong character development alongside academic progression.

Quite rightly, the main focus in schools is on the development and improvement of pupils, but as teachers this is something we need to constantly address in our own performance. Technology can be hugely influential in this regard because it allows for more targeted teaching and reporting, as well the time-saving aspect previously mentioned.

The diversity of a teacher's role, particularly in an independent school, where one frequently teaches a full timetable followed by games (before even thinking of lesson planning and marking) means time is precious. The speed and efficiency with which we can now make information available to staff is crucial.

Efficiency in the technology we utilise can firstly allow for consistent planning and prep task setting, but it can also allow a level of feedback to students and parents unlike anything we have had previously.

As with most schools across the country, we use CEM data from the University of Durham for our Key Stage Four and Five students. From this we use the 'Chances Graph' produced, which provides predicted grades, but we then do something very few schools do – we share this data with pupils and parents. This provides a narrative which you can engage the pupil with, as they are able to clearly see where they need to progress and how they do that. They can now take ownership of the behaviours which are most crucial to their progress.

The next step once we had access to this data was clear, and that was to make this readily available to both staff and students by using ClassCharts. This means every teacher has access to a 'card' for each student which is populated with academic and behavioural information pertinent to that child, which has become to be crucial for tracking development.

The behavioural aspect of this has been particularly important to Pangbourne, because we operate with our seven Flag Values of kindness, selflessness, moral courage, initiative, industry, resilience, and integrity, at the heart of everything we do. With the ClassCharts app we have been able to 'mark' children on how they 'perform' in these fields which are so key to us, and the ease of access to these has made the vernacular thorough throughout the school.

The range of devices, programmes, apps and initiatives is so vast now that it makes the choices of the school all the more important. We need to engage rather than distract, and the values which a school is built on must remain central, whilst the information and access we provide to our students cannot become overwhelming. The implementation of these initiatives needs to be seen as a positive for students, teachers and parents. We need to raise the academic ante, without sacrificing the pastoral support.

*For more information about Pangbourne College see page 94*

# Future thinking: how to think, adapt, develop and succeed

**As artificial intelligence begins to exert its influence on every career, Andrew Johnson, Headmaster of St Benedict's, outlines how we can prepare young people to thrive in a time of rapid change**

It's sometimes said that education is what is left when you have forgotten what you were taught. Einstein himself used this quote to make the point that the core value of education is not in the subjects studied, but in the acquisition of mental skills – the ability to think well.

Beyond educating and preparing pupils to achieve the best academic results they are capable of, schools need to teach them how to analyse information in an information age; to distinguish between fact and fiction – the true and the fake; to arrive at reasoned judgements and to articulate their own arguments when evaluating complex issues such as war, euthanasia, nuclear arms, or the environment.

At every stage, education needs to challenge children; to encourage them to think; to learn and research independently; to be curious, ask questions and go beyond the syllabus.

At St Benedict's, students in all years, including in the Junior School, are given the opportunity to follow their curiosity and explore whatever interests them. They follow up independent research on their chosen topics with presentations, given to an invited audience of peers and parents. In Year 7, pupils explore the apparently simple question 'Who am I?', guided by subject teachers and using a wide range of interdisciplinary sources: some take a historical perspective and delve into their family tree, others take a scientific approach, looking at genes; a few even choose to focus on the philosophical nature of self, or include self-portraits and creative writing. At this important junction in their senior school careers, they enjoy having the opportunity to explore their identity, and having a free rein in deciding how to approach it.

In the Sixth Form, an open forum for debate and discussion helps students to explore difficult concepts,

As technology improves, and occupies an ever increasing part of our lives, it is human qualities which will matter more and more. Imagination, empathy, reliability, compassion, perseverance – these are the qualities that will hopefully remain when students have forgotten what they've learned for those exams.

share ideas and hone their arguments. The emphasis is on thinking outside the box, intellectual creativity and fun. Students also engage in short, group research projects, such as reviewing books or podcasts. The forum is a valuable space for exploring ideas, and challenging each other's thinking.

The future of work is arguably more uncertain now than it's ever been. Our children will be employed in jobs that haven't even evolved yet, and it's unlikely that they'll stay within one area of work, or one career. Artificial intelligence is increasing exponentially, and many jobs which are familiar to us now, in virtually every sphere, will soon be performed by computers. Schools therefore need to equip pupils to take their place in the world, and to find the kind of employment that best suits their talents.

Careers Departments have had to evolve dramatically since the days of handing out booklets or showing the occasional video. At St Benedict's, pupils benefit from our active partnership with alumni and parents, who regularly visit to talk about their work and provide work experience. Our Careers Fair is a professional, live-streamed conference attended by hundreds of organisations and representatives from careers covering every profession, STEM, service, third economy and active work. There is also information on apprenticeships and sponsored degrees, which are increasingly popular alternatives to traditional university degrees.

Perhaps most valuable of all, however, beyond this first-hand, specific and practical advice, a keynote speaker concludes the Careers Fair by talking about their personal experience en route to success. The same powerful message invariably comes through: that future success is unpredictable, often defies a plan, requires tenacity and depends upon an individual's growth mindset: not on initially being the 'best', but on constantly learning, growing and being a person that people want to work with.

As technology improves, and occupies an ever increasing part of our lives, it is human qualities which will matter more and more. Imagination, empathy, reliability, compassion, perseverance – these are the qualities that will hopefully remain when students have forgotten what they've learned for those exams.

So it is vital that, as well as teaching the curriculum, we help our children to develop these qualities in the first place; to be self-starters – independent learners, creative thinkers, team-workers and effective communicators. As they exchange the orderly, structured familiar environment of school for a highly competitive, uncertain world, young people will need to be versatile and adaptable. Good study skills and the acquisition of knowledge certainly have their place, but they are really only the beginning. It is determination which will see them through when they face enormous challenges, or when things don't go to plan.

Co-curricular opportunities have an enormous part to play in arming pupils with this resilience, and their place in education is essential, not subsidiary. It takes self-discipline and independence to practise a musical instrument, or to learn the lines of a play. Performing in a concert or play develops confidence and self-belief.

In sport, when you're 4-0 down with 10 minutes to go, it takes gritty determination to keep going to the end; and if you can encourage your team-mates along the way, so much the better.

Outward bound activities take children out of their comfort zones, teaching them map reading, survival skills and team work. My own sons still talk about their Duke of Edinburgh's Award Gold expedition as one of the best things they ever did when they were at school: four days of navigating their way around the mountains of North Wales in horizontal rain and icy gales taught them a great deal about perseverance and pulling together.

Stellar exam results alone are really only just the beginning. We also need to develop to the full all that makes us human and unique.

*Andrew Johnson has been Headmaster of St Benedict's School, Ealing, since 2016. For more information about St Benedict's, see page 70*

# Nurturing the qualities that define us

**Nicola Baldwin, Principal of Dolphin School, explains her school's guiding philosophy**

"Courage, Kindness, Friendship, Character. These are the qualities that define us as human beings, and propel us, on occasion, to greatness."
R.J.Palacio, *Wonder*

The recent film, *Wonder*, reminds us once again that it is who we are on the inside that really matters.

Sometimes pupils can feel that their value is measured by their tangible achievements. Thus whether they secured a place in the 'A' team, which secondary school accepted them, what grades they achieved at GCSE and A level or what university they attended, can, at various stages in their academic career, be seen as the be all and end all of their worth. At other times, pupils link their value to their self image, becoming overly concerned with how they appear. They can become obsessed with using social media to perpetuate a 'perfect' life, looking the 'right' way, wearing the 'right' clothes, being seen at

the 'right' places and creating a fabricated version of a perfect on-line life. The gap between this created persona and the reality of life can be considerable. The danger of on-line friends is well documented. The desire to have a high number of on-line friends who 'like' whatever you have posted can become a goal in itself. It can also have a damaging impact on a young person's mental health and well-being.

So, in schools, how important it is that we actively promote the qualities we value. Our pupils need to know how to form friendships, deal kindly with others and have the courage of their convictions. Friends are real people you can talk to about your hopes and your fears. They are companions who are 'walking the walk' alongside you. We need to make time in our curriculum to develop character and establish values. Our young people need to experience and show kindness and know what courage looks like, in order to develop their own moral compass to allow them to tackle all the vagaries of life. Neither teachers nor parents will always be on hand to tell them what to do. It is not enough to hope that through osmosis our youngsters will have necessarily absorbed the values on which their future decisions should be founded.

We recognise that the impact of peer pressure can be very great. Are those peers always going to be offering wise counsel? It can take courage, moral grounding and a secure sense of self to make the 'right' decision when faced with challenging situations. How valuable a preparation for life it is to have spent time collaborating, learning to respect alternate views while not sharing them, to know how to say 'No' clearly, firmly but not angrily or offensively. In fact we all continue to hone these skills throughout our lives, trying to be forward thinking and open to new ideas, but not swayed by every new fad and fashion.

The groundwork needs to be done in schools. Pupils must have repeated opportunities to practise the character traits that we wish to encourage. Whether it is younger pupils being helped or mentored by older pupils, pupils raising money to help a worthy cause, or lending a listening ear to support a friend in need, these actions will build the character of the individual. School will thus promote a true understanding and acceptance of each individual's worth. Each pupil will become a person with ideas and ideals, with empathy and passion for the world and its issues, able to forge friendships and relate empathetically to others, quick to show kindness and consideration, for are not these qualities the true measures of mankind? We must ensure that we equip our pupils to value themselves for who they are rather than what they have achieved.

It is not easy to have league tables showing character, friendship, kindness and courage. A school cannot be measured nationally by its results in these areas. But, just because something cannot be measured, does it mean it is not valued and important?

How vital that schools do not become consumed by a results-driven agenda but rather consider the wider reaching impact of education. How critical to devote time to enable pupils to lay the foundation for the people they will become.

At Dolphin School one way we ensure due time is given to exploring what it is to be human is through our daily dedicated Relationship Time sessions which are part of our Life Education programme. Here, through reflection and consideration, the nuts and bolts of how we get along with each other and how we want our world to be can be addressed.

All children have immense potential. A vital part of our role as educators is to ensure that pupils are allowed the opportunity to develop the qualities that will enable them to become the best version of themselves that they can be – healthy in body, mind and spirit. In thirty years' time, whatever they are doing, we want them to be kind, considerate, caring people who have found their passions in life and know how to be a good friend. We want them to prize what is on the inside, the qualities that truly can propel them to greatness.

> It is not easy to have league tables showing character, friendship, kindness and courage. A school cannot be measured nationally by its results in these areas. But, just because something cannot be measured does it mean it is not valued and important?

*For more information on Dolphin School see page 49*

MP Nicky Morgan (centre) with LVS Ascot Head of Junior School Rachael Cox and sixth form student Daniel Walker

# The importance of character education

**Rachael Cox, Head of Junior School at all ability all-through school LVS Ascot, discusses the importance of character education in developing students for the future**

During the primary phase of education, children develop a set of life long values and beliefs about the process of learning and about themselves as learners. Alongside this they begin to understand how they fit as part of a wider community, the importance of tolerance and acceptance, of humility and sportsmanship, of effort and resilience to name but a few. Developing these characteristics takes time, focus and skill.

As primary school practitioners we hold this immense responsibility in our hands and at LVS Ascot we are determined that every child will move up to our senior school with positive attitudes towards learning and be confident about the role they play in our community. Our mission is to create confident, caring citizens of the future and that is certainly what we strive towards from the first moment children enter our school. By building warm, caring relationships with pupils and knowing the individual strengths and character of each child, teachers are able to ensure that every lesson challenges and engages them.

Happiness and well-being are the cornerstones of academic success and it is important to give children the confidence to believe in themselves and follow their dreams. Providing space for our children to enjoy childhood whilst providing a forward-looking, nurturing and ambitious curriculum that includes outdoor learning, independent projects and character education can only be of benefit to their development.

Central to the curriculum at LVS Ascot are five pairs of Learning Values and Skills:

- Empathy and reflection
- Creativity and curiosity
- Independence and initiative
- Risk taking and resilience
- Collaboration and self-confidence

These develop the character of pupils so that they are equipped with the qualities they need to be successful in the ever-changing world they will enter as young adults. These Learning Values are intertwined through every aspect of school life, and children are able to use the language and attributes with confidence.

MP and former Secretary of State for Education Nicky Morgan visited LVS Ascot in January where she addressed parents on the importance of character education and praised the school for its development in this area. She said: "Character isn't a one-size fits all concept, it is a combination of traits that sets people apart so they can achieve their dreams. I think LVS Ascot is probably much further along on this journey than other schools".

Nicky, who has been MP for Loughborough since 2010, was invited to LVS Ascot's theatre where she discussed with parents of pupils from the junior school up to sixth form the benefits developing positive character traits brings. She detailed the advantages this provides to students when applying for jobs and, having been Secretary of State for Education from 2014 to 2016, was perfectly placed to talk about key strengths that employers are looking for from students. She said employers are looking for candidates that they can train fully in a specific role, but who arrive with key personal skills that will help them to succeed within that training and career.

Nicky said: "The LVS Ascot learning values including self-confidence and collaboration, risk taking and resilience, creativity and curiosity are great values that we all want to see developed in our young people. The resilience, empathy and initiative traits will really help set the pupils apart in terms of making a success of life, and alongside persistence when things don't go so well those are the things employers will say they want and they help in terms of high academic attainment too".

In addition to the learning values and skills being woven into everyday life at LVS Ascot, specific engaging events have allowed the students to focus on the skills and their importance, such as during Outdoor Learning Day. All 160 students in the LVS Ascot Junior School enjoyed a captivating day of activities in October as Outdoor Learning Day took them from the classroom into the school's 25 acre grounds to explore and discover new things, with some students making the trip to the World Heritage Site of Stonehenge in Wiltshire. The youngest pupils in Reception Class to Year 2 enjoyed a scavenger hunt around the school grounds to encourage them to use their imaginations to find items which met certain criteria including bugs and plants. The sessions were overseen by one of the school's Outdoor Pursuit teachers, Mr Wyndham-Smith who leads sixth formers on Duke of Edinburgh trips, demonstrating the benefit of being an all-through school with teaching expertise shared across age-groups. Year 4 pupils were given a session on trust and communication which involved a number of teamwork activities and problem solving tasks, whilst all pupils enjoyed an opportunity to read outdoors. Older students in Year 6 were taught map reading skills as part of an orienteering session which involved following a series of instructions to move from point to point within the leafy school grounds.

Pupils in Year 5 made the exciting trip to Stonehenge in Wiltshire where they discovered the history of the famous monument and learned how prehistoric man lived and how they managed to create the iconic ring of stones.

By having a day like Outdoor Learning Day outside the classroom, where every child is involved, they are able to work together across year groups and show collaboration and self-confidence, take risks and do things that they might not otherwise do. It was an inspiring day that really engaged them with learning and trying new things.

Increasing evidence suggests characteristics such as creativity, empathy and collaboration can be learnt. Acquiring such positive character traits is associated with a range of positive life outcomes, so it is essential we instil these values in our young people to give them the greatest chance of success in life.

*For more information about LVS Ascot, see page 96*

# Knowledge based is knowledge aced

**Sarah Gillam, Head Teacher of Maple Walk Prep School, explains the inspiration behind the school's teaching practices**

In North West London, Maple Walk School's central aim is for pupils to be thoroughly prepared for the next phase of their education; in order for this to happen, pupils need to gain mastery of knowledge and have an imaginative engagement with and understanding of the world around them.

The New Model School Company (NMS), proprietors of Maple Walk and its sister school Faraday (in the City), was set up in 2004 and the founders were strongly influenced by the American educator and academic Professor Eric Donald Hirsch Jr, who, interestingly, has had a huge impact on the UK Government and the changes to the national curriculum since 2010.

Hirsch believes that to thrive in a free and democratic society, children must secure a shared, foundational knowledge necessary to exercise effective citizenship. His fundamental precepts are:

1. We all need cultural literacy ... certain facts, ideas and knowledge of literary works that he says people need to know in order to operate effectively as citizens of the country in which they live.
2. Children need to learn facts in a highly organised and structured way ... therefore creating the imperative to get back to the basics with a robust core curriculum.

Maple Walk School uses Core Knowledge Curriculum books (developed by Civitas) as a starting point for the curriculum; the books place the knowledge of complex subjects at the centre of the children's school experience.

Whilst Hirsch's work was primarily to close the social gap, it is clear that a child who has a good basic knowledge of a subject can achieve greater depth and mastery with this knowledge based approach as they have the skills to read and debate more widely; "Knowledge is Power" (Michaela Secondary School, Brent).

Toby Young (2009) stated the importance of "powerful knowledge" and how it can provide ways to think about the world and discuss reliable explanations. At Maple Walk, "powerful knowledge" is the focus of the curriculum; it involves thinking not just about the 'what' but the 'how' and the 'why'.

We place the knowledge of complex subjects and its mastery at the centre of the children's school experience; the study of grammar, of chronological history, of physical and political geography, the knowledge of classical literature are all very important.

At Maple Walk, pupils receive a meaningful overview of British and European history as a whole, so that they can come, in time, to view the 21st Century within the context of a larger picture. For instance, we believe that it is impossible to understand the UK's political and legal system without a knowledge of the Saxons, Normans, Civil War, etc. The children need this knowledge and indeed they have a right to it, as it is the foundation of the parliamentary political system they are growing up in.

In addition, we agree with the principle: "Critical thinking processes such as reasoning and problem solving – are intimately intertwined with factual knowledge that is stored in long-term memory" (Daniel T. Willingham, a cognitive scientist at the University of Virginia).

The key to this knowledge-based approach is the teacher who can change children's lives by bringing these topics and subject areas to life; opening their minds to worlds outside their pre-existing experiences, and enabling children to grasp the relevance of other epochs and cultures. Cavemen and Plantagenets both produced astonishingly powerful works of art and architecture, plenty of which are still visible today; they made crucial discoveries and inventions, which we rely on everyday of our lives; and in the case of the Plantagenets, their language, laws, customs and institutional structures are still the foundation of our public world.

Maple Walk continues to consider the best pedagogical practices to introduce our children to coherent, overlapping bodies of knowledge, engaging their interest and enthusiasm.

We ensure that the teachers have an excellent subject knowledge and high expectations; they put in a huge effort into preparing lessons to make them creative, dynamic and interesting. Great emphasis is placed on the marking of work and supporting the learning of the pupils and the use of textbooks consolidates the learning.

*For more information on Maple Walk Prep School, see page 59*

# The importance of relationships for behaviour management

## Aaron Williams, Co-Principal of Lloyd Williamson Schools (LWS), shares a model for successful intervention

At LWS we believe in the importance of developing the children's emotional literacy, supporting them to understand themselves, take account of others they come into contact with and make the best of situations they find themselves in. We aim for all children to benefit as much as possible from their school experience so that they leave us with a high sense of achievement, self-esteem and personal responsibility.

We encourage children to think, feel and behave in ways appropriate to the here and now reality they find themselves in so they can take responsibility for who they are and how they behave and learn in any given moment.

Children come to school with values and beliefs from a range of sources: home (their immediate and wider family), stories they read, television programmes they watch (or which may just be on in the background),

popular culture they absorb both in ways we know and in ways we can only imagine. There are messages they have 'swallowed whole', and fully understood, as well as others they have swallowed whole but which remain not thought through. They bring in other ideas of their own, which are assimilations of how they think they are supposed to think, feel and behave. Often these values and beliefs are helpful in supporting them to make the most of their school life and to enjoy a satisfying enough experience; sometimes they are not, and they hinder their enjoyment and learning!

Here I would like to focus on behaviour as an interconnected product of thinking and feeling.

All children bring personalities as unique as snowflakes to their experience of school and we aim to support them to make the best of who they are, who they hope to be and to work out how to get there!

What we as teachers have in common with them is our own experience of childhood, and whilst for some (myself especially) it is firmly set in the days of black and white television and original episodes of Upstairs Downstairs, we all aim to understand life in the here and now as we experience it. There are social situations that children experience today that most of us did not have to face when we were growing up – the world is changing in ways that as an adult I sometimes struggle to understand – I try to imagine how it must be for some of our pupils and how they make sense of these changes.

At our school, we support the staff through training in self-reflection to understand themselves in relation to the children. In this respect we understand that education happens in relationship – not just the content of lesson plans and meticulously planned topics, but in the process of being together in a room with others, all of us learning something new about each other at the same time.

Whilst my main ethos of education evolved in the 70s and 80s through 'child centred' education, it was the head of my first school who taught me to understand the real value of relationship through teaching me to deeply reflect on "Who am I? Who are the children in my class? What will we learn together?"

This led me to explore my own sense of how I learned (how did I feel about my own experience of school?), what I learned (what did I know or not know? What were my passions and why?), how did I feel about myself (what parts of me had been allowed to emerge, or gone into hiding, which parts of me did I feel driven to show others and why?). In answering these questions I began to think about how I might either consciously or unconsciously influence the children in my care either in ways that would benefit them or otherwise. I realised that in order to understand them I had to understand me!

The main area this first came to light in was behaviour, and when faced with 38 children in my class I realised I needed to work on some common consensual ideas. What this turned into was a class contract. Not the first of its kind but a radical thought back in the early '80s when most behaviour management in schools seemed to me to be about the enforcement of rules and children adapting to them.

At Lloyd Williamson Schools we use a tool to support intervention in behaviour called the Awareness Ladder, which we have adapted from a Transactional Analysis tool called the Discount Matrix (Mellor and Sigmund 1975). It is based on four levels:

**Level 1:** Does the person know that what they're doing is a problem? If not then the intervention must be at this level – there may be a cultural (perhaps between home and school) difference, or generational difference, or a developmental sense that they don't understand that this is a problem and why. Sometimes an intervention at this level is enough to support the person to change what they are doing. This can facilitate a conversation between two children or the child and staff member involved to see each other's perception.

Once Level 1 is achieved we can proceed, if necessary, to:

**Level 2:** Does the person understand the impact of what they're doing? Once level 1 is achieved, we can help children to understand the effect they have on others and support them to de-escalate what they are doing and minimise the impact. To do this we need to understand the impact we in turn have on our children.

**Level 3:** Do they know what their options are to do something different? This might be about the child understanding their emotions and how they might be acting out, in which case how else might they process their anger, sadness or fear. There may be options to do things differently but some children have never been talked through these options. This may be a one-off intervention or a stage that needs a planned support period.

**Level 4:** How willing are they to invest in the changes they need to make? This is about motivation and readiness. This may be a tough one to crack. They may well know what to do; what is it about making the changes they are struggling with? Teachers need to have their own reference for this in order to have empathy.

Often teachers come in with a Level 4 intervention too early and think the child is stubborn, even when they are not, which is sometimes where the clash comes. We believe it is more useful to work through each level without presuming!

Pitching the intervention is crucial to challenging everyone's perception about what is happening and why, and offering children a route towards making amends and understanding how to take responsibility for who they are.

Not only have we found this model a useful barometer in our everyday interactions with children, it is useful for us as parents and in our adult relationships and staff management.

*For more information about Lloyd Williamson Schools, see page 57*

# Technology in the classroom: what are the benefits?

**Harriet Connor-Earl, Headmistress of St Mary's School Hampstead, looks at the challenge of balancing IT with traditional practices**

When I meet the girls at the front door each morning, they burst into St Mary's School. They run, they skip and scooter at record breaking speeds! They are smiling, giggling or often brimming with something new to tell me.

As Headmistress, my primary goal is to help the girls and boys become their best selves. Within education, increasingly people seem to believe that our purpose is to teach children and solely focus on the knowledge required to pass a particular set of exams thus moving them forward to the next school, university or indeed career.

However, I believe that by fixating upon this, we often fail our children by forgetting to teach key habits of learning and essential life skills. If we can instil these habits and practical skills at a young age, they become embedded and of real value for life in the 21st century.

As an independent school with charitable status, we enjoy the advantage of being able to implement new initiatives very quickly. Investing in the latest IT equipment and bringing learning to life is a key priority at St Mary's School.

When I first arrived at the School, we decided to remove the dedicated IT suite. In a world where technology is embedded in every aspect of our daily lives, it felt alien to say to the girls: "Let's stop what we're doing and go to a separate room to use technology."

We have invested in new iPads and Chromebooks so they are more accessible to every pupil in the classrooms and fully integrated to support all areas of learning from Pre-Nursery to Year 6. The School has also invested in MacBooks for the music department to create digital music.

Children fully embrace and are excited by the opportunities that technology offers. We believe that incorporating the latest technology helps to promote independent learning, improves pupil engagement and encourages more active participation in the class. In turn, as our pupils are interested in the lessons, we've seen an improvement in knowledge retention.

Technology also offers numerous benefits for teachers. Direct access to the internet and online resources through our interactive whiteboards allows teachers to enhance and build on more traditional teaching methods. Another advantage that we've seen is improved sharing of resources and collaboration between colleagues.

In place of the IT suite, we were able to open a new Science Room to support and enhance the Science curriculum. This new facility allows outdoor learning to become a reality. For instance, in the curriculum there is a specific experiment on habitats. The children create different habitats for woodlice in the classroom such as damp, warm, dark or light. We put wood lice in this fake environment and see which one they go to. As we are lucky enough to have an amazing outdoor space, we are then able to go outside to find the woodlice in our garden and explore the habitats that they naturally choose.

Our focus on technology is equally balanced with an emphasis on creative and physical development. Music, drama, art and sports are also an essential part of life at St Mary's School and involve everyone. Children demonstrate great enthusiasm and build valuable and social skills that last a lifetime.

To support the integration of technology in our teaching, St Mary's School is currently undergoing an extensive refurbishment programme to deliver the most up-to-date and engaging classroom facilities.

In my office, I have three separate work areas. We, as adults, use different seating for different tasks to improve our concentration and efficiency. So, when designing our new classrooms, I wanted to include a variety of learning spaces to reflect the wide range of individual learning styles. Gone are name labels stuck to an assigned desk. Pupils can now choose between soft staged seating, a stand up desk or a collaborative working pod. All the furniture is flexible and can be moved easily. This allows teachers to group the children in varied ways according to the lesson. It follows that if you feel comfortable at your work station, you are going to work better and more effectively.

By having non-allocated seating and a variety of spaces, we have seen the children's output of work increase and improve. We also removed the teacher desk from the classroom to allow the teachers to sit amongst the children. In turn, this has meant the removal of a line of children waiting to ask the teacher a question and eliminating the requirement for a pupil to publicise that

they are finding an aspect of learning difficult. For the child who is reluctant to share that they do not understand a concept, this has been revolutionary. They are now able to quietly speak to the teacher who may be sitting next to them.

Used together – the integrated technology, the flexible seating and the broad curriculum – the girls at St Mary's are flourishing. They are adopting habits of learning which they can take forth into their secondary education to ensure they truly thrive and achieve their individual potential. They are active and interested learners who are able to collaborate, communicate and develop their learning independently.

**St Mary's School Hampstead** provides an outstanding and inspirational Catholic education to girls from 3-11 years and boys from 3-7 years.

The School celebrates the uniqueness of every pupil and their achievements. The rigorous, challenging curriculum places a strong emphasis on high academic achievement within a culture of care and support.

Leavers achieve impressive results, gaining offers and Academic Scholarships from the best schools in the country, including City of London School for Girls, Francis Holland School, Highgate School, North London Collegiate, South Hampstead High School and St Paul's Girls' School.

*For more information about St Mary's School Hampstead see page 74 or visit www.stmh.co.uk*

# Learning is not a pathology

## Sarah Raffray, Headteacher of St Augustine's Priory, looks at the words that shape our times

Did you know that 'whatevs' has entered the English dictionary? You probably knew that 'mankini' is used frequently enough to have become a 'real' word but did you know that words which have evolved from texting have formally been acknowledged? Do you use 'Truthiness (n): the quality of seeming or being felt to be true, even if not necessarily true'? How about 'Grrrl (n): A young woman regarded as independent and strong or aggressive, especially in her attitude to men or in her sexuality (A blend of 'Grrrr' and 'Girl.')' or 'Guyliner (n): Eyeliner that is worn by men.'? Have you come across or used 'Bromance (n): A close but non-sexual relationship between two men'?

All of these coinings reflect the dynamic nature of language and our sense of identity and relationships in 21st Century Western society. What we say reflects our culture. Indeed the portmant*bros* very specifically convey much of the current debate and legislation around gender. The increasing acceptance of the LGBTQ movement has of course been mirrored in a proliferation of new words as well as attitudes. A voice has literally been given to people about the nature of sexuality and whether or not, like language, it is or can be fixed.

These examples of language change also reveal something of our cultural norms and how these paradigms are shifting. The addition or blending of the prefix to create words like guyliner and bromance foregrounds the fact that eyeliner is presupposed to be a feminine accoutrement while 'romance' has conventionally denoted a heterosexual relationship. These apparently small linguistic changes say a great deal about what it is to be male or female today.

Feminist writers on discourse have often explored semantic space as a literal and figurative place. They have long commented on the ways in which language is a useful barometer of social status. In the past, the nouns 'courtier' and 'courtesan' had an equality – both referred to someone who worked in the aristocratic courts. 'Madam' and 'sir', 'spinster' and 'bachelor' should carry equivalence but note how in both of these cases (and in others) the female word slides into a negative space. The latest 'hoo-ha' (great word – now in the OED) around sexual harassment cannot be surprising when our language routinely diminishes women and the words associated with them. If we want to change behaviour, we must challenge language. In short, does the way we speak reflect our society or shape it?

I would argue that we should resist the usage of a word like 'grrrl' because once again it suggests that if a woman takes on so called male attributes, she risks a criticism which reflects our society's discomfort with women in power. We should challenge assumptions that women must not dare to tread where men go. While we seem capable of accepting a completely new status quo around gender identity, we seem to be incapable of moving on from old stereotypes or judgements and our language reflects that.

That we have become more informal in our discourse is probably agreed. Generation Z would be very comfortable with the fact that '**D'oh (ex):** an exclamation used to comment on a foolish or stupid action, especially one's own, has entered the Oxford English Dictionary. But what about the new entry of 'worstest'? Surely that is an example of child language acquisition where children work out the rules of grammar and apply them, often delightfully. My favourite example would be the child who had been watching the news about demonstrations when Margaret Thatcher tried to introduce the poll tax. The child's favoured insult at the time was to call someone a poll tack. She had worked out that the word tax sounded like a plural and needed to become singular. This is a brilliant example of the language of protest as well as fascinating in showing how we pick up social and grammatical nuances without realising it.

If you have never mined the Oxford English Dictionary (OED) I recommend it highly and you can gain access to it online, for free, through your public library membership. For a word to gain entry it must pass a number of tests. Often it will have been in use for many, even hundreds of years. Indeed it transpires that worstest, added in 2017, has been around for a while and not just as a childish quirk. Thus – '1892 News & Observer (Raleigh, N. Carolina) 23 Sept. Worst – oh, worstest thing of all! I have to stay a girl.' In other words, the OED captures not just language use, but it also acknowledges the moment when language as a living thing becomes fixed – or at any rate as fixed as it can be.

Yet 'd'oh' and 'worstest' also reflect another aspect of language use. For years I have been challenging my sons' use of words which I was brought up to regard as impolite; those words, like 'jerk', it transpires are now used routinely in children's cartoons and books. Like the shifts in notions of sexuality, we have to acknowledge that we are in the midst of a culturally seismic change. Our children

*For years I have been challenging my sons' use of words which I was brought up to regard as impolite; those words, like 'jerk', it transpires are now used routinely in children's cartoons and books.*

and the young people we educate have grown up in a world as different from their parents' as those Industrial Revolution children whose parents had experienced the world before railways. I don't regard myself as especially old, but I did start teaching when we still used blackboards and Banda machines – this is enough to make me feel ancient as young teachers have absolutely no idea what I am talking about, though some might remember the distinctive chemical smell of a fresh handout produced in this way.

There is nothing new about language changing – our inventiveness with language is one of the things which makes us human. The words we use also reflect historic moments – rightly there has been much interest in the film *Hidden Figures* about the black women whose mathematical expertise put the first man on the moon. The women were called computers because they were conducting the calculations. During that period the IBMs arrived to help speed up the process. Like hoovers, the product was named after the company that produced them. Unlike hoovers, IBMs became known as computers – replacing in every sense the human beings whose job they replicated. The product's resilience was mirrored in its ability to change name.

Many of our new words reflect emerging technologies and linguistic colonisation; our words reveal the invasion of cultural changes. The English language in times gone by absorbed new words in enormous swathes through physical incursions. The Battle of Hastings saw almost every member of the English aristocracy die to be replaced by French lords. English became the language of the servant and so developed one source of the richness of our vocabulary and its synonyms, which also reflected the class system. The English farmers cared for the sheep, cows and pigs (Old English words) to put the mutton, beef and pork (French words) on the tables of their French overlords. The Renaissance then brought further hundreds of Latinate words with the flourishing of rediscovered texts and thus it was during the 14th century that the OED records the arrival of the word 'creativity'. Does that mean that the concept of creativity had not existed before? Or did the Latinate word suggest that it had become something of intellectual value? The

word feminism only arrives in the OED in the 1970s. We know women had agitated for equality for hundreds of years before this word was acknowledged by the OED. Once again a word's inclusion in the dictionary reveals something of our society's acceptance of the ideas it represents.

So new words reflect the signs of the times. New applications of old words also say something of our values or preoccupations. I am interested in the proliferation of terms used to support students who are struggling with their learning. More specifically they are probably not quite reaching a bar for public examinations. We have a whole raft of activities now for young people where none existed before. We 'workshop' to brainstorm ideas – a term expressive of manufactured output or worse; we have 'surgeries' for those who cannot manage aspects of Chemistry or other subjects. Does your school have 'clinics' for extra Maths? Why have we medicalised the language and enjoyment of learning? Learning is not a pathology and it concerns me that we have turned helping with learning into the linguistic equivalent of an A and E. Perhaps we should intubate if someone cannot understand a poem or begin compressions if a student is unable to tackle an essay with confidence. We already 'monitor' progress and conduct lesson 'observations' as we subject teachers to the same level of scrutiny. Much is said about the reduction of pupils to mere data – yet a more sinister reduction of their humanity and individuality is occurring through the ways in which we judge educational activity and measurements.

Perhaps we should look to our language use for some of the reasons we now have escalating rates of acute anxiety amongst young people and an apparent epidemic of eating disorders. We could all, teachers and pupils, benefit from ditching meetings in favour of 'encounters' or 'conversations'. We are not automatons – teachers and pupils need life changing and thought provoking experiences. We urgently need a new vocabulary for engaging in learning which is inspired and creative; we seem to be able to find new words for everything else under the sun but we need an equal inventiveness to reclaim education and learning as a space of joy and enthusiasm and playfulness.

*For more information about St Augustine's Priory see page 72*

# Going co-educational

**Matthew Burke, Head of Mount House School in Hadley Wood, North London, looks at the process of going co-educational, and the opportunities that such a move presents.**

This September, Mount House School will open its doors to its first ever intake of boys. We will be admitting boys to the First Form (Year 7) and Sixth Form and, by 2022, the school will be entirely co-educational.

In many ways – apart from the obvious! – little will change when we go co-educational. The fundamentals will remain; we will still be a warm and welcoming school, where every individual will be valued and every child's unique talents will be identified and nurtured. Our school ethos of being a caring and respectful community, where children feel supported and where individuality and self-confidence are fostered, will remain at the heart of all we do.

For us, welcoming boys is a natural step, but we didn't take the decision to go co-ed lightly. Given that Mount House had been blessed with a more than respectable reputation in its former life as an all-girls school, it was

very important to us that the great traditional strengths of the school continue to be felt by both genders from the outset.

We recognise that moving from an all-girl environment to co-education is going to be a challenge, both for the girls currently at the school and the boys joining from September.

In becoming co-ed, we aim to open up new opportunities to a wider audience. We hope to foster a new sporting culture, where the girls will, literally, compete on a level playing field with the boys. We aim to break down the traditional perceptions that netball and hockey are for girls, while the boys tackle rugby, football and cricket.

Both boys and girls will have full access to all the main school sports and we are organising a full

*In becoming co-ed, we aim to open up new opportunities to a wider audience. We hope to foster a new sporting culture, where the girls will, literally, compete on a level playing field with the boys.*

calendar of fixtures against local schools and in national competitions.

We also plan to set a trend for new mixed-sex teams which, while unable to compete at league or county level, will be able to play friendly matches against teams from other schools.

Another advantage is the further enrichment of our pastoral system. The sense of extended family that our house and tutor system gives pupils will be stronger by including boys, ultimately aiding the culture of mutual respect and good manners required for relationships throughout life.

Likewise, a mixed Sixth Form means students will be more confident when taking those first, often faltering, steps into employment or further education, being at ease when studying or working alongside the opposite sex.

We live in an age which believes everyone has the right – and ability – to achieve, whatever their gender.

Our girls already excel at maths and sciences and will certainly give the boys a run for their money in all subject fields.

More than half the current (female) sixth form at Mount House is studying A-level Maths and last year's A-level results for Maths were in the top 5% nationally.

Able students are encouraged to take their Maths GCSE at the end of Year 10 and 70% of them gained As and A*s in Maths in 2017. Following this outstanding success, we are now looking to create a centre of excellence for Maths and Physics, as well as Music and Sport.

For the majority of our teaching staff, co-education will not provide any new challenges. Most teachers have experience, and a proven track record of success, in co-ed schools. For those that haven't had that experience, we will be providing top quality in-service training prior to the start of the next school year.

It is clear that there will need to be a full review of the texts and resources used in the classroom. Where necessary, these will be revised to reflect the change in pupil population and to ensure the enthusiasm of both genders in every lesson.

In addition, we will be providing a new Computing & Technology course from September - not using wood, metal and plastics, but technology based around electronics, control systems and robotics.

With the move to co-education will come the need to provide basic facilities for boys. We are currently creating high quality changing rooms, showers and toilets for male pupils which will be fully functioning by September.

It's a far cry from 1903, when Mount House – formerly St Martha's Catholic School for Girls – was opened by the Sisters of the Order of St Martha.

Girls were taught to cook, sew and know their place. Interestingly, there remains more school provision for girls in the Barnet area than for boys – another reason we decided to open our doors to boys.

Mount House School will be one of only a small handful of independent co-educational senior day schools in North London. This, coupled with our small class sizes – which we will maintain – and our family school ethos, we believe makes our offering somewhat unique.

There will always be some parents who prefer single sex schooling. Every child is different and one size does not necessarily fit all, that we accept.

But, at the end of the day, good teachers are the key to academic success. That – and happy students.

We believe our future plans for Mount House will tick both of these boxes.

*'Coeducational Excellence, Where Everyone Is Known, Cherished and Challenged'*

*For more information about Mount House School, see page 88*

# Healthy and happy minds

## Maria Edwards reports on how Orchard House School works hard to make sure the children are happy

The late Agatha Christie said: "One of the luckiest things that can happen to you in life is to have a happy childhood." Here at Orchard House School we aim to maintain above all a happy ethos. But we don't rely on luck to do this. We have introduced a number of initiatives to build a fulfilling and productive environment for the whole Orchard House school community.

According to the Mental Health Foundation, mental health problems affect about 1 in 10 children. Problems that include depression, anxiety and conduct disorder are often a direct response to what is happening in a child's life. Of course, the vast majority of children are resilient, happy people but every child may on occasion need help to rebound back to a state of happy equanimity.

The issue for any school is how to recognise a child with a growing issue and help him or her with early intervention. Following extensive discussions, my staff and I have introduced additional whole school initiatives which we believe have had a significant impact. We began the process with a review of the school's Pastoral Plan. The new plan has broken new ground in that it involves children in their own pastoral care and enables staff to monitor much more closely how each pupil feels. A simple questionnaire, easily completed by the children, allows each child to record his or her feelings confidentially. This in turn helps the children to enjoy school life to a fuller extent, as it alerts teachers to any little anxieties or concerns and allows them to address these quickly before they escalate.

In addition to working with individual children, the school has a specialist Life Coach who works with children to help each to resolve any emotional queries, often equipping a child with a tool kit he or she can use on other occasions to overcome difficulties. We have also introduced sessions for both staff and parents. As a result, teachers have implemented additional child-centred techniques into their classroom practice, parents have learnt additional positive techniques to deploy at home and across the school we have seen marked improvements in the children's self-esteem.

We have also further developed the school's behaviour policy, which now focuses additionally on pupils taking responsibility for their own behaviour and learning from their mistakes.

Following an extensive consultation with pupils, the playground was redesigned to enable more activities to take place. This has been hugely successful. Alongside traditional playground games, themed days have been introduced to encourage further interaction and these too have proved a winner with the children.

We have also introduced breathing techniques, and brief yoga sessions and meditation takes place daily, as a calm and relaxed child will always perform better. Indeed, despite being a non-selective school for children entering

at nursery and reception, our academic results at 11+ are enviable, with many scholarships gained to the top London schools. Holiday homework tasks have also been changed, to encourage families to spend time together while each child adds to his or her learning experience.

As Graham Greene once said, "There is always one moment in childhood when the door opens and lets the future in." That is our job at Orchard House as educators, to open the doors and let the future in: the happier we can make each child's experience of school, the greater for certain will be each child's success.

*For more information about Orchard House School see page 44*

# Choosing a school – the key questions

## However much a school may appeal at first sight, you still need sound information to form your judgement

Schools attract pupils by their reputations, so most go to considerable lengths to ensure that parents are presented with an attractive image. Modern marketing techniques try to promote good points and play down (without totally obscuring) bad ones. But every Head knows that, however good the school prospectus is, it only serves to attract parents through the school gates. Thereafter the decision depends on what they see and hear. Research we have carried out over the years suggests that in many cases the most important factor in choosing a school is the impression given by the Head. As well as finding out what goes on in a school, parents need to be reassured by the aura of confidence that they expect from a Head. How they judge the latter may help them form their opinion of the former. In other words, how a Head answers questions is important in itself and, to get you started, we have drawn up a list of points that you may like to consider. Some can be posed as questions and some are points you'll only want to check in your mind. They are not listed in any particular order and their significance will vary from family to family, but they should be useful in helping you to form an opinion.

Before visiting and asking questions, **check the facts** – such as which association the school belongs to, how big it is, how many staff *etc*. Is there any form of financial pie chart showing how the school's resources are used? The answers to questions like these should be in the promotional material you've been sent. If they aren't, you've already got a good question to ask!

**Check the website.** Is it up-to-date? Almost certainly not 100% because that's just about impossible, but it shouldn't be obsolete. And that first impression is very important.

**When you get to the school** you will want to judge the overall atmosphere and decide whether it will suit you and your child. Are any other members of the family going to help to pay the fees? If so, their views are important and the school's attitude towards them may be instructive.

When you make it to the inner sanctum, **what do you make of the Head as a person?** Age? Family? Staying? Moving on? Retiring? Busted flush? Accessible to children, parents and staff? If you never get to see the Head, but deal with an admissions person of some sort, it may not mean you should rule the school out, but it certainly tells you something about the school's view of pupil recruitment.

**Academic priorities** – attitude towards league tables? This is a forked question. If the answer is 'We're most concerned with doing the best for the child', you pitch them a late-developer; if the answer is, 'Well, frankly, we have a very high entry threshold', then you say 'So we have to give you a foolproof academic winner, do we?'

### Supplementary questions:

- What is the ratio of teachers to pupils?
- What are the professional qualifications of the teaching staff?
- What is the school's retention rate? In prep schools this means how many pupils do they lose at 11 when the school goes on to 13.
- How long is the school day – and week?
- What are the school's exam results?
- What are the criteria for presenting them?
- Were they consistent over the years?
- Is progress accelerated for the academically bright?
- How does the school cope with pupils who do not work?
- Where do pupils go when they leave?
- How important and well resourced are sports, extra-curricular and after school activities, music and drama?
- What cultural or other visits are arranged away from the school?

### Other topics to cover:

- What is the school's mission?
- What is its attitude to religion?
- How well is the school integrated into the local community?
- How have they responded to the Charities Act initiatives?
- What are the responsibilities and obligations at weekends for parents, pupils and the school?
- Does the school keep a watching brief or reserve the option to get involved after a weekend incident?

Dolphin School – see editorial on page 18

- What is the school's attitude to discipline?

- Have there been problems with drugs, drink or sex? How have they been dealt with?

- What is the school's policy on bullying?

- How does the school cope with pupils' problems?

- What sort of academic and pastoral advice is available?

- What positive steps are taken to encourage good manners, behaviour and sportsmanship?

- What is the uniform?

- What steps are taken to ensure that pupils take pride in their personal appearance?

- How often does the school communicate with parents through reports, parent/teacher meetings or other visits?

- What level of parental involvement is encouraged both in terms of keeping in touch with staff about your own child and more generally, eg a Parents' Association?

- Is it possible to have the names and addresses of parents with children at the school to approach them for an opinion?

And finally – and perhaps most importantly – what does your child make of the school, the adults met, the other children met, pupils at the school in other contexts, and the website?

# Initial advice

**Educational institutions often belong to organisations that encourage high standards. Here we give a brief guide to what some of the initials mean.**

# BSA

## The Boarding Schools' Association

Association (BSA) has had the twin objectives of the promotion of boarding education and the development of quality boarding through high standards of pastoral care and boarding accommodation. Parents and prospective pupils choosing a boarding school can, therefore, be assured that the 550 schools in membership of the BSA are committed to providing the best possible boarding environment for their pupils.

A school can only join the BSA if it is in membership of one of the ISC (Independent Schools Council) constituent associations or in membership of SBSA (State Boarding Schools' Association). These two bodies require member schools to be regularly inspected by the Independent Schools' Inspectorate (ISI) or Ofsted. Boarding inspection of independent schools has been conducted by ISI since September 2012. Ofsted retains responsibility for the inspection of boarding in state schools. Boarding inspections must be conducted every three years. Boarding is judged against the National Minimum Standards for Boarding Schools (revised 2011) with considerable input from the BSA.

### Relationship with government

The BSA is in regular communication with the Department for Education (DfE) on all boarding matters. The Children Act (1989) and the Care Standards Act (2001) require boarding schools to conform to national legislation and the promotion of this legislation and the training required to carry it out are matters on which the DfE and the BSA work closely. The key area is in training.

### Boarding training

The programme of training for boarding staff whose schools are in membership of the BSA has been supported and sponsored in the past by the DfE. The BSA maintains the high standards expected as a consequence of that support. The Utting Report on the Safeguards for Children Living Away from Home highlighted the importance of the development of 'policy, practice and training for services for children who live away from home'. It focuses on the right of parents to expect that staff looking after children

are competent to do so, and points out the responsibility of central government to secure consistent national standards in promoting the welfare of children away from home. The Singleton Review (March 2009) reiterated the importance of rigorous safeguarding of such children.

In addition the BSA organises five residential conferences, five one-day conferences and more than 90+ day seminars a year for governors, Heads, deputies, housemasters and housemistresses, and matrons and medical staff where further training takes place in formal sessions and in sharing good practice. The BSA provides professional qualifications for both teaching and non-teaching staff in boarding schools. The BSA has been responsible for the development of courses leading to university validated Certificates of Professional Practice in Boarding Education. These certificates, the result of at least two years' study, are awarded by the University of Roehampton.

### State Boarding Forum

The BSA issues information on the 38 state boarding schools in England and Wales and the BSA should be contacted for details of these schools. In these schools parents pay for boarding but not for education, so fees are substantially lower than in an independent boarding school.

Chief Executive: Robin Fletcher MBA, MPhil, FRSA
Director of Operations: Aileen Kane
Director of Training: Andrew Lewin
Boarding Schools' Association
4th Floor, 134-136 Buckingham Palace Road
London SW1W 9SA
Tel: 020 7798 1580
Fax: 020 7798 1581
Email: bsa@boarding.org.uk
Website: www.boarding.org.uk

# GSA

## The Girls' Schools Association, to which Heads of leading girls' schools belong

The Girls' Schools Association represents the heads of many of the top performing day and boarding schools in the UK independent schools sector and is a member of the Independent Schools Council.

The GSA encourages high standards of education for girls and promotes the benefits of being taught in a largely girls-only environment. GSA schools are internationally respected and have a global reputation for excellence. Their innovative practice and academic rigour attract pupils from around the world. As a whole, students at GSA schools tend to achieve disproportionately high results and are more likely to study and do well in STEM (science, technology, engineering, maths) subjects than girls in other schools. A high percentage – 96% – progress to higher education.

Twenty first century girls' schools come in many different shapes and sizes. Some cater for 100% girls, others provide a predominantly girls-only environment with boys in the nursery and/or sixth form. Some follow a diamond model, with equal numbers of boys but separate classrooms between the ages of 11 to 16. Educational provision across the Association offers a choice of day, boarding, weekly, and flexi-boarding education. Schools range in type from large urban schools of 1000 pupils to small rural schools of around 200. Many schools have junior and pre-prep departments, and can offer a complete education from 3/4 to 18. A significant proportion of schools also have religious affiliations. Heads of Girls' Day School Trust (GDST) schools are members of the GSA.

The Association aims to inform and influence national educational debate and is a powerful and well-respected voice within the educational establishment, advising and lobbying educational policy makers on core education issues as well as those relating to girls' schools and the education of girls. The Association liaises with the Department for Education, the Office for Standards in Education, the Qualifications and Curriculum Authority and other bodies.

The GSA also provides its members and their staff with professional development courses, conferences, advice and opportunities to debate and share best practice, ensuring that they have every opportunity to remain fully up-to-date with all aspects of their profession.

As the GSA is one of the constituent bodies of the Independent Schools' Council (ISC), its schools are required to undergo a regular cycle of inspections to ensure that these rigorous standards are being maintained. GSA schools must also belong to the Association of Governing Bodies of Independent Schools, and Heads must be in membership of the Association of School and College Leaders (ASCL).

The Association's secretariat is based in Leicester.

Suite 105, 108 New Walk, Leicester LE1 7EA
Tel: 0116 254 1619
Email: office@gsa.uk.com
Website: www.gsa.uk.com
Twitter: @GSAUK
President 2018: Gwen Byrom, Loughborough High School
Chief Executive: Vivienne Durham

# HMC

## The Headmasters' and Headmistresses' Conference, to which the Heads of leading independent schools belong

Founded in 1869 the HMC exists to enable members to discuss matters of common interest and to influence important developments in education. It looks after the professional interests of members, central to which is their wish to provide the best possible educational opportunities for their pupils.

The Heads of some 289 leading independent schools are members of The Headmasters' and Headmistresses' Conference, whose membership now includes Heads of boys', girls' and coeducational schools. International membership includes the Heads of around 53 schools throughout the world.

Within HMC there are schools with continuous histories as long as any in the world and many others trace their origins to Tudor times, but HMC continues to admit to membership recentlyfounded schools that have achieved great success.

The great variety of these schools is one of the strengths of HMC but all must exhibit high quality in the education provided. While day schools are the largest group, about a quarter of HMC schools consist mainly of boarders and others have a smaller boarding element including weekly and flexible boarders.

All schools are noted for their academic excellence and achieve good results, including those with pupils from a broad ability band. Members believe that good education consists of more than academic results and schools provide pupils with a wide range of educational co-curricular activities and with strong pastoral support.

Only those schools that meet with the rigorous membership criteria are admitted and this helps ensure that HMC is synonymous with high quality in education. There is a set of membership requirements and a Code of Practice to which members must subscribe. Those who want the intimate atmosphere of a small school will find some with around 350 pupils. Others who want a wide range of facilities and specialisations will find these offered in large day or boarding schools. Many have over 1000 pupils. About 30 schools are for boys only; others are coeducational throughout or only in the sixth form. The first girls-only schools joined HMC in 2006. There are now about 25 girls-only schools.

Within HMC there are schools with continuous histories as long as any in the world and many others trace their origins to Tudor times, but HMC continues to admit to membership recently-founded schools that have achieved great success. The facilities in all HMC schools will be good but some have magnificent buildings and grounds that are the result of the generosity of benefactors over many years. Some have attractive rural settings, others are sited in the centres of cities.

Pupils come from all sorts of backgrounds. Bursaries and scholarships provided by the schools give about a third of the 220,000 pupils in HMC schools help with their fees. These average about £30,000 per annum for boarding schools and £13,000 for day schools. About 170,000 are day pupils and 43,000 boarders.

Entry into some schools is highly selective but others are well-suited to a wide ability range. Senior boarding schools usually admit pupils after the Common Entrance examination taken when they are 13.

Most day schools select their pupils by 11+ examination. Many HMC schools have junior schools, some with nursery and pre-prep departments. The growing number of boarders from overseas is evidence of the high reputation of the schools worldwide.

The independent sector has always been fortunate in attracting very good teachers. Higher salary scales, excellent conditions of employment, exciting educational opportunities and good pupil/teacher ratios bring rewards commensurate with the demanding expectations. Schools expect teachers to have a good education culminating in a good honours degree and a professional qualification, though some do not insist on the latter especially if relevant experience is offered. Willingness to participate in the whole life of the school is essential.

Parents expect the school to provide not only good teaching that helps their children achieve the best possible examination results, but also the dedicated pastoral care and valuable educational experiences outside the classroom in music, drama, games, outdoor pursuits and community service. Over 90% of pupils go on to higher education, many of them winning places on the most highly-subscribed university courses.

All members attend the Annual Conference, usually held in a large conference centre in September/October. There are ten divisions covering England, Wales, Scotland and Ireland where members meet once a term on a regional basis, and a distinctive international division.

The chairman and committee, with the advice of the general secretary and membership secretary, make decisions on matters referred by membership-led sub-committees, steering groups and working parties. Close links are maintained with other professional associations in membership of the Independent Schools Council and with the Association of School and College Leaders.

Membership Secretary: Ian Power
Tel: 01858 465260
General Secretary: Dr William Richardson
Tel: 01858 469059
12 The Point
Rockingham Road
Market Harborough
Leicestershire LE16 7QU
Email: gensec@hmc.org.uk
Website: www.hmc.org.uk

Leading Independent Schools

# IAPS

## The Independent Association of Preparatory Schools (IAPS) is a membership association representing leading headteachers and their prep schools in the UK and overseas

With more than 650 members, IAPS schools represent a multi-billion pound enterprise, educating more than 160,000 children and employing more than 20,000 staff.

Schools are spread throughout cities, towns and the countryside and offer pupils the choice of day, boarding, weekly and flexible boarding, in both single sex and coeducational settings. Sizes vary from 100 to more than 800 per school, with the majority between 150 and 400. Most schools are charitable trusts, some are limited companies and a few are proprietary. There are also junior schools attached to senior schools, choir schools, those with a particular religious affiliation and those that offer specialist provision as well as some schools with an age range extending to age 16 or above.

IAPS only accredits those schools that can demonstrate that they provide the highest standards of education and care. Member schools offer an all-round, values-led, broad education, which produces confident, adaptable, motivated children with a lifelong passion for learning. In order to be elected to membership, a Head must be suitably qualified and schools must be accredited through a satisfactory inspection. IAPS offers its members and their staff a comprehensive and up-to-date programme of professional development courses to ensure that high professional standards are maintained.

Pupils are offered a rich and varied school life. The targets of the National Curriculum are regarded as a basic foundation, which is greatly extended by the wider programmes of study offered. Specialist subject teaching begins at an early age and pupils are offered a range of cultural and sporting opportunities. Together with more than 30 recreational games, music, art and drama form part of curricular and extra-curricular activities. In addition, IAPS organises holiday and term-time sporting competitions for pupils to take part in, including skiing, sailing, judo, swimming, golf, fencing and squash, amongst many others.

IAPS has well-established links with senior independent schools, and experience in methods of transfer and entry to them. As the voice of independent prep school education, it has national influence and actively defends and promotes the interests of its members. It lobbies the government on their behalf and promotes prep school issues on a national and international stage. IAPS works directly with ministers and national policy advisers to ensure that the needs of the prep school sector are met.

IAPS
11 Waterloo Place,
Leamington Spa,
Warwickshire CV32 5LA
Tel: 01926 887833
Email: iaps@iaps.uk
Website: iaps.uk

# ISA

## The Independent Schools Association, with membership across all types of school

The Independent Schools Association (ISA), established in 1879, is one of the oldest of the Headteachers' associations of independent schools that make up the Independent Schools' Council (ISC). It began life as the Association of Principals of Private Schools, which was created to encourage high standards and foster friendliness and cooperation among Heads who had previously worked in isolation. In 1895 it was incorporated as The Private Schools Association and in 1927 the word 'private' was replaced by 'independent'. The recently published history of the association, Pro Liberis, demonstrates the strong links ISA has with proprietorial schools, which is still the case today, even though boards of governors now run the majority of schools.

Membership is open to any Head or Proprietor, provided they meet the necessary accreditation criteria, including inspection of their school by a government-approved inspectorate. ISA's Executive Council is elected by members and supports all developments of the Association through its committee structure and the strong regional network of co-ordinators and area committees. Each of ISA's seven areas in turn supports members through regular training events and meetings.

ISA celebrates a wide-ranging membership, not confined to any one type of school, but including all: nursery, pre-preparatory, junior and senior, all-through schools, coeducational, single-sex, boarding, day and performing arts and special schools.

Promoting best practice and fellowship remains at the core of the ISA, as it did when it began 140 years ago. The association is growing, and its 431 members and their schools enjoy high quality national conferences and courses that foster excellence in independent education. ISA's central office also supports members and provides advice, and represents the views of its membership at national and governmental levels.

Pupils in ISA schools enjoy a wide variety of competitions, in particular the wealth of sporting, artistic and academic activities at area and national level.

President: Lord Lexden
Chief Executive: Neil Roskilly, BA PGCE NPQH FRSA FRGS

ISA House,
5-7 Great Chesterford Court,
Great Chesterford, Essex CB10 1PF
Tel: 01799 523619
Email: isa@isaschools.org.uk
Website: www.isaschools.org.uk

# The Society of Heads

## The Society of Heads represents the interests of the smaller independent secondary schools

The Society of Heads represents the interests of the smaller, independent, secondary schools. The Society celebrated its 50th Anniversary in 2011. The Society has as its members over 110 Heads of well-established secondary schools, many with a boarding element, meeting a wide range of educational needs. All member schools provide education up to 18, with sixth forms offering both A and AS levels and/or the International Baccalaureate. Also some offer vocational courses. Many have junior schools attached to their foundation. A number cater for pupils with special educational needs, whilst others offer places to gifted dancers and musicians. All the schools provide education appropriate to their pupils' individual requirements together with the best in pastoral care.

The average size of the schools is about 350, and all aim to provide small classes ensuring favourable pupil:teacher ratios. The majority are coeducational and offer facilities for both boarding and day pupils. Many of the schools are non-denominational, whilst others have specific religious foundations.

The Society believes that independent schools are an important part of Britain's national education system. Given their independence, the schools can either introduce new developments ahead of the maintained sector or offer certain courses specifically appropriate to the pupils in their schools. They are able to respond quickly to the needs of parents and pupils alike.

Schools are admitted to membership of the Society only after a strict inspection procedure carried out by the Independent Schools Inspectorate. Regular inspection visits thereafter ensure that standards are maintained.

The Society is a constituent member of the Independent Schools Council and every full member in the Society has been accredited to it. All the Society's Heads belong to the Association of School and College Leaders (ASCL) (or another recognised union for school leaders) and their schools are members of AGBIS.

The Society's policy is: to maintain high standards of education, acting as a guarantee of quality to parents who choose a Society school for their children; to ensure the genuine independence of member schools; to provide an opportunity for Heads to share ideas and common concerns for the benefit of the children in their care; to provide training opportunities for Heads and staff in order to keep them abreast of new educational initiatives; to promote links with higher and further education and the professions, so that pupils leaving the Society's schools are given the best advice and opportunities for their future careers; and to help Heads strengthen relations with their local communities.

The Society of Heads' Office,
12 The Point, Rockingham Road,
Market Harborough,
Leicestershire LE16 7QU
Tel: 01858 433760
Email:
gensec@thesocietyofheads.org.uk
Website: www.thesocietyofheads.org.uk

# The Independent Schools Council

**The Independent Schools Council (ISC) works with its members to promote and preserve the quality, diversity and excellence of UK independent education both at home and abroad**

### What is the ISC?

ISC brings together seven associations of independent schools, their heads, bursars and governors. Through our member associations we represent over 1,300 independent schools in the UK and overseas. These schools are ranked among the best in the world and educate more than half a million children each year.

ISC's work is carried out by a small number of dedicated professionals in our offices in Central London. We are assisted by the contributions from expert advisory groups in specialist areas. Our priorities are set by the board of directors led by our Chairman, Barnaby Lenon. We are tasked by our members to protect and promote the sector in everything we do.

### ISC schools

ISC schools are at the forefront of educational achievement in every way. They are the most academically successful schools and offer excellent teaching, extensive facilities and an astonishing breadth of co-curricular activities. There are schools to suit every need, whether you want a day or boarding school, single sex or co-education, a large or a small school, or schools offering specialisms, such as in the Arts.

Our schools are very diverse. Some of our schools are selective and highly academic, offering a chance to stretch the bright child. Others have very strong drama or music departments full of creative opportunities in plays, orchestras and choirs. For children with special needs such as dyslexia or autism there are many outstanding independent schools that offer the best provision in the country.

And of course, our schools have very strong track records of high achievement at sport, offering superb facilities, excellent coaches and a full fixture list. Independent schools excel at the traditional sports like football and rugby, but also offer more unusual sports like rowing, fencing and even rock climbing.

There is also a wealth of co-curricular opportunity available. Whether your child is into debating, sailing, the Model United Nations or is interested in army training in the Combined Cadet Force, most schools offer numerous clubs and activities. It all adds up to an exciting, broad and stimulating all-round education.

### Academic results

In 2017 47.9% of A-level subjects taken at independent schools were graded A*/A – this is almost double the national average of 26.3%. This year also saw nearly two-thirds of independent school GCSE entries being awarded an A*/A or 9/8/7, three times the national average. This is especially impressive given many fee-charging schools are not academically selective. In 2017, there was an increase in Year 13 candidates taking Extended Project, Pre-U, and BTEC qualifications. The average points score for pupils taking the IB Diploma was 37, roughly equivalent to 4.5 As at A-level. In the International Baccalaureate, 3.7% of pupils obtained 45 points, the highest mark, which is only achieved by 0.1% of candidates worldwide.

### Fee Assistance

ISC schools are sympathetic to the financial challenges facing many parents and the amount of bursaries and scholarships available has grown to reflect this. A third of pupils receive fee assistance; the value of this help totals over £900m.

### ISC Associations

There are seven member associations of ISC each with its own distinctive ethos:

**Girls' Schools Association (GSA) – see page 36**
**Headmasters' and Headmistresses' Conference (HMC) – see page 36**
**Independent Association of Prep Schools (IAPS) – see page 38**
**Independent Schools Association (ISA) – see page 38**
**The Society of Heads – see page 39**
**Association of Governing Bodies of Independent Schools (AGBIS)**
www.agbis.org

**Independent Schools' Bursars Association (ISBA)**
www.isba.org.uk
The ISC can be contacted at: First Floor, 27 Queen Anne's Gate, London, SW1H 9BU
Telephone: 020 7766 7070
Website: www.isc.co.uk

# Profiles

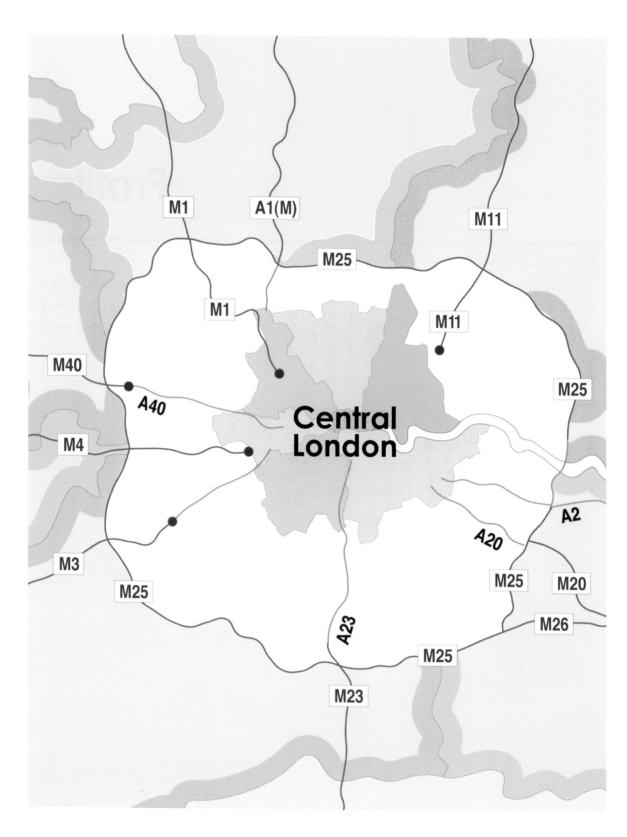

# Schools in Central London

# Bassett House School

BASSETT
HOUSE SCHOOL

(Founded 1947)

60 Bassett Road, London, W10 6JP
**Tel:** 020 8969 0313
**Email:** info@bassetths.org.uk
**Website:** www.bassetths.org.uk
**Headmistress:** Mrs Philippa Cawthorne
MA (Soton) PGCE Mont Cert
**Appointed:** January 2014

**School type:** Co-educational Day
**Age range of pupils:** 3–11
**No. of pupils enrolled as at 01/01/2018:** 190
**Fees per annum as at 01/01/2018:**
*Day:* £8,520–£17,760
**Average class size:** 20
**Teacher/pupil ratio:** 1:7

At Bassett House, last year we marked 70 years of educating young children to achieve their very best. The school's founder, Sylvia Rentoul, recognised children as individuals, and encouraged them to express themselves, helping to grow their achievements and self-confidence.

Focused attention remains our hallmark. We believe tailor-made teaching opens up young minds to endless possibilities, encouraging them to think creatively. We start by ensuring high staff-to-pupil ratios and many specialist teaching staff. Our teachers know every child in their care inside out and use great teaching supported by our excellent equipment (including cutting-edge IT) to bring lessons to life for each child. Our 'sport for all' ethos encourages all our children to think of themselves as athletes, while allowing our sporting stars to shine. We offer football, netball, tag rugby, hockey, tennis, rounders, athletics, gymnastics and eurhythmics as part of the core curriculum and clubs in swimming, fencing, yoga and dance.

We don't stop there. Vibrant music and drama give our children a passion for participation and performance, fostering a sense of achievement and boosting self-confidence. Our children first take to the stage from age 3 and have many opportunities to shine throughout life at Bassett House, whether in whole-school assemblies, stage shows or concerts. We have choirs, musical ensembles and an orchestra and provide individual instrumental music lessons from specialist music teachers.

Our extra-curricular clubs, together with our weekly enrichment hour, expand our children's horizons beyond the core curriculum. Each term children can choose to add a variety of activities to the school day, be it Lego modelling, computer coding, Scottish dancing, origami, chess, geography, cookery, arts and crafts or Zumba.

Residential trips from year 3 onwards create a sense of adventure and build self-reliance. The glow of a 7-year-old's face recounting a nighttime bug-hunting expedition, a 9-year-old's thrill at working with a friend to sail a dinghy, a 10-year-old embracing the challenge of sleeping out under a self-made shelter: we create these memorable moments, knowing that their positive effects will last a lifetime.

All of this makes not only for well-rounded individuals, it translates into excellent academic results. When they leave aged 11, Bassett House children are ready to thrive at London's best senior schools. And they do: our children win places to the cream of London's senior schools. For those who want to board, Bassett House prepares them well for life at leading boarding schools.

We collaborate closely with our sister schools, Orchard House and Prospect House, sparking off new ideas to promote ever more successful teaching practices. The three schools share a common ethos but each retains its unique personality.

The schools (brought together under the umbrella of House Schools Group) are proudly non-selective. True to our belief, children are not tested and judged at the tender age of 3 or 4 years. Our outstanding results repeatedly show all children can fulfill their potential, regardless of early learning ability. We encourage our high fliers to skyrocket, whilst children who need a little extra help are given the support they need to reach their fullest potential.

Our last full ISI inspection awarded us 'excellent' and 'outstanding' in all areas and we flew through our 2016 compliance inspection.

This year, we look forward to another year of stellar success in education.

# Dallington School

(Founded 1978)

8 Dallington Street, Islington,
London, EC1V 0BW
**Tel:** 020 7251 2284
**Email:** hercules@dallingtonschool.co.uk
**Website:** www.dallingtonschool.co.uk
**Headteacher:** Mrs M C Hercules MBE
**Appointed:** 1978

**School type:**
Coeducational Day and Nursery
**Age range of pupils:** 3–11
**No. of pupils enrolled as at 01/01/2018:** 134
**Boys:** 82 **Girls:** 52
**Fees per annum as at 01/01/2018:**
*Day:* £9,978–£12,630
**Teacher/pupil ratio:** 1:16 (with full time TA)

**A family-run, independent, co-educational day school for children aged 3 to 11, in the heart of London**

*"My passion and determination, combined with an unerring belief that children should be included in their learning and listened to, as they expressed their thoughts, ideas and opinions drove me to create my own school. I did this in 1978 and this characteristic spirit of our school is still in evidence and works!"*
Mogg Hercules MBE. Headteacher, Proprietor and Founder
Ted Wragg Lifetime Achievement Award (with Distinction) 2009

At Dallington, we want children to enjoy their childhood, develop a love of learning, independence of thought and retain their individuality. Our expectation is for every child to understand the part it has to play in its learning. The relationships between the staff and the children are informal, but considerate. First names are used and we do not have a school uniform.

We encourage our children to become confident, enthusiastic learners. We offer a topic-based curriculum which is broad, creative and balanced; The Arts are a strong element of our curriculum. Our school is widely creative and the children are encouraged to assume responsibility in a self-regulated, purposeful way.

Our children work and play together in a co-operative, supportive way and great emphasis is placed on nurturing the development of the powers of reasoning and reflective, critical thinking. We provide an environment where children can openly relate to others and expect to be listened to and respected for their points of view.

We have an exemplary record of attaining places prior to and at Secondary level. Children are prepared for external exams in a non-competitive, stress-free environment. A non-competitive ethos does not mean the children lack purpose in their learning.

Personal tours each day of the week. Non-selective entry policy. Early registration advised.

# Devonshire House Preparatory School

(Founded 1989)

2 Arkwright Road, Hampstead,
London, NW3 6AE

**Tel:** 020 7435 1916

**Email:** enquiries@
devonshirehouseprepschool.co.uk

**Website:**
www.devonshirehouseschool.co.uk

**Headmistress:** Mrs S. Piper BA(Hons)

**School type:** Preparatory, Pre-preparatory
& Nursery Day School

**Religious Denomination:**
Non-denominational

**Age range of boys:** 2½–13

**Age range of girls:** 2½–11

**No. of pupils enrolled as at 01/01/2018:** 670

**Boys:** 360 **Girls:** 310

**Fees per annum as at 01/01/2018:**

*Day:* £9,750–£17,985

## Academic & leisure facilities

The school is situated in fine premises in the heart of Hampstead with its own walled grounds. The aim is to achieve high academic standards whilst developing enthusiasm and initiative throughout a wide range of interests. It is considered essential to encourage pupils to develop their own individual interests and a good sense of personal responsibility.

## Curriculum

Early literacy and numeracy are very important and the traditional academic subjects form the core curriculum. The younger children all have a class teacher and classroom assistant and their day consists of a mixture of formal lessons and learning through play. Whilst children of all ages continue to have a form teacher, as they grow older an increasing part of the curriculum is delivered by subject specialists. The combined sciences form an increasingly important part of the timetable as the children mature. The use of computers is introduced from an early stage, both as its own skill and as an integrated part of the pupils' education.

Expression in all forms of communication is encouraged, with classes having lessons in art, music, drama and French. Physical exercise and games also play a key part of the curriculum. Much encouragement is given to pupils to help widen their horizons and broaden their interests. The school fosters a sense of responsibility amongst the pupils, and individuality and personal attention for each pupil is considered essential to make progress in the modern world.

The principal areas of the National Curriculum are covered, though subjects may be taken at a higher level, or at a quicker pace. For the girls approaching the eleven plus senior schools' entry examinations, special emphasis is given to the requirements for these, and in the top two years for the boys, Common Entrance curriculum is taught. The pupils achieve great success in these examinations and a number also sit successfully for senior school scholarships.

The school has its own nursery, The Oak Tree Nursery, which takes children from two-and-a-half years of age.

## Entry requirements

The Oak Tree Nursery: For children entering the Oak Tree Nursery, places are offered on the basis on an informal assessment made at the nursery. Children in The Oak Tree Nursery transfer directly to the Junior School.

The Junior School: For children entering the junior school from the ages of three to five, places are offered on the basis of assessment made at the school. From the age of six places are usually subject to a written test taken at school. At eight, children transfer directly into the upper school. Parents and their children are welcome to visit for interview and to see around the school.

The Upper School: Entry to the upper school is principally from the junior school. For pupils seeking to join the school from elsewhere places are normally subject to a written entrance test.

# DLD College London

DLD
COLLEGE
LONDON

ESTABLISHED 1931

(Founded 1931)

199 Westminster Bridge Road, London, SE1 7FX

**Tel:** +44 (0)20 7935 8411
**Email:** dld@dld.org
**Website:** www.dldcollege.co.uk
**Principal:**
Irfan H Latif BSc (Hons) PGCE FRSA FRSC
**Appointed:** January 2018
**School type:**
Coeducational Day & Boarding

**No. of pupils enrolled as at 01/01/2018:** 440
**Boys:** 224 **Girls:** 216
**No. of boarders:** 220
**Fees per annum as at 01/01/2018:**
**Day:** £19,000–£23,000
**Full Boarding:** £16,500–£24,000
**Average class size:** 10-12
**Teacher/pupil ratio:** 1:6

DLD College is a leading independent boarding and day school that offers over 500 students a wide-ranging curriculum in a superb and modern learning environment, delivered by teachers who are selected for their academic strength, enthusiasm and their ability to relate positively to young people. We are helping students achieve grades they often didn't believe possible and preparing them to access the university courses and destinations of their choice. DLD College is a dynamic place to study providing high quality GCSE, A Level & BTEC courses.

Our lessons are lively and encourage students to discuss ideas, ask questions and actively learn. We recognise that choosing the most appropriate programme of study is a very important part of the application process and we therefore invite all those interested in enrolling at DLD to an interview to discuss their subject choices.

We believe small class sizes encourage a more purposeful learning environment and allows for a greater measure of individual attention, helping students to be more focused on their studies and building their confidence. Students learn important study skills including note taking, essay writing, time management, revision and exam technique. On average, class sizes at DLD are around 10-12 students. Each student is allocated a Personal Tutor who monitors his or her progress as they move through the course. The welfare of students is paramount and the personal tutors are backed up by a team of dedicated Directors of Studies.

In September 2015, DLD College relocated to brand new, purpose built premises in the heart of London,

overlooking Westminster and the River Thames. DLD College London is a truly unique college campus, with facilities including:

- 55 classrooms – 60 touch screens
- Theatre with state of the art LED lighting. The theatre is also equipped with a cinema screen and surround sound.
- Two 1st floor music rooms fully equipped with the latest iMacs and software, a studio complex in the basement with three rooms. The music technology lab comprises state of the art iMac computers with the latest versions of Logic and Sibelius software on them. In addition, we have three practice rooms equipped with a top end acoustic and digital pianos as well as a drum kit.
- Three art studios, graphic suite and a photography studio and classrooms.
- Separate laboratories for Biology,

Chemistry and Physics equipped with interactive touch screens.
- Four dedicated learning zones with quiet booths and water fountains.
- Learning centre equipped with state of the art technology.
- Under 16's study areas equipped with computers (supervised) and open space learning.
- 5 private tuition rooms for one on one learning.
- The Refectory provides a multifunctional space for eating, studying and socialising, and has a mixture of long bench style tables and booths. In addition, students also have access to a Starbucks Café from 8am.
- Atrium with film projectors and surround sound.
- Gallery with seating for student group work.
- College nurse with onsite medical facilities.

# Dolphin School
## (incorporating Noah's Ark Nursery Schools)

(Founded 1986)
106 Northcote Road, London, SW11 6QW

**Tel:** 020 7924 3472
**Email:** admissions@dolphinschool.org.uk
**Website:** www.dolphinschool.org.uk
**Principal:** Mrs. N. Baldwin
**Appointed:** September 2016
**School type:**
Coeducational Day and Nursery
**Age range of pupils:** 2.5–11

**No. of pupils enrolled as at 01/01/2018:** 301
**Fees per annum as at 01/01/2018:**
*Day:* £5,640–£12,885
**Average class size:**
18 in school: 8 in Nursery
**Teacher/pupil ratio:** 1:8 Nursery,
1:9 (Lower School), 1:18 (Upper School)

### Curriculum
Our small class sizes enable us to get to know your child extremely well so that we can not only set specific individualised academic targets, but also discover how he or she learns best. We give priority to English and maths as well as hands-on science, colourful geography, history (with outings to the real thing) and whole-school Spanish.

### Games and the arts
We train pupils in the arts with fantastic specialist teaching and a plethora of performing and exhibiting opportunities. We also coach children in a wide range of sports through dynamic teaching and a superb fixture list.

### Pastoral care
We are committed to giving both time and care to grow your child's character on his or her journey from Reception to Year 6. Our Christian ethos leads us to believe that personal growth ultimately matters more than anything. So while we are thrilled that our leavers win academic or sporting scholarships to a range of excellent secondary schools, we are even more excited about who they are – and pleased that they enjoyed the journey.

### Entry requirements
Reception class: appointment with the Principal. Years 1-6: assessment day and past school reports.

### Principal's philosophy
If we want children to be the best they can be, academically, artistically, in sport or as people, we must start by valuing them for who they are.

### Outstanding characteristics
The combination of nurture and dynamism. The passionate commitment of the staff. A fantastic all-round education.

### Examinations offered
11+ entry examinations.

**Senior exit schools:** Alleyn's, City of London Schools, Downe House, Ibstock Place, Royal Russell, Dulwich College, JAGS, Streatham & Clapham High, Trinity School, Emanuel, TCC, Lady Margaret, Putney High School, Whitgift, Francis Holland, Frensham Heights.

*Dolphin School Trust is a registered charity (No. 1145113) and exists to promote a high quality of education for all its children based upon Christian principles.*

# École Jeannine Manuel – London

(Founded 2015)

43-45 Bedford Square, London WC1B 3DN

**Tel:** 020 3829 5970
**Email:** contact@jmanuel.uk.net
**Website:**
www.ecolejeanninemanuel.org.uk
**Head of School:** Pauline Prévot
**School type:** Coeducational Day

**Age range of pupils:** 3–18 years
**No. of pupils enrolled as at 01/01/2018:** 350
**Fees per annum as at 01/01/2018:**
*Day:* £17,460
**Average class size:** 16
**Teacher/pupil ratio:** 1:10

École Jeannine Manuel in London is a French, bilingual, international school which opened its doors in September 2015 in three contiguous mansions on Bedford Square, steps away from the British Museum. Our school currently welcomes pupils from all nationalities and cultural backgrounds, from Nursery to Year 10. Starting from September 2018, we will welcome pupils up to Year 11 and will develop gradually thereafter, with the opening of our Year 13 planned for September 2020. Pupils will be able to take the International Option of the French Baccalaureate (British Section) or the International Baccalaureate.

École Jeannine Manuel is the young sister school of its Paris namesake, a UNESCO associated school founded in 1954 and one of France's most prestigious schools, ranked first among French high schools (public and independent) for overall academic performance for the past five years. As is the case in France, École Jeannine Manuel London's mission is "to promote international understanding through the bilingual education of a multicultural community of students, the fostering of pedagogical innovation, and the constant exploration of best practices in the context of an ever-changing global environment."

### A bilingual education

École Jeannine Manuel offers an enriched, bilingual adaptation of the French national curriculum, including English, Science and Chinese programmes developed by its sister school in Paris. In History, the French national curriculum is complemented to help pupils gain coherent knowledge and understanding of Britain's past and that of the wider world. Extra-curricular activities include sports – with outdoor facilities within walking distance of the school – as well as a broad range of artistic and tech-based clubs.

English and French are spoken equally in class. Our aim is to bring pupils to a native proficiency – orally and in writing – in both languages. We welcome non French-speaking students at all levels and help them adapt to the demands of a bilingual curriculum. With respect to English, the school accommodates beginners up to Year 7. Experience shows that studying in French and in English yields a strong and mutually reinforced command of both languages as well as a deep understanding of the cultures they express. A bilingual education enhances pupils' capacity for abstract, conceptual thinking and develops a sense of nuance, nurtured by exposure to multiple perspectives.

### A multicultural community of students

Looking beyond French and bi-national families, the school welcomes pupils from all nationalities, cultural traditions and native languages. École Jeannine Manuel in London is positioned, as is the case in Paris, as a unique, truly bicultural institution with a multicultural student body representing more than 40 nationalities. We attract international and internationally minded families deeply invested in the education and well being of their children. Living within this cultural melting pot every day yields a special consciousness of one's place in the world, an appreciation for the broad landscape of culture and civilizations that we learn to understand and value together.

### The fostering of pedagogical innovation

The key drivers of our school's pedagogy are coherence and innovation. Whether inspired by current research in the cognitive sciences, by best practices from around the world or home-grown, our teaching methods are constantly evolving. Our international teams of teachers stimulate new ideas that lead to a creative, pioneering education. Hands-on manipulations in math, inquiry-based learning in the sciences, and teamwork are among the practices that foster pupil engagement and growth. Our aim is to have pupils think, do and share. The school's pedagogical principles are founded on four pillars: the early mastery of core academic skills; the development of autonomy; the encouragement of collaborative work; and the nurturing of curiosity, creativity and a lifelong appetite for culture.

© Paul Riddle

# Faraday School

FARADAY SCHOOL
TRINITY BUOY WHARF

Old Gate House, 7 Trinity Buoy Wharf,
London, E14 0JW
**Tel:** 020 8965 7374
**Email:** info@newmodelschool.co.uk
**Website:** www.faradayschool.co.uk
**Executive Head Teacher:** Mrs. S. Gillam

**School type:** Coeducational Day
**Age range of pupils:** 4–11
**No. of pupils enrolled as at 01/01/2018:** 105
**Fees per term as at 01/01/2018:**
**Day:** £3,284

Faraday is a small, independent prep school situated at the historic setting of Trinity Buoy Wharf, close to the City and Canary Wharf.

Faraday School is committed to giving every child a first-class education in the arts and sciences, drawing as a resource upon the Core Knowledge approach, which imparts knowledge through traditional academic subjects.

Although we believe in a traditional approach, our lessons reflect modern thinking on how children learn most effectively and our small classes and quality staff allow for a very personal approach to learning.

We feel literacy and numeracy are important, however, our curriculum is broad and stimulating, including specialist teaching in French, Music and Physical Education. Our aim is to educate the whole child through a rich curriculum with many stimuli, in order to support an atmosphere of life-long learning.

We also provide a wide range of after school clubs and, to help working parents, a private school bus runs before and after school from 22 different locations, including south of the river.

We were founded in 2009 and maintain strong links with our sister school, Maple Walk, in North West London. Our setting beside the River Thames, opposite the iconic O2 arena and beside the Trinity Lighthouse, gives our pupils an inspirational location in which to learn. We are fortunate enough to be surrounded by creative industries and we make the best of all that London has to offer, with regular trips to museums, historic attractions and galleries.

Our June 2014 ISI Inspection found Faraday School pupil attainment to be *"well-above national age-rated expectations."*

# Hawkesdown House School Kensington

**Hawkesdown House School**
Endeavour • Courage • Truth

27 Edge Street, Kensington,
London, W8 7PN

**Tel:** 020 7727 9090
**Email:** admin@hawkesdown.co.uk
**Website:** www.hawkesdown.co.uk
**Headmistress:**
Mrs. J. A. K. Mackay B.Ed (Hons)
**Appointed:** April 2017
**School type:** Coeducational
Independent Preparatory Day

**Religious Denomination:**
Non-denominational
**Age range of pupils:** 3–11
**No. of pupils enrolled as at 01/01/2018:** 130
**Fees per annum as at 01/01/2018:**
*Day:* £16,020–£18,435
**Average class size:** 15
**Teacher/pupil ratio:** 1:9

Hawkesdown House is an independent prep school for girls and boys from the age of four to eleven, with a Nursery class for children of three years old. It is housed in a fine building in Edge Street just off Kensington Church Street where bright and airy classrooms provide a creative and welcoming environment.

Hawkesdown House is dedicated to providing an outstanding early education. The children are prepared for examinations at 11+ to a wide range of London's selective prep and senior schools. Pupils may also choose to sit entrance examinations at 8+ to London's prep schools and country boarding schools.

The excellence of the broad and creative educational provision enriches the pupils' lives across the curriculum and in all co-curricular and extra curricular activities, so fencing, judo, chess and coding, for example, are all included in the timetable.

The ethos and aims of the School embrace high academic standards and expectations. Hawkesdown House prides itself on its outstanding pastoral care, thoughtful teaching and individual attention. Right from the beginning, Hawkesdown House provides advice, support, reassurance and the preparation to give pupils and parents a very happy start at school.

The School's motto, "Endeavor, Courage, Truth", reflects the aspirations for the pupils; that they grow into kind, capable and considerate adults, well prepared to make sound judgements and take responsibility for themselves and others. Hawkesdown House pupils are actively encouraged to develop both their initiative and their intellectual curiosity.

Mrs Jenny Mackay, the Headmistress, has a deep commitment to pastoral care, academic excellence and the development of the individual. With a degree in Education from Oxford, she also has extensive experience of some of the best education in Britain, at some of London's most highly sought after and outstanding schools.

Hawkesdown House is a happy, nurturing and successful school. There is a fantastic, dedicated staff body and a wonderful collaborative approach which ensures that the curriculum meets the needs of each and every child. The school exudes busyness and celebrates the excellence and achievements of all.

# Hill House International Junior School

**HILL HOUSE**
INTERNATIONAL JUNIOR SCHOOL

(Founded 1949)
17 Hans Place, Chelsea,
London, SW1X 0EP
**Tel:** 020 7584 1331
**Email:** info@hillhouseschool.co.uk
**Website:** www.hillhouseschool.co.uk

**Principals:** Richard, Janet, William & Edmund Townend
**Appointed:** 2002
**Founders:** Lt Col Stuart Townend OBE & Mrs Beatrice Townend
**School type:** Coeducational Day
**Age range of pupils:** 4–13
**No. of pupils enrolled as at 01/01/2018:** 740

**Boys:** 410 **Girls:** 330 **Sixth Form:** 70
**Fees per annum as at 01/01/2018:**
**Small & Lower School:** £13,200–£14,100
**Middle & Upper School:** £15,000–£16,200
**Senior School & Transitus:** £16,500
**Lower & Upper Sixth:** £17,100–£17,400
**Average class size:** 12-14
**Teacher/pupil ratio:** 1:7

'A child's mind is not a vessel to be filled, but a fire to be kindled.'

Hill House was founded in Switzerland in 1949 moving to La Tour-de-Peilz in 1951 when the building in Hans Place, London was opened. We hold fast to the guiding vision set by the founders that the modern child must be educated for a world community. He or she must be taught to understand that all nations depend on one another; learn to live with children of other nationalities; respect that which is unknown and often very foreign to them, and thus open the doors to a world which each day becomes smaller. Hill House became the first school to teach in two different countries at the same time with the same children. The purpose-built house in Glion, 2,500 feet above Lac Leman, hosts specialist courses throughout the year for selected pupils from London, providing experience of a boarding school environment in the setting of a mountain village in the French speaking canton of Vaud.

Hill House is the oldest London school in which every aspect of the daily administration of the school remains in the care and control of the founding family. It is a school that enables children from all over the world to have the opportunity to follow an English curriculum while learning that every nation is equal but different and that peaceful co-existence comes from mutual respect, understanding and consideration for others from diverse backgrounds. A full academic programme, enriched by outstanding teaching in small classes, leads to pupils consistently going on to the leading day and boarding secondary schools of their choice with many scholarships awarded each year. We passionately believe in supporting and stretching all our pupils to seek the highest levels of academic achievement. There is a particular emphasis on Art, Drama, Music and Sport all of which are taught by over thirty specialist teachers. Throughout the year there are over seventy concerts, recitals and drama evenings in Founders' Hall where pupils can showcase their artistic talents and the school year ends with a celebratory Field Day culminating in the famous Gun Run.

### Admissions

Children can enter Hill House at any age between four and eleven years old if places are available. There is no formal entry examination. Parents are invited to visit Hans Place any Monday, Tuesday, Thursday or Friday during term time at 8.30am for a tour of the school. There is no need for an appointment – please just come when it is convenient for you. After the tour, if you wish, you may complete the simple entry application form. All entry forms must be completed by the parents, in person, at Hans Place. We will not send forms by post.

### Contacts

Mrs Janet Townend (Director of Admissions), Miss Beryl Lang (Registrar)
Tel: 020 7584 1331, admissions@hillhouseschool.co.uk

# Lloyd Williamson Schools

## LLOYD WILLIAMSON
### —SCHOOLS—

(Founded 1999)

12 Telford Road, London, W10 5SH

**Tel:** 020 8962 0345

**Fax:** 020 8962 0345

**Email:** admin@lws.org.uk

**Website:** www.lloydwilliamson.co.uk

**Co-Principals:**

Ms Lucy Meyer & Mr Aaron Williams

**Appointed:** December 1999

**School type:** Coeducational Day

**Age range of pupils:**

4 months–16 years (18 in 2019)

**Fees per annum as at 01/01/2018:**

*Day:* £13,950

**Average class size:** 12-16

**Teacher/pupil ratio:** 1:12

Over the past twelve years, Lloyd Williamson Schools have built an excellent reputation for being schools with high academic standards, personalised learning for individual children and a friendly, happy environment in which to learn. We foster initiative and a love for learning. 'Outstanding' (Ofsted).

We are pleased to offer parents important extras:

- Breakfast and after-school club at no extra cost (the school and nurseries are open 7.30am – 6pm).
- Holiday clubs (we are open 50 weeks of the year).

- Small classes (maximum of 16).
- Competitive fees.
- Home-cooked meals freshly prepared every day by our in-house chefs.

We boast an outstanding playground with excellent facilities, a homely atmosphere with school pets, and dedicated teachers who support the children to be focused, positive and enthusiastic.

'Throughout the school, relationships between staff and children are excellent, which gives the pupils security and confidence to succeed.' (Ofsted)

**In the words of our children:**

"I'm really happy here – the teachers really listen and if I get stuck they help!"

"There is always someone who listens to me."

"I like the way the big children look after the little children."

**And the parents:**

"You always know a Lloyd Williamson child – they're so polite!"

"I think the school is, beyond doubt, the best I could wish for."

"The best-kept secret in London!"

To visit the school or nurseries, please contact the school administrator, Emma Cole on: 020 8962 0345.

# L'Ecole de Battersea
## International Bilingual School
### TROTT STREET, BATTERSEA, LONDON SW11 3DS

Founded in 1977

**Principal:** Mme Brisset

**Head:** Mr L Balerdi

**Founder:** Mme Otten

**School type:** Independent Bilingual Pre-Primary and Primary (Ecole Homologuée)

**Age range of pupils:**
3–11 years, boys and girls

**No of pupils enrolled as at 1.9.17:**
260 pupils

**Fees per annum as at 1.9.17:**
£12,150 - £12,300

**Religious denomination:**
All denominations welcome

**Entry requirements:**
Interview with parents and school tour

L'Ecole de Battersea opened in 2005 following on from the success of its sister school, L'Ecole des Petits.

The school is unique in that it offers a **continuous bilingual education from age three through until age eleven** at the end of primary, where both the French and English educational systems operate together. The teaching emphasis throughout the school is fundamentally based on the French system, into which aspects of the English curriculum and methodology are integrated.

The highly motivated bilingual team of teachers are qualified in both the English and French educational systems.

This bilingual facility enables children and parents to choose to progress on to either the English private school system or on to the French Lycée system, and is also ideal for the increasingly popular International Baccalaureate.

The school welcomes bilingual pupils from a range of cultures, and so aims to generate a **truly international atmosphere**.

**Partnership with the family** is paramount in the school's ethos, and the school successfully seeks **to develop confident and balanced children** with experience of a wide range of activities, an appreciation of artistic and cultural heritage and a thoughtful and considerate attitude towards others.

**Class sizes are small** and the school occupies a recently refurbished building with **top quality facilities**, and with good outside spaces for a Central London school. The school is only **five minutes drive from Chelsea** and operates a twice daily school bus service between South Kensington and Battersea, as well as a link to its sister school in Fulham, ten minutes distance.

The school is inspected by both the French Inspectorate and Ofsted and achieves excellent academic results. **OFSTED 2015 report said the school was** "*Outstanding in all categories*" and it has been selected as one of the top 225 private schools in the country in *The Tatler Education Guides 2009–2018*.

TEL. 020 7371 8350    admin@lecoledespetits.co.uk    www.lecoledespetits.co.uk

**Founded in 1977**

# L'Ecole des Petits

*International Bilingual School*

## 2 HAZLEBURY ROAD, FULHAM, LONDON SW6 2NB

**Principal:** Mme Brisset

**Deputy:** Miss E Mesnage

**Founder:** Mme Otten

**School type:** Independent Bilingual Pre-Primary (Ecole Homologuée)

**Age range of pupils:**
3–6 years, boys and girls

**No of pupils enrolled as at 1.9.17:**
132 pupils

**Fees per annum as at 1.9.17:**
Full day £11,895 - £11,985

**Religious denomination:**
All denominations welcome

**Entry requirements:**
Interview with parents and school tour

L'Ecole des Petits is a flourishing pre-primary school situated in Fulham, just **ten minutes from Chelsea**, with easy access by public transport. The school also runs its own daily morning and afternoon **bus service between South Kensington and Fulham**, and between its sister school in Battersea.

The school was founded in 1977 to cater for English and French families who want their children to **grow up in a bilingual environment**. By combining the Early Years curriculum with the French National curriculum, the school provides all aspects of education in both French and English, and today has a wonderfully **international flavour with children from 22 different countries** attending.

Children are taught by qualified and highly-motivated bilingual teachers. The school aims to provide **an education that enhances early learning skills in the controlled environment of small classes**.

The school has a warm and friendly atmosphere which encourages children to express themselves whilst following the structured bilingual curriculum. We consider maintaining **traditional family values** a very important aspect of our approach.

Our philosophy is to develop confident and happy children by providing **the best possible all-round education and care**, with an abundance of sports, drama, clubs, school outings and events as well as academic lessons.

We prepare our children to move onto both English and French schools, and many also continue their primary education at our sister school, L'Ecole de Battersea.

According to one of our parents, *"This is an exceptional school that provides a nurturing environment, as well as good discipline and a wonderful education, and my child could not be happier and more confident about going to school."*

**OFSTED 2017 report:** *"Outstanding in all categories"*.

TEL. 020 7371 8350      admin@lecoledespetits.co.uk      www.lecoledespetits.co.uk

# Lyndhurst House Prep School

**LYNDHURST HOUSE**
PREPARATORY SCHOOL

(Founded 1952)
24 Lyndhurst Gardens, Hampstead,
London, NW3 5NW

**Tel:** 020 7435 4936
**Email:** office@lyndhursthouse.co.uk
**Website:** www.lyndhursthouse.co.uk
**Head of School:** Mr Andrew Reid MA
(Oxon)
**Appointed:** September 2008
**School type:** Boys' Day

**Age range of boys:** 4–13
**No. of pupils enrolled as at 01/01/2018:** 165
**Fees per annum as at 01/01/2018:**
*Day:* £5,735–£6,410
**Average class size:** 18
**Teacher/pupil ratio:** 1:8

Lyndhurst House Pre-Prep & Prep School for boys was founded by Vernon Davies in 1952, in a tall, handsome Willett-style building in leafy Lyndhurst Gardens, Hampstead.

For over 60 years Lyndhurst has played a full part in the range of local independent educational provision, sending on its thirteen year olds to the many renowned senior schools in London, and some to boarding further afield with an excellent record of academic success and achievement, matched by a strong participation in sports, music and art.

Pupils develop a good knowledge of their own and other cultures and traditions. Visits to theatres, museums and art galleries feature prominently throughout the year. A significant strength of the school is the way pupils from a wide range of cultural backgrounds work and play together harmoniously.

One of the smaller prep schools in the area, Lyndhurst provides a structured but individually responsive education from reception at four-plus up to Common Entrance and scholarship at 13, delivered by an experienced, well-qualified, and stable staff team, and the abiding characteristics of its pupils seem to be a lively enthusiasm and sense of engagement and belonging. Lyndhurst House is a non-denominational school.

For all enquiries, please contact:
Mrs Dawn Lewis
Lyndhurst House Preparatory
24 Lyndhurst Gardens
Hampstead
London NW3 5NW
Tel: 020 7435 4936
Email: dlewis@lyndhursthouse.co.uk
Website: www.lyndhursthouse.co.uk
We look forward to meeting you.

# Maple Walk School

62A Crownhill Road, London, NW10 4EB

**Tel:** 020 8963 3890

**Email:** admin@maplewalkschool.co.uk

**Website:** www.maplewalkschool.co.uk

**Head Teacher:** Mrs S Gillam

**School type:** Coeducational Day

**Age range of pupils:** 4–11

**No. of pupils enrolled as at 01/01/2018:** 200

**Fees per term as at 01/01/2018:**

**Day:** £3,190

**Average class size:** 20

Maple Walk is a small, independent prep school in North West London.

Maple Walk School is committed to giving every child a first-class education in the arts and sciences, drawing as a resource upon the Core Knowledge approach, which imparts knowledge through traditional academic subjects.

Although we believe in a traditional approach, our lessons reflect modern thinking on how children learn most effectively and our small classes and quality staff allow for a very personal approach to learning.

We feel literacy and numeracy are important, however, our curriculum is broad and stimulating, including specialist teaching in French, Music, Drama, Dance and Physical Education. Our aim is to educate the whole child through a rich curriculum with many stimuli, in order to support an atmosphere of life-long learning.

Our sports teams compete in a range of competitions and have seen growing success, particularly at Cross Country, Football and Gymnastics. We also provide a wide range of after school clubs and care.

Maple Walk was founded in 2004 and we maintain strong links with our sister school, Faraday School, in East London. We are easily accessible by road and public transport and make use of the local facilities, including the Green-Flag awarded Roundwood Park for PE and Willesden Sports Centre for swimming lessons. We take full advantage of the extensive cultural opportunities London has to offer, with termly trips to a wide range of museums, galleries, theatres and places of scientific, historical and religious interest.

Our March 2012 ISI Inspection found that *"the personal development of pupils is excellent"*.

In 2016 Maple Walk was named in *The Telegraph* newspaper as one of the Top 10 Best Value Prep Schools.

# Mander Portman Woodward – London

Mander Portman Woodward

(Founded 1973)

90-92 Queen's Gate, London, SW7 5AB
**Tel:** 020 7835 1355
**Fax:** 020 7259 2705
**Email:** london@mpw.ac.uk
**Website:** www.mpw.ac.uk
**Principal:** Mr John Southworth BSc MSc
**Appointed:** August 2016

**School type:** Coeducational Day
**Age range of pupils:** 14–19
**No. of pupils enrolled as at 01/01/2018:** 724
**Fees per annum as at 01/01/2018:**
*Day:* £9,075–£9,833
**Average class size:** 6
**Teacher/pupil ratio:** 1:6

MPW London was founded in 1973 by three Cambridge graduates. The academic experience for students is modelled on the Oxford and Cambridge tutorial, with lessons being more relaxed and informal than those of a typical school, but also intellectually stimulating and demanding. MPW's mission is to help our students develop their confidence, maturity, knowledge and skills, turning their academic aspirations into reality.

Through our bespoke lessons, we aim to make working hard good fun and equip our alumni with the independence and aptitudes they need for success at university and beyond. With fewer than 10 students in any class, and an average student:teacher ratio more like 6:1, lessons are intensive but rewarding with plenty of opportunity for individual attention and personalised learning. Over 40 subjects are offered at A level and 25 at GCSE.

Our academic programme aims not only to enable students to achieve their best in GCSE and A level examinations but also to prepare them for life at university and beyond. We prepare students for a range of universities, including Oxford and Cambridge, University of the Arts, and competitive degree specialists such as Medicine or Law. Each year, over 70% of our graduates head to top tier universities and our modal A level grade is consistently A/A*. We are especially proud of this given that our admissions policy is academically non-selective; MPW's 'value-add' (the distance travelled by students at A level relative to where they were at GCSE) is exceptional.

As well as expert tuition, students benefit from pastoral care, mentoring and university advice provided by a team of Directors of Studies. A student's Director of Studies provides detailed counsel on university entrance and support for submitting the application, from personal statement critique to organising tutoring for entrance tests or mock interviews. The role of a Director of Studies only begins at UCAS and additional, day-to-day, support is provided to all students throughout their studies. *"They have put themselves out to be helpful"* said one parent to the Good Schools Guide.

Parents are invited to the college regularly to discuss progress with their child's Director of Studies and also for events such as our Art Show, Principal's lecture series or UCAS Week, where we provide advice on university applications. We also run a number of ad-hoc parental seminars throughout the year on relevant topics, such as 'how to support a teenager through exam stress'.

An extensive extra-curricular programme caters for all tastes, from sports – rugby and football are the most popular – to creative arts, language lessons, guitar lessons, drama, journalism, chess club and everything in between. The Duke of Edinburgh award scheme is available to all students and year 10 complete the Bronze award together over the course of the year.

MPW is academically rigorous but socially relaxed and the college prides itself on maintaining a relatively informal, personalised and supportive atmosphere, allowing our students to develop the independence and responsibility that they will need in the future. Our focus on equipping students with the skills they need for life encourages success across a wide range of disciplines. Recent alumni include Harry Stebbings, Europe's youngest ever venture capitalist (*"I would not be who I am without MPW"*) and Tom Charman, CEO of KOMPAS (*"nothing could have prepared me better for the role that I play today"*).

# More House School

(Founded 1953)

22-24 Pont Street, Knightsbridge, London, SW1X 0AA

**Tel:** 020 7235 2855

**Fax:** 020 7259 6782

**Email:** office@morehouse.org.uk

**Website:** www.morehouse.org.uk

**Co-Heads:** Mrs. Amanda Leach & Mr. Michael Keeley

**Appointed:** April 2014 & July 2017

**School type:** Independent Girls' Day

**Age range of girls:** 11–18

**No. of pupils enrolled as at 01/01/2018:** 206

**Fees per annum as at 01/01/2018:**

*Day:* £18,930

**Average class size:** 16

**Teacher/pupil ratio:** 1:5

More House School provides an environment where pupils and staff are valued and supported as individuals and where their rights and dignity are maintained. Our School fosters an ethos of spiritual growth, not only for those within the Roman Catholic Church but also for those who adhere to other Christian traditions and other faiths.

The school was founded in 1953 by the Canonesses of St Augustine, at the request of a group of parents determined to send their daughters to a Catholic London day school. It occupies two interconnecting townhouses in the heart of Knightsbridge. Pupils of all faiths or none are welcome and the school has a broad cultural mix. Girls are provided with a rounded education, designed to allow individual strengths to shine through.

Academic results are good, balanced by a wide range of extra-curricular activities. Music, drama, and art are well supported and pupils regularly achieve local success in sports such as netball and running. The Duke of Edinburgh's Award is popular and there is an active commitment to fundraising for charity.

Our mission at More House is to provide an environment for pupils to not only gain the qualifications they need to pursue the courses and careers of their choice, but also the confidence and self assurance to meet the challenges that lie ahead in an ever-changing world.

Academic, music, drama, and art scholarships are available at 11+ entry and sixth form. Bursaries are also available.

# North Bridge House

 **North Bridge House**

(Founded 1939)
65 Rosslyn Hill, London, NW3 5UD
**Tel:** 020 7428 1520
**Email:** admissionsenquiries@
northbridgehouse.com
**Website:** www.northbridgehouse.com

**Head of Nursery & Pre-Prep Schools:**
Mrs. Christine McLelland
**Head of Prep School:** Mr. Brodie Bibby
**Head of Senior Hampstead:**
Mr. Brendan Pavey
**Head of Senior Canonbury:**
Mr. Jonathan Taylor
**School type:** Co-educational Day
**Age range of pupils:**
2 years 9 months–18 years

**No. of pupils enrolled as at 01/01/2018:** 1375
**Fees per annum as at 01/01/2018:**
*Nursery:*
 £6,840 (half day)–£13,680 (full time)
*Pre-Reception & Reception:* £15,975
*Pre-Prep – Prep:* £16,575 –£17,340
*Senior Hampstead:* £17,295
*Senior School & Sixth Form Canonbury:*
£17,295 –£18,555
**Average class size:** 20

Founded in 1939, North Bridge House extends its warm, family atmosphere to five prestigious sites across North London, providing a unique and personalised education for pupils aged 2 years 9 months to 18 years. With its newest campus, North Bridge House Canonbury, the first Independent Senior School and Sixth Form in Islington, students can now complete their A-Levels in a stunning Grade II listed building and in a school rated 'Outstanding' by Ofsted in 2015.

At North Bridge House we celebrate the individual, develop their character and nurture their aspirations. As well as happy, our pupils are also high-achieving. Our Key Stage 1 standards of reading, writing and maths score well above the national average. Our Prep School is renowned for first-class results in the girls' 11+ and boys' 13+ senior school entrance exams, whilst NBH Senior Schools celebrate GCSE and A-Level results that evidence significant value added to academic performance.

All North Bridge House students benefit from a rich and varied range of academic and extra-curricular activities which, together with our outstanding pastoral support, encourage them to grow in confidence and gain their independence. We focus on educating the whole child and providing a breadth of learning experience that takes pupils much further than the curriculum itself.

Pupils also enjoy a wide range of sports, with weekly PE and Games sessions designed to develop the individual's physical and emotional wellbeing, as well as essential team skills.

At the heart of the school is a highly qualified and inspirational team of teachers, dedicated to helping every child to fulfil their potential. From the fundamental foundations that are established in the early years of education to the expert UCAS and careers advice that is provided at A-Level, North Bridge House is a platform to success and a gateway to the top universities. Ultimately, with excellent grades and indispensable life skills, North Bridge House prepares students for the challenges and rewards of adult life and the real world.

**Our schools**
**North Bridge House Nursery School**
33 Fitzjohn's Avenue, Hampstead,
London NW3 5JY
**North Bridge House Pre-Prep School**
8 Netherhall Gardens, Hampstead,
London NW3 5RR
**North Bridge House Prep School**
1 Gloucester Avenue, London NW1 7AB
**North Bridge House Senior Hampstead**
65 Rosslyn Hill, London NW3 5UD
**North Bridge House Senior Canonbury**
6-9 Canonbury Place, London N1 2NQ

# Orchard House School

ORCHARD
HOUSE SCHOOL

(Founded 1993)

16 Newton Grove, Bedford Park, London,

W4 1LB

**Tel:** 020 8742 8544

**Email:** info@orchardhs.org.uk

**Website:** www.orchardhs.org.uk

**Headmistress:**

Mrs Maria Edwards BEd(Beds) PGCE(Man)
Mont Cert

**Appointed:** September 2015

**School type:** Co-educational Day

**Age range of pupils:** 3–11

**No. of pupils enrolled as at 01/01/2018:** 290

**Fees per annum as at 01/01/2018:**

*Day:* £8,520–£17,760

**Average class size:** 20

**Teacher/pupil ratio:** 1:7

At Orchard House School, children are loved first and taught second. Our Pupil Pastoral Plan monitors the well-being of each child and was recently shortlisted for a TES (Times Educational Supplement) national award for educational innovation. This emphasis on a nurturing environment is not, however, at the cost of academic excellence. In fact, our outstanding results show how creating the right environment enables every child to thrive academically and emotionally. We believe learning should be exciting and fun, and the children should positively want to come to Orchard House every day. And they do: we harness the exuberance and energy of every child in our care, and instil within them a lifelong love of learning.

Orchard House's diverse curriculum creates a sense of adventure, developing the children's appetite for risk. This feeds into greater academic and creative achievements. Whether it's a whole-school skipping day, a project with Jaguar to enable our 10- and 11-year-old mathematicians to engineer performance cars or learning archery in Normandy (taught solely in French), Orchard House children embrace novel tasks throughout their time with us. By the time they sit 11+ exams, they are past masters at tackling new challenges with verve: this shows in our stellar results.

Sport at Orchard House encourages a respectful, competitive attitude, teaching children the value of camaraderie and the buzz of going for gold, or goal. We offer football, netball, rugby, hockey, lacrosse, cross country, tennis, athletics, triathlon, cricket, rounders, swimming and gymnastics and arrange regular team-sport fixtures against other schools, often lifting the trophy but always relishing the match.

Similarly, music and drama build confidence and self-esteem, as well as many opportunities for every child to perform. Visiting music teachers offer individual instrumental tuition on a variety of instruments. We have a school orchestra, Pippin choir, chamber choir, senior and junior choir and a parent and staff choir. There are many other instrumental groups including a pupil-led rock band.

We collaborate closely with our sister schools, Bassett House and Prospect House, sparking off new ideas to promote ever more successful teaching practices. The three schools share a common ethos but each retains its unique personality. The schools (brought together under the umbrella of House Schools Group) are proudly non-selective. True to our belief, children are not tested and judged at the tender age of 3 or 4 years. Our educational success shows all children can fulfil their potential, regardless of early learning ability.

The Independent Schools Inspectorate recently awarded Orchard House the highest accolades of 'excellent' in all areas and 'exceptional' in achievements and learning. These are mirrored in our first-class academic results and the scholarships our pupils win to their next schools.

# Prospect House School

PROSPECT
HOUSE SCHOOL.

(Founded 1991)

75 Putney Hill, London, SW15 3NT
**Tel:** 020 8246 4897
**Email:** info@prospecths.org.uk
**Website:** www.prospecths.org.uk
**Headmaster:**
Mr Michael Hodge BPED(Rhodes) QTS
**Appointed:** September 2017

**School type:** Co-educational Day
**Age range of pupils:** 3–11
**No. of pupils enrolled as at 01/01/2018:** 300
**Fees per annum as at 01/01/2018:**
*Day:* £8,520–£17,760
**Average class size:** 20
**Teacher/pupil ratio:** 1:7

At Prospect House School, we focus on making each child feel valued and secure and on making their educational experience both challenging and fun. This allows us to develop every child to their fullest potential, as our outstanding results demonstrate. Our most recent full Independent Schools Inspectorate inspection, in 2013, rated us 'excellent' against all the inspectors' criteria and we flew through our 2017 regulatory compliance inspection.

Prospect House's superb teachers provide a supportive and encouraging academic environment in which children excel. The sound of laughter is never far away, as Prospect House children discover their aptitude for sport, music, art, computing, drama or a whole host of other

opportunities both within the curriculum or before or after school. Whether taking up the trombone, building a go-cart or orienteering on Putney Heath, our children relish each new challenge and emerge better able to face the next challenge that comes their way.

Music is an important part of life at Prospect House. We have over 200 individual music lessons taking place each week and a school orchestra, chamber choir and senior and junior choirs, as well as a number of ensembles. All children act in assemblies, school plays, musical productions and concerts throughout the year. Children in Years 1 to 6 enjoy drama lessons and our high-quality staging, lighting, sound and props give every production a professional feel.

Physical activity promotes wellbeing, so we offer a busy sports programme. This includes football, netball, hockey, running, cross country, tennis, athletics, cricket, rounders, swimming, dance and gymnastics. Our approach to fixtures and tournaments successfully balances participation for everyone with letting our sports stars shine.

Residential trips thrill the children with the sense of adventure, encouraging risk-taking and building self-reliance, whether on a history expedition, a bushcraft adventure or a week in Normandy immersed in the French language and culture.

We encourage our children to think for themselves, to be confident and to develop a sense of responsibility for the world in which they live. By the time they leave us aged 11, Prospect House children are ready to thrive at London's best senior schools. This is reflected in our impressive 11+ results. In 2017, academic, sports or music scholarships made up over 12% of our overall senior school offers.

We collaborate closely with our sister schools, Bassett House and Orchard House, sparking off new ideas to promote ever more successful teaching practices. The three schools share a common ethos but each retains its unique personality.

The schools (brought together under the umbrella of House Schools Group) are proudly non-selective. True to our belief, children are not tested and judged at the tender age of 3 or 4 years. Our stellar results repeatedly show all children can fulfil their potential, regardless of early learning ability. We encourage our high-flyers to soar, whilst children who need a little extra help are given the support they need to reach their fullest potential. At Prospect House, every child is helped to achieve a personal best.

# Ravenscourt Park Preparatory School

(Founded 1991)

16 Ravenscourt Avenue, London, W6 0SL

**Tel:** 020 8846 9153

**Fax:** 020 8846 9413

**Email:** secretary@rpps.co.uk

**Website:** www.rpps.co.uk

**Headmaster:**

Mr Carl Howes MA (Cantab), PGCE (Exeter)

**Appointed:** September 2015

**School type:** Coeducational Day

**Age range of pupils:** 4–11

**No. of pupils enrolled as at 01/01/2018:** 419

**Fees per term as at 01/01/2018:**

*Day:* £5,626

**Average class size:** 20

Ravenscourt Park Preparatory School (RPPS) is a lively, co-educational and non-selective independent school for children aged 4 to 11 in West London. Owned by the Gardener Schools Group, a family founded company set up in 1991, RPPS was the first of three schools to open, followed by Kew Green Prep and Kew House Senior School.

RPPS is situated next to Ravenscourt Park, a twenty-acre park which provides the setting for the majority of PE and Games lessons. RPPS has specialist on-site facilities such as a multi-purpose Auditorium, Library, Music Suite, Art Studio and Science Laboratory. Additional facilities include a designated gymnasium, ICT suite and large outdoor playground space.

The school provides an education of the highest quality with an engaging curriculum that is varied, exciting and forward-looking, whilst also preparing pupils for transfer at the end of Year 6 to London Day Schools and 11+ boarding schools.

We are a thriving school, taking pride in a holistic approach to the attainment of each child's potential – intellectual, physical, social and spiritual. Our talented and dedicated team of teachers nurture and inspire the children so that they flourish academically and emotionally.

Our pupils engage in the excitement of learning and develop the confidence to question, analyse and express their opinions. We encourage children to develop a Growth Mindset so that they become resourceful, resilient, reflective and enthusiastic learners who are able to learn from their mistakes and build on their successes.

We form strong and trusting partnerships with our parents. We operate an 'Open Door Policy', where parents' comments, views, contributions and suggestions are valued.

The Independent Schools Inspectorate (ISI) visited RPPS in 2016 and we were delighted to have received the judgement of 'excellent' in all areas.

# Rosemead Preparatory School & Nursery, Dulwich

**ROSEMEAD**
**PREPARATORY**
**SCHOOL & NURSERY**
*DULWICH*

*inspirans flammas*
*posteritatis*

(Founded 1942)

70 Thurlow Park Road, London, SE21 8HZ

**Tel:** 020 8670 5865

**Fax:** 020 8761 9159

**Email:**
admin@rosemeadprepschool.org.uk

**Website:**
www.rosemeadprepschool.org.uk

**Headmaster:** Mr Phil Soutar

**School type:** Coeducational Day

**Age range of pupils:** 2½–11

**No. of pupils enrolled as at 01/01/2018:** 366

**Boys:** 176 **Girls:** 190

**Fees per annum as at 01/01/2018:**

*Day:* £10,272–£11,286

**Average class size:** 18-20

Rosemead Preparatory School and Nursery is a coeducational independent school in Dulwich, which caters for just under 370 pupils.

Rosemead prepares its pupils for private and maintained schools in the Dulwich area and elsewhere, giving them a thorough understanding of learning and a competitive edge that helps the vast majority secure places at their first choice schools. Each year, a high percentage of pupils are given academic, sports, music and art scholarships, exhibitions, bursaries and other awards at a wide range of schools.

Phil Soutar, who joined the school in 2017 as Headmaster, has increased the provision of drama opportunities and residential experiences through the school, whilst continuing to invest in the expansion of the school's extracurricular sports and clubs, which now number just under 100 per week.

The opening of the new playground area in the Pre-Prep department and further internal expansion intended for the near future, make the school a growing proposition for the young children of Dulwich. Having it's own refurbished Nursery taking children from 2 1/2 years of age has also enabled the school to provide further educational opportunities for its families, which is an important part of Rosemead.

What has not changed, however, is Rosemead's renowned unique ethos and sense of community, and the high standards of behaviour expected of its pupils. Rosemead produces kind, caring individuals who are ready to take on the challenges of life in the classroom and beyond. Friendships are forged that last well beyond school – and that includes among the parents. It is the kind of place where pupils cry when they leave, not when they arrive.

There is no doubt that Rosemead aims to do things a bit differently, as its hugely successful annual family skiing trip to Switzerland and camping weekends, demonstrate. To find out more about the difference that Rosemead makes, please email admissions@rosemeadprepschool. org.uk.

# St Benedict's School

(Founded 1902)

54 Eaton Rise, Ealing, London, W5 2ES

**Tel:** 020 8862 2000

**Fax:** 020 8862 2199

**Email:** admissions@stbenedicts.org.uk

**Website:** www.stbenedicts.org.uk

**Headmaster:** Mr A Johnson BA

**Appointed:** September 2016

**School type:** Co-educational Day

**Age range of pupils:** 3–18

**No. of pupils enrolled as at 01/01/2018:** 1073

**Boys:** 715 **Girls:** 361 **Sixth Form:** 219

**Fees per annum as at 01/01/2018:**

**Day:** £12,500–£16,104

**Average class size:** (Junior School) Max 23;

(Senior School) Max 24;

(Sixth Form) Max 14

**Teacher/pupil ratio:** 1:10

St Benedict's is London's leading independent Catholic co-educational school, situated in leafy Ealing. The School is a successful blend of the traditional and the progressive; proud of its heritage but also forward thinking and innovative. Within a caring, happy community, our pupils thrive, benefiting from a seamless education which can begin at the age of 3 and continue through to the Sixth Form.

St Benedict's has strong academic standards, with considerable ambition for future academic success. The School is committed to supporting all children to develop their full potential, by treating them as individuals, and catering for their particular needs and talents at every stage. Inspirational teaching, tutorial guidance and exceptional pastoral care are at the heart of the education we offer.

The Junior School and Nursery provide a supportive and vibrant environment in which to learn. Sharing excellent facilities with the Senior School and a programme of cross-curricular activities help ease the transition at 11+ to the Senior School, which is on the same site.

At St Benedict's, there is a vital focus on personal development, and our outstanding co-curricular programme helps pupils to thrive by enabling them to find and develop their unique gifts and talents. St Benedict's has a distinguished sporting tradition: while many boys and girls train and compete at county and national level, everyone is encouraged to enjoy sport, teamwork and fitness. Music and Drama are both excellent; there is a strong choral tradition, renowned Abbey Choir and many instrumental ensembles. Termly Drama productions have recently included *Amadeus*, *West Side Story* and *A Midsummer Night's Dream*.

We encourage principled leadership, resilience and character in our pupils, and promote the Christian values of integrity, fairness and generosity to others. This is a hallmark of the School, informed by the 1500 year-old Rule of St Benedict, and there could be no better way of equipping young people for the future.

Recent developments include a fine new Sixth Form Centre and Art Department, opened in 2015. A new Nursery and Pre-Prep Department opened in September 2017, providing our youngest pupils with a first-rate learning environment.

St Benedict's School is unique. Come and visit, and see what we have to offer. You can be sure of a warm Benedictine welcome.

# St Augustine's Priory

(Founded 1634)

Hillcrest Road, Ealing, London, W5 2JL

**Tel:** 020 8997 2022

**Fax:** 020 8810 6501

**Email:** office@sapriory.com

**Website:** www.sapriory.com

**Headteacher:**

Mrs Sarah Raffray M.A., N.P.Q.H

**Appointed:** September 2012

**School type:** Girls' Independent Day School

**Religious Denomination:** Catholic

**Age range of boys:** 3–4

**Age range of girls:** 3–18

**No. of pupils enrolled as at 01/01/2018:** 456

**Fees per annum as at 01/01/2018:**

*Day:* £10,656–£15,162

**Average class size:** 20-24

**Teacher/pupil ratio:** 1:12.2

St Augustine's Priory is Ealing's top performing Catholic school, rated 'Outstanding' in all areas in the Westminster Diocesan Report in 2016. We are a Catholic, Independent day school for girls aged 3-18. As an all-through school we expect the majority of pupils to move seamlessly up through the school. We are experts in educating girls and we are dedicated to preparing girls to be highly effective women in the workplace and in the world.

St Augustine's is a unique London school set in 13 acres of beautiful grounds looking out over the Thames Valley to the North Downs. Here girls have the physical, mental and emotional freedom to grow intellectually in an environment which both supports and provides plenty of challenges. Our results are excellent and we pride ourselves on instilling in girls a love of learning.

We are a Catholic school which means that the care of the whole person is at the core of what we do. Founded in 1634 in France, St Augustine's Priory has nearly 400 years' experience of educating children and, until the mid-1990s, was led by a community of Augustinian nuns. We are proud to continue their legacy and cherish their heritage, our children are their heirs. Each child is valued, each a treasured individual with potential and talent. We pride ourselves on producing well-rounded young women, people who, when they emerge from the community that is St Augustine's Priory, are ready to serve and contribute to the wider community and lead lives enriched by their experience at this school.

In 2015 we celebrated "100 years of Faith" – one hundred years since the school moved into its current site in Ealing. We represent a wonderful continuity of expertise in educating women of the future. We offer a broad and varied curriculum with rich opportunities for personal development. Whatever your daughter's ambitions St Augustine's Priory will equip her with the tools she needs to achieve her goals.

We know that self-knowledge and an awareness of how we work with and affect others is crucial to mental health and success in the workplace. We are passionate about our work!

# St John's Wood Pre-Preparatory School

(Founded 1982)
St Johns Hall, Lords Roundabout,
London, NW8 7NE
**Tel:** 020 7722 7149
**Fax:** 020 7586 6093
**Email:** info@sjwpre-prep.org.uk

**Website:** www.sjwpre-prep.org.uk
**Principal:** Adrian Ellis
**School type:** Coeducational Day
**Age range of pupils:** 3–7
**Average class size:** 16
**Teacher/pupil ratio:** 1:8

Happiness is at the heart of the philosophy at St Johns' Wood Pre-Prep School, and it works. This small school, described by owner and Principal, Adrian Ellis, as feeling more like a private members' club, is a 7+ specialist school. The school is immensely proud of the 2018 Year 2 pupils for their outstanding entrance test results. Of the 11 children in the class two girls will go to City of London School for Girls, one to South Hampstead High School. Two boys will head to St Paul's Juniors, four to UCS and two to Westminster Under School.

With a friendly and caring environment as its strength for three-to seven year-old boys and girls, Mr Ellis believes that the excellent ratio of staff to pupils allows each child to reach their full potential. "*Of course, together with parents, we look to establish each child's unique qualities and particular talents and aim to develop them as fully as possible,*" said Mr Ellis.

Parents have high expectations of the school. Mr Ellis points out this is a two way street, "*Equally, we have high expectations of our parents. This combination is the recipe for success*".

Following this year's excellent results, St John's Wood Pre-Prep remains a recommended 'feeder' to many of London's top prep schools.

# St Mary's School Hampstead

## ST MARY'S SCHOOL HAMPSTEAD

(Founded 1871)

47 Fitzjohn's Avenue, Hampstead,
London, NW3 6PG

**Tel:** 020 7435 1868

**Fax:** 020 7794 7922

**Email:** enquiries@stmh.co.uk

**Website:** www.stmh.co.uk

**Head Teacher:** Mrs Harriet Connor-Earl

**Appointed:** September 2016

**School type:** Coeducational Day

**Religious Denomination:** CISC

**Age range of boys:** 2 years 9 months–7 years

**Age range of girls:** 2 years 9 months–11 years

**No. of pupils enrolled as at 01/01/2018:** 300

*Boys:* 17 *Girls:* 283

**Fees per annum as at 01/01/2018:**

*Day:* £7,305–£13,500

**Average class size:** Max 20

**Teacher/pupil ratio:** 1:9.5

St Mary's School Hampstead provides an outstanding and inspirational Catholic education to girls from 3-11 years and boys from 3-7 years.

St Mary's School celebrates the uniqueness of every pupil and their achievements. The rigorous, challenging curriculum places a strong emphasis on high academic achievement within a culture of care and support.

The School aims to instil four key habits of learning in their pupils. The children are encouraged to be risk takers, not only in their play, but also in their learning. They are also taught to be resilient and not to fall at the first hurdle. Staff ask the children to make mistakes because in the process of challenging themselves, they make more academic progress and in turn excel not only in the classroom, but in their own self confidence. The boys and girls at St Mary's School are respectful, not just of each other, but of themselves. Finally, pupils are encouraged to be reflective, on their faith, their behaviour and their academic work.

Computer Science and digital literacy skills are integrated superbly within the classroom. Technology is used to support and enhance all curriculum areas and learning every day from Nursery to Year 6.

Music, drama, art and sports are also an essential part of life at St Mary's School and involve everyone. Children demonstrate great enthusiasm and build valuable and social skills that last a lifetime.

St Mary's School is an unexpected oasis amidst the bustle and activity of Hampstead. The outdoor space at St Mary's School is extensive, and the leafy playground makes it easy to forget you are in London. The children in Nursery have their own dedicated garden, aptly named 'The Secret Garden', where they can dig in the mud, play at the water tables, dress up and spend time in the sensory room.

Leavers achieve impressive results, gaining offers and Academic Scholarships from the best schools in the country, including St Paul's Girls' School, North London Collegiate, City of London School for Girls and St Mary's Ascot.

# SINGING FROM THE HEART

Being a chorister at St Paul's Cathedral is the experience of a lifetime.

— 100% tuition fees for all choristers
— Assistance with boarding fees available
— One of the top preparatory schools in the country
— The finest musical education
— An amazing start to life

Entry is in Year 3 or Year 4. If your son shows musical promise, he could become one of the next generation of choristers at St Paul's.

For more information please contact:
Clare Morgan, Registrar, St Paul's Cathedral School
020 7248 5156 · admissions@spcs.london.sch.uk

ST PAUL'S
CATHEDRAL
SCHOOL

# The Roche School

(Founded 1988)
11 Frogmore, London, SW18 1HW
**Tel:** 020 8877 0823
**Fax:** 020 8875 1156
**Email:** office@therocheschool.co.uk
**Website:** www.therocheschool.com

**Headmistress:** Mrs V Adams BA(Hons), PGCE, MA
**Appointed:** September 2010
**School type:** Co-educational Day
**Religious Denomination:**
Non-denominational
**Age range of pupils:** 2–11 years

**No. of pupils enrolled as at 01/01/2018:** 305
**Boys:** 153 **Girls:** 152
**Fees per annum as at 01/04/2018:**
**Day:** £14,280–£14,970
**Average class size:** 18
**Teacher/pupil ratio:** 1:9

## Curriculum

The Roche School offers good, clear teaching well adapted to pupils' understanding in a pleasant, encouraging and homely atmosphere so that all can take pride in their progress and no one feels left behind. Classes are kept small so children benefit from the personal attention. Pupils are encouraged to respect each other sympathetically and we offer a wide variety of academic, artistic and sporting opportunities. The school seeks continually to build on its fine academic reputation. Art, Music, French and Sport are taught by specialists.

## Entry requirements

Prospective pupils spend a morning in class during which their work is assessed. There is no testing at nursery and reception entry.

## Examinations offered

Children are prepared for 11+ examinations and placed in a variety of top London schools.

# Schools in Greater London

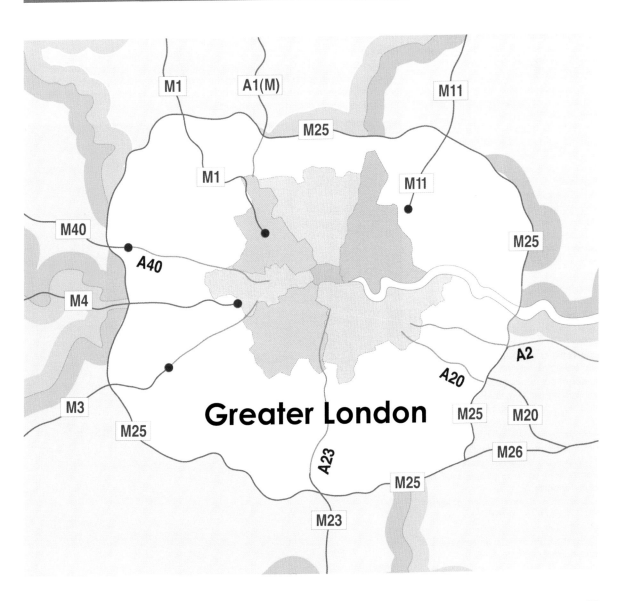

# Babington House School

(Founded 1887)

Grange Drive, Chislehurst, Kent BR7 5ES

**Tel:** 020 8467 5537

**Fax:** 020 8295 1175

**Email:** enquiries@babingtonhouse.com

**Website:** www.babingtonhouse.com

**Headmaster:** Mr Tim Lello MA, FRSA, NPQH

**Appointed:** 2013

**School type:** Coeducational Day

**Age range of boys:** 3-11 & 16-18

**Age range of girls:** 3–18

**No. of pupils enrolled as at 01/01/2018:** 364

**Fees per term as at 01/01/2018:**

**Nursery:** £3,000 (inclusive of lunches)

**Preparatory (Reception to Year 6):** £4,204 (inclusive of lunches)

**Seniors (11 to 18):** £5,236 (inclusive of lunches)

**Teacher/pupil ratio:** 1:20

At Babington House, *"pupils throughout the school display excellent attitudes to learning that are evident in all that they do, and an atmosphere of happy endeavour permeates school life"*, independent school inspectors find.

The school received the highest grade possible in all categories and across every age group in an Educational Quality and Compliance Inspection by the Independent Schools Inspectorate (ISI) in November 2016. Under the new more robust Inspection Framework, this is described as 'Excellent' and is very rare indeed. Babington could not have done better and such a result is a remarkable achievement.

Babington House School is an independent day school from 3 to 18 years, situated in a beautiful group of buildings on Grange Drive in Chislehurst, near Bromley.

We are co-educational up to 11 years old; girls only from 11 to 16 and have a mixed Sixth Form.

Our commitment is to provide an academic and well-rounded education with small class sizes which is tailored to the needs of our pupils, believing that bright children benefit from carefully monitored and well directed learning, where self-discipline is highly prized and where each pupil is known as an individual. This helps Babington House pupils grow into confident, accomplished, creative young people with emotional intelligence and high standards.

Babington is an academic school. Our academic, social and sporting endeavours are underpinned by core Christian values. There is a strong sense of community at Babington House.

The girls Senior School is academically selective with an Entrance Examination for Year 7 entry. In Babington's co-educational Sixth Form, the focus is very much on A-level study in small sets whilst at the same time providing the opportunity for work experience, which helps university applications stand out and provides great self-confidence.

Headmaster, Mr Tim Lello says *"I am immensely proud to lead such a vibrant community. Babington House is an excellent school in every way. The boys and girls receive a first class education in a supportive and academic environment."*

# Bancroft's School

(Founded 1737)
High Road, Woodford Green,
Essex IG8 0RF

**Tel:** 020 8505 4821
**Email:** office@bancrofts.org
**Website:** www.bancrofts.org
**Head:** Mr Simon Marshall MA, PGCE
(Cantab), MA, MPhil (Oxon)
**Appointed:** September 2016
**Head of Prep:** Mr Joe Layburn MA
**School type:** Coeducational Day
**Age range of pupils:** 7–18

**No. of pupils enrolled as at 01/01/2018:** 1143
*Sixth Form:* 245
*Prep:* 261
**Fees per term as at 01/01/2018:**
*Prep:* £4,718
*Senior:* £5,794
**Average class size:** 22
**Teacher/pupil ratio:** 1:8

Situated in north east London, adjacent to Epping Forest, Bancroft's is London's best kept educational secret. We feel we have got much to shout about and want to share what makes us special.

Pupils join Bancroft's Prep at the age of 7. Prep pupils are marked out by their enthusiasm, friendliness and confidence. There is a real "buzz" in the Prep – a sense of enjoyment from pupils and teachers alike. Most Prep pupils stay with us at 11, when they are joined by 65 children from a range of schools.

Academic results at Bancroft's are fantastic. Summer 2017 saw 89% of all GCSEs graded either A*or A. A Levels were equally impressive with 91% graded A* to B. The majority of Bancroftians progress to Russell Group institutions. These results put Bancroft's firmly amongst the very top of co-educational schools in the London area.

Life here isn't just about exams. Bancroft's is a busy, energetic school. Pupils of all ages are eager to take part in a multitude of clubs and societies catering for all interests. The Duke of Edinburgh Award scheme is particularly popular, with around 200 pupils working towards awards every year. We offer a lively Cub pack, a Sea Scout Troop and a thriving Combined Cadet Force. Drama productions are ambitious and technically daring with productions at the Edinburgh Fringe. Musicians are well catered for and a variety of ensembles and choirs offer chances for regular performances. Sports facilities are first class; teams have a full programme of fixtures against local schools and also enjoy success in national competitions. Our much praised and strong Pastoral Care, with a traditional house system, underpins life at Bancroft's.

The best way of getting to know about a school is to visit. Please join us on one of our Open Days, details of which are on our website: www.bancrofts.org.

# Bromley High School GDST
## A GDST School

**FIDES et OPERA**

(Founded 1883)

Blackbrook Lane, Bickley,

Bromley, Kent BR1 2TW

**Tel:** 020 8781 7000/1

**Email:** bhs@bro.gdst.net

**Website:** www.bromleyhigh.gdst.net

**Head:**

Mrs A M Drew BA(Hons), MBA (Dunelm)

**Appointed:** September 2014

**Head of Junior School:**

Mrs Claire Dickerson BA (Hons) (Anglia)

**School type:** Independent Selective Day

School for Girls

**Age range of girls:** 4–18

**No. of pupils enrolled as at 01/01/2018:** 912

*Sixth Form:* 120

*Senior School (ages 11-18):* 590

*Junior School (ages 4-11):* 310

**Fees per annum as at 01/01/2018:**

*Day:* £13,356–£16,563

**Average class size:** 20-24

Set in leafy parkland and benefitting from first rate facilities, Bromley High School provides a beautiful and buzzy environment where bright girls will flourish.

In the classroom, each girl's intellectual potential is challenged and developed by inspirational teachers whose concern for your daughter ranges infinitely beyond her performance in examinations; teachers who have a capacity to develop a love of learning, a spirit of enquiry and an independence of mind. Our girls learn to collaborate and to compete; to be creative and intellectually curious and their learning is underpinned by the

school's ethos of achievement for all and by the subject passion, enthusiasm and expertise of their teachers.

In 2016, the school's outstanding teaching earned the rare accolade of an 'Exceptional' rating for Learning and Achievement from the Independent Schools' Inspectorate (ISI). The school's academic results are consistently excellent 85% A*-B at A level in 2016; 88% A*-B in 2015. We are most proud of the school's impressive Value Added results at GCSE and A level which demonstrate the care taken to bring out the best in every girl.

However, outstanding success at Bromley High School is not purely academic. Bromley High girls are resilient and well-rounded young women participating with enthusiasm and commitment in Music, Drama, Art, Sport, Duke of Edinburgh and an overabundant range of activities – and where they have interest or talent or enthusiasm, it is nurtured so that they learn to excel. Sport is exceptional: with 25 acres of top class facilities and multiple teams across a range of sports allowing for both wide participation and elite performance.

Our pastoral care is thoughtful and developmental, actively encouraging girls to develop key attributes: Confidence, Composure, Courage, Compassion and Commitment. Every class takes on the responsibility of supporting its own individual charity and the school has a highly valued tradition of volunteering and charitable activity.

We welcome you very warmly to our Open Events and Taster Days both allowing for wide participation and elite performance. We hope that you will like what you see – confident, cheerful, considerate girls enthusiastic about the myriad of opportunities their school has to offer.

For 4+, 7+, 11+ and 16+ Entry in September 2019 please visit us at our Open Events on Friday May 4th and Saturday October 6th 2018. Booking is Essential.

Please contact the school via our website: www.bromleyhigh.gdst.net or our admissions office on admissions@bro.gdst.net or Tel 020 8781 7066 to arrange a visit.

# Cumnor House School for Boys

(Founded 1931)

168 Pampisford Road, South Croydon, Surrey CR2 6DA

**Tel:** +44 (0)20 8660 3445

**Email:** admissions@cumnorhouse.com

**Website:** www.cumnorhouse.com

**Headmaster:** Mr Daniel Cummings

**Appointed:** September 2017

**School type:** Boys' Day

**Age range of boys:** 2–13

**No. of pupils enrolled as at 01/01/2018:** 440

**Fees per term as at 01/01/2018:**

*Day:* £3,375–£4,250

Located in leafy South Croydon on the outskirts of Surrey, but 20 minutes by train to London Bridge, Cumnor House School provides a high quality all round education for boys. A day at Cumnor House School is one of purposeful industry and following 'The Cumnor Way', we subscribe to those timeless values that embrace good manners, courtesy, self-respect, respect for others, and a sense of duty and responsibility. We challenge our boys to take risks in order to discover that the seemingly impossible can be achieved.

Our recent excellent ISI inspection in 2017, with comments ranging from *'the quality of the pupils' academic and other achievements is excellent. Pupils exhibit a deep love of learning and are highly motivated.'* Our boys are successful throughout their journey at Cumnor House School, we believe strongly in the lessons of teamwork and personal achievements, this is evident in multiple achievements within Music, Sport and the Arts at all levels. We aspire to high academic standards and we are proud of our record scholarship and examination success to leading HMC schools, the Whitgift Foundation and local Grammar Schools.

Children who start nursery in our new 2017 state-of-the-art setting receive an outstanding introduction to their education in an exciting, stimulating and creative environment; with the added benefits of our main school staff supporting developments in Sports, Music and the Arts.

In order for our boys to make a smooth transition from nursery to reception, our boys' reception class is located in the gated Webb estate, Purley, providing a secure, nurturing start to their education. Our dedicated Pre-Prep team focus on the core skills of reading, writing and mathematics and start to identify talents and wider learning interests amongst our pupils. Upon entering our Prep school, our pupils have the opportunity to discover and develop their talents in Sports, Music, and the Arts, as well as receiving a broad and balanced academic curriculum. Our Upper School, as well as continuing an all-round development of our boys, focuses on tailoring the curriculum to our pupils' academic ability, in order to give them the best preparation for entrance in the senior school of choice at either 11+ or at 13+.

At Cumnor House School, we are proud of our sporting and musical achievements, our dedicated sports staff and wonderful sporting facilities offer the opportunity for all our boys to develop their teamwork skills. Pupils have the prospect to tour overseas to play sport in diverse locations, such as Dubai, South Africa and the West Indies. These valuable experiences give our boys the opportunities to explore new cultures and life outside the classroom.

We pride ourselves on our music curriculum, with all boys in Year 3 receiving a curriculum based peripatetic one on one lesson with music teachers on a variety of instruments. Our choirs, instrumental ensembles have all experienced formal and informal concerts including our yearly choir tour and have performed across Europe and at the Royal Opera House.

### Admissions

Our Open Mornings run throughout the year and we also offer the opportunity for personal tours. We provide taster days for registered applicants to give your child the opportunity to experience life at Cumnor, this will take the form of classroom lessons, sport, music and an informal meeting with the Head.

Find out more at cumnorhouse.com

# Cumnor House School for Girls

(Founded 2010)
1 Woodcote Lane, Purley, Surrey CR8 3HB
**Tel:** +44 (0)20 8660 3445
**Email:** admissions@cumnorhouse.com
**Website:** www.cumnorhouse.com
**Headmistress:** Mrs Amanda McShane

**Appointed:** April 2018
**School type:** Girls' Day
**Age range of girls:** 4–11
**No. of pupils enrolled as at 01/01/2018:** 165
**Fees per term as at 01/01/2018:**
*Day:* £3,375–£4,250

Located in the exclusive Webb Estate, Purley, Cumnor House School for Girls provides an enriching all round education, where talent and potential are recognised and nurtured and where all successes are celebrated. We are founded on a commitment of academic excellence and moral integrity and our aim is to prepare girls to achieve the best possible choice of senior school.

We treat each pupil as an individual, all of whom have different strengths, aspirations and dreams. Our school offers outstanding teaching in a nurturing and caring environment, and our girls are brimming with enthusiasm and confidence to exceed in all of their future endeavours.

The genuine happiness of a Cumnor girl is palpable, with proven evidence that not only are they learning well, but are also forming friendships and experiencing a safe and nurturing environment where they can be themselves and perform at their best.

Our team of dedicated and professional staff enable the girls to achieve success both in and out of the classroom by providing them with the learning tools to achieve and by instilling a love of learning. We have created an enriching curriculum, focusing on the core skills of reading, writing and mathematics combined with Music, the Arts, and Sports.

Our pupils have an impressive record of participation at Regional and National sporting events, with sport forming a regular part of the curriculum, our facilities include a six acre playing field, swimming pool and a large number of sports teams and fixtures throughout the year.

We pride ourselves on our Music, Drama and Arts curriculum, with all girls in Year 3 receiving free lessons with a variety of instruments. Our choir and orchestra have all experienced formal and informal concerts and perform regularly within the local community. Our dedicated music, drama and arts studios, give our pupils the opportunity to develop their confidence, teamwork and performance skills with annual drama productions, concerts and art exhibitions. As part of the ISA, we compete both regionally and nationally in sport, achieving huge successes.

At Cumnor House School for Girls, we are very proud of our scholarship record and the offers our girls receive from their first choice senior schools. As a preparatory school, we ensure that the girls are ready for their onward journey to senior school, ensuring that their journey from Reception through to Year 6 has been a happy and valuable experience that prepares them for their future.

**Admissions**

Our Open Mornings and personal tours run throughout the year. We provide taster days for registered applicants to give your child the opportunity to experience life at Cumnor, this will take the form of classroom lessons, sport, music and an informal meeting with the Head.

Find out more at cumnorhouse.com

# Kew Green Preparatory School

(Founded 2004)

Layton House, Ferry Lane, Kew Green,
Richmond, Surrey TW9 3AF
**Tel:** 020 8948 5999
**Fax:** 020 8948 4774
**Email:** secretary@kgps.co.uk
**Website:** www.kgps.co.uk
**Headmaster:** Mr J Peck
**Appointed:** September 2011

**School type:** Coeducational Day
**Age range of pupils:** 4–11
**No. of pupils enrolled as at 01/01/2018:** 270
**Fees per term as at 01/01/2018:**
**Day:** £5,626
**Average class size:** 20
**Teacher/pupil ratio:** 1:6.4

Kew Green Prep School (KGPS) is a lively, co-educational and non-selective independent school for children aged 4 to 11 near Kew Gardens in Richmond. Owned by the Gardener Schools Group, a family founded company set up in 1991, KGPS is the sister school to Ravenscourt Prep School (RPPS) and Kew House Senior School.

KGPS is housed in an attractive building, surrounded by mature trees and nestled in a peaceful corner of Kew Green. It is flanked by The Royal Botanical Gardens and The River Thames and we use these regularly along with the green itself.

We offer our children the opportunity to succeed, be recognised and be valued. Our pupils grow with the faculties required to tackle the many challenges that life may have to offer. We instil tolerance and respect for others and the capacity to celebrate diversity, embrace change and understand the importance of contributing to society. Above all, we believe that children need to be nurtured, guided, motivated and inspired to allow them to blossom. We are a school of smiles, laughter and happiness where pupils fulfil their maximum potential.

We believe children thrive in an environment that is loving and supportive. Physically, socially, emotionally and intellectually – our children develop and achieve their full potential in their time with us. Our aim is that they leave as skilled and adaptable young citizens who will grow to meet the challenges of the 21st century. We believe in a broad and balanced curriculum, nurturing creativity and the development of high self-esteem in each individual child. We enthusiastically share our children's education with their parents through our "open door policy".

Kew Green is a thriving school community where laughter and enjoyment go hand in hand with the process of delivering a first-rate education.

# Kingston Grammar School

70 London Rd, Kingston upon Thames,
Surrey KT2 6PY
**Tel:** 020 8456 5875
**Email:** enquiries@kgs.org.uk
**Website:** www.kgs.org.uk
**Head:** Mr Stephen Lehec
**Appointed:** 2014

**School type:** Independent
Coeducational Day
**Age range of pupils:** 11–18
**No. of pupils enrolled as at 01/01/2018:** 829
**Fees per term as at 01/01/2018:**
*Day:* £6,225
**Average class size:** 22

With a history dating back to the 12th century, and founded in 1561 by Royal Charter, Kingston Grammar School is a school with one foot in the past but both eyes firmly on the future. It is one of the most successful co-educational day schools in the country and has a long tradition of developing individual talent and encouraging high aspirations.

The present site has a range of buildings representing architectural styles from the 1870s to the present day. The modern Queen Elizabeth II Performing Arts Centre has a theatre, music school, drama department and Sixth Form Centre. The school enjoys excellent state-of-the-art facilities and 22 acres of playing fields by the Thames, opposite Hampton Court Palace.

Academic standards are high and examination results are excellent. A strong tutorial programme encourages pupils to develop their individual talents. Our pupils are bright and enthusiastic; their joy in life and spirit of curiosity makes education here a real pleasure.

International GCSEs and Extended Projects inter-weave with more traditional examinations to produce an exciting and vibrant academic diet, designed to challenge expectations and to engage pupils in a love of learning.

We make sure that our pupils are drawn into investigation and enquiry beyond the confines of the various examination specifications. They develop their skills and thinking in ways which give them the fullest advantage at university, and

the resilience and flexibility to make the most of the opportunities that come their way. Our co-curricular programme pays a central part in this. The opportunity to engage in an extraordinary range of trips, expeditions and activities allows pupils to develop their self-awareness, skills and competence in all sorts of ways and contributes significantly to the rounded individuals they become.

For many, the world outside the formal academic curriculum will provide the key to their future lives. Physical Education and Sport in Independent Schools (2012), edited by Malcolm Tozer, contains a survey of the number of sporting internationals to have come from independent schools since 2000. Kingston Grammar School is ranked equal fifth, and third for Olympians – quite an achievement for a school of our size.

You will also find a strong tradition of theatre, art and music here, with Kingstonians making their mark on the stage, in performance and in all aspects of the design world. For all our pupils, whatever their skill or ambition, the opportunities we provide both inside and outside the curriculum are enriching and empowering.

We offer Bronze and Gold Duke of Edinburgh, Community Service, Young Enterprise, Combined Cadet Force, a wide variety of trips and adventurous activities as well as links with our partnership school in Ghana. We typically offer over 60 clubs and activities from Photography to Politics and from Music Recording Club to GibSoc (Debating). Our educational partnerships across the world open up all sorts of opportunities in fostering international understanding, collaborative enquiry, leadership, exploration and adventure.

# Kew House School

Kew House, 6 Capital Interchange Way,
London, Middlesex TW8 0EX

**Tel:** 0208 742 2038
**Email:** info@kewhouseschool.com
**Website:** www.kewhouseschool.com
**Headmaster:** Mr Mark Hudson
**School type:** Coeducational Day

**Age range of pupils:** 11–18
**No. of pupils enrolled as at 01/01/2018:** 450
**Fees per term as at 01/01/2018:**
*Day:* £6,849
**Average class size:** 22

Located in West London, Kew House School is a co-educational independent senior school for students aged 11-18 years. Owned by the Gardener Schools Group, a family founded company set up in 1991, Kew House is the sister school to Ravenscourt Park Prep and Kew Green Prep.

Kew House School takes a modern and pioneering approach to every aspect of school life. The school recognises and enhances the individual abilities of each child, welcoming students with varying academic profiles and placing emphasis on confidence, self-esteem and creativity.

By operating a true 'open door' policy that welcomes parents and members of the wider community to become a part of school life, Kew House has developed the feeling of a family and social hub that provides emotional support and security for all students and employees.

Sport is an important part of the Curriculum and its students achieve national and regional championship. Students benefit from using state of the art facilities at sporting locations just a stone's throw away from the school, including professional tennis courts and cricket grounds. Just a short walk from the River Thames, rowing is part of the curriculum.

In September 2017, Kew House opened a brand new Sixth Form Centre which benefits from a beautifully designed independent learning centre on the ground floor. This building reflects the fact that sixth form students are approaching adulthood and encourages independent study in an attractive environment. Facilities include a Sixth Form Café, library, roof terrace, audio-visual suite, recording studio and Sixth Form Seminar rooms.

Following an inspection of the school in February 2018 by the Independent Schools Inspectorate (ISI) Kew House was particularly delighted to learn from the lead inspector that the results of the student and parent questionnaires were the most positive they had ever seen.

# Marymount International School London

(Founded 1955)

George Road, Kingston upon Thames, Surrey KT2 7PE

**Tel:** +44 (0)20 8949 0571

**Fax:** +44 (0)20 8336 2485

**Email:** admissions@marymountlondon.com

**Website:** www.marymountlondon.com

**Headmistress:** Mrs Margaret Frazier

**School type:** Girls' Day & Boarding

**Age range of girls:** 11–18

**No. of pupils enrolled as at 01/01/2018:** 250

**Fees per annum as at 01/01/2018:**

*Day:* £20,015–£22,860

*Weekly Boarding:* £34,365–£37,210

*Full Boarding:* £36,030–£38,875

**Average class size:** 12

**Teacher/pupil ratio:** 1:6

Marymount International School is an independent Catholic day and boarding school – welcoming girls of all faiths, aged 11-18.

A small school with 250 pupils (of which 80 are boarders), Marymount offers a supportive, nurturing environment with small classes and bespoke study programmes. With a student-teacher ratio of 5:1, teaching is relevant and flexible, keeping students highly motivated.

Marymount adopted the International Baccalaureate (IB) in 1979. The Middle Years Programme (MYP) is taught as the best preparation possible for the Diploma. This stretches students without the need for incessant testing allowing them to develop inquiring, critical minds and to become confident, creative, independent thinkers.

Marymount was the first School in the UK to install its own, fully equipped Fab Lab (fabrication laboratory) designed to facilitate the teaching of computer programming, coding and robotics. This has resulted in a rigorous, inter-disciplinary curriculum, in support of the STEM subjects.

With over 40 nationalities in the School, students are prepared for life in a global setting and develop a cultural fluency so sought after by today's employers.

The largest national group is British and tuition is in English; however, additional languages taught include Spanish, German, French, Italian, Japanese, Korean and Mandarin (Russian and Arabic when required) for native speakers.

The School consistently delivers excellent academic results. In 2017, 25% of graduates achieved 40 points and above (which is higher than A*A*A*A* at A-levels) and over 50% graduated with a Bilingual Diploma. Students regularly achieve a full score of 45 points.

Students gain places at top universities worldwide including Ivy League in the USA and Oxbridge. In 2017, 87% of students studying in the UK, gained places at Russell Group Universities.

Set in a secure, leafy campus, school buses cover routes from amongst others Sloane Square, South Kensington, Fulham, Putney, Wimbledon and Richmond.

# Mount House School

**MOUNT HOUSE SCHOOL**

(Formerly St Martha's School)

Camlet Way, Hadley Wood, Barnet,
Hertfordshire EN4 0NJ
**Tel:** 020 8449 6889
**Email:** admissions@mounthouse.org.uk
**Website:** www.mounthouse.org.uk
**Headmaster:** Mr Matthew Burke
**Appointed:** September 2013

**School type:** Co-educational Day (taking boys in Year 7 and 12 from September 2018)
**Age range of pupils:** 11–18
**No. of pupils enrolled:** 180
**Fees per annum as at 01/01/2018:**
*Day:* £14,820
**Average class size:** 12-18

Mount House School is a non-selective, co-educational independent day school for the 21st century where children develop into confident learners.

Located in the North London suburb of Hadley Wood, Mount House School enjoys a tranquil and peaceful setting, whilst still being close to all major road and rail links.

Mount House is not a 'one size fits all' school. Here, every individual is valued and each child's unique talents will be identified and nurtured. Students leave as able, articulate, balanced, caring, and well-rounded individuals with a genuine love of learning, ready to take on life's challenges and opportunities, aware of the needs of others and confident in their ability to make a difference.

With our small class sizes and highly experienced, committed teaching staff, we are able to maximise the learning potential of every pupil.

Mount House is a happy and successful school, with an excellent record of GCSE and A level results and an outstanding record of students achieving places at top universities.

We place a high priority on personal development. Growth in moral, spiritual and cultural values is encouraged as part of the everyday ethos of the school. Pastoral care is centred around our supportive tutor system, which enhances the feeling of belonging to a very special family community, where everyone feels valued.

Our innovative curriculum, offering ground-breaking opportunities for students aged 11–18, is at the heart of the school, while our 'Growing Foxes' programme teaches pupils the kind of ingenuity and strategic thinking utilised in the city's best boardrooms.

Pupils are encouraged to become self-motivated learners, critical thinkers, to express thoughts and feelings, to write creatively and use their imaginations. They enjoy using their numeracy skills, interpreting and using data and applying their knowledge to problem solving situations. Pupils' education is supplemented through a wide variety of educational visits and visitors from the community, such as theatre groups and interactive workshops.

We believe a child's education is a shared responsibility between school and home and we positively encourage the support of parents, offering a partnership that embraces regular contact and communication, leading to the building of strong relationships that are a key factor in the school's popularity.

A significant amount of funding has already been invested in Mount House in recent months, including the provision of new music, drama and IT facilities, refurbished classrooms and the creation of a new café, which is open to parents as well as to sixth formers, and with plans for further investment, including a brand new sports hall, new technology suite and a new library, Mount House will become a school fit to support and develop both the curricular and extra-curricular talents of its growing pupil population.

The move to co-education (Mount House was previously the all-girls St Martha's School), together with our policy of non-selection, form the basis of our vision of making Mount House School much more inclusive and accessible to all. We believe everyone is capable of achieving, given the right tools and inspiration, and are proud that our members of staff always go the extra mile to help our pupils succeed.

Mount House School is in Camlet Way, Hadley Wood, Herts – 10 minutes walk from Hadley Wood station and three miles from J24 of the M25.

For further information, visit www. mounthouse.org.uk

# Trinity School

(Founded 1596)
Shirley Park, Croydon, Surrey CR9 7AT

**Tel:** 020 8656 9541
**Fax:** 020 8655 0522
**Email:** admissions@trinity.croydon.sch.uk
**Website:** www.trinity-school.org
**Head:** Alasdair Kennedy MA (Cantab)
**Appointed:** September 2016
**School type:** Boys' Day, Co-educational Sixth Form

**Age range of boys:** 10–18
**Age range of girls:** 16–18
**No. of pupils enrolled as at 01/01/2018:** 1007
**Fees per annum as at 01/01/2018:**
*Day:* £16,656
**Average class size:** 21
**Teacher/pupil ratio:** 1:11

Situated within twenty seven acres of land on the outskirts of Croydon, Trinity School is a dynamic, modern and welcoming school for boys aged 10-18, with a co-educational sixth form.

Trinity is a lively and inclusive community which provides an extraordinary variety of opportunities for its pupils to enjoy and excel in. Inspirational teaching, small class sizes, outstanding facilities and an exceptional co-curricular programme ensure that pupils achieve academic excellence and develop into emotionally intelligent adults ready for life beyond school.

Trinity's strong academic results regularly place it among the top schools in the country. In 2017, Trinity was ranked 41st in the Parent Power list of Top 100 Independent Schools in the UK, making it the top ranked independent school in Croydon for the second year in a row.

Trinity's Music Department is one of the best-known in Britain and pupils can take part in over 50 different ensembles. The School was awarded the Pro Corda Special Award for Schools in recognition of its "outstanding contribution" to chamber music playing and, in 2012, became London's first All-Steinway secondary school. Trinity Boys' Choir celebrated 50 years in 2015, culminating in a spectacular celebration of musical excellence at Glyndebourne.

The school has an outstanding reputation for sporting excellence and extremely high overall participation rates. The pupils' commitment, enthusiasm and enjoyment of their sporting life is testament to the manner in which coaching staff at Trinity balance excellence and inclusivity.

Pupils make use of good transport links to travel to Trinity from a wide geographical area. Around half benefit from the Whitgift Foundation's generous bursary scheme and the School's scholarship awards. Entry at ages 10+, 11+ and 13+ is via an examination in Maths, English and Verbal Reasoning, followed by an interview. Entry at 16+ is via entrance examination and interview.

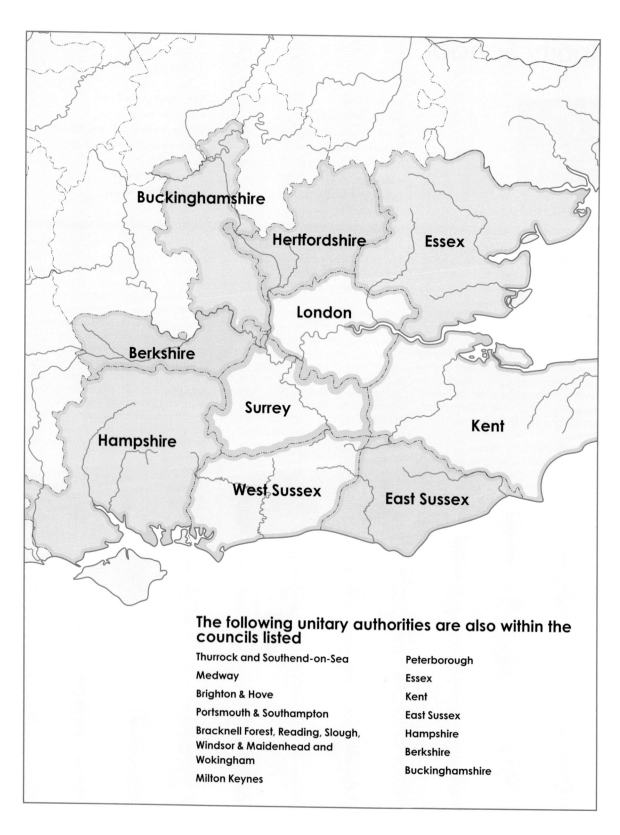

**The following unitary authorities are also within the councils listed**

| | |
|---|---|
| Thurrock and Southend-on-Sea | Peterborough |
| Medway | Essex |
| Brighton & Hove | Kent |
| Portsmouth & Southampton | East Sussex |
| Bracknell Forest, Reading, Slough, Windsor & Maidenhead and Wokingham | Hampshire |
| | Berkshire |
| Milton Keynes | Buckinghamshire |

# Schools in the South-East

# Berkhamsted School

**BERKHAMSTED**
— 1541 —

(Founded 1541)
Overton House, 131 High Street,
Berkhamsted, Hertfordshire HP4 2DJ

**Tel:** 01442 358001
**Email:**
admissions@berkhamstedschool.org
**Website:** www.berkhamstedschool.org
**Principal:**
Mr Richard Backhouse MA(Cantab)
**Appointed:** January 2016
**School type:** Co-educational & single-sex, day & boarding
**Age range of pupils:** 3–18

**No. of pupils enrolled as at 01/02/2018:** 1772
*Sixth Form:* 402
*Pre-Prep/Prep:* 552
*Senior Boys:* 439
*Senior Girls:* 379
**Fees per annum as at 01/09/2017:**
*Day:* £10,365–£20,250
*Weekly Boarding:* £27,115
*Full Boarding:* £32,255
**Average class size:** 20

With a history dating back to 1541, an excellent reputation and an accessible location, Berkhamsted School offers much to make it worthy of consideration by parents across London and the South East. Our patron, pictured on a visit to mark the School's 475th anniversary in 2016, is Her Majesty The Queen.

Located in the historic market town of Berkhamsted, the School is a 30 minute train journey from Euston Station, and a short drive from Junction 20 of the M25. Full and weekly boarding, as well as term time and holiday wraparound care for younger pupils, are on offer to support working parents.

Berkhamsted is one of only a small number of schools in the country to offer a 'diamond' structure that combines both single-sex and co-educational teaching. Boys and girls are taught together until the age of 11, separately from 11-16, before coming back together again in a joint Sixth Form. In senior school, boys and girls are taught separately on different sites, but share in academic trips and visits and in some co-curricular activities, such as drama productions, orchestras, Duke of Edinburgh's Award and the Combined Cadet Force.

Academic results are consistently strong with an average of 80% A*- B grades at A level over the last five years. In 2017, GCSE students achieved 68.7% of grades at A* to A and 78% of leavers were placed at either their first or second choice university with 53% going on to study at a Russell Group university.

Berkhamsted offers all the key components of a traditional independent school education: small class sizes, specialist staff and excellent standards of teaching throughout the school. Alongside this, an outstanding co-curricular programme seeks to foster and develop a wide range of interests and hobbies – music, sport, drama, public speaking and a vibrant outdoor education programme. The school timetable is structured to accommodate a wide selection of clubs and societies within core school hours. Berkhamsted also has a strong tradition of undertaking service within the local community from Year 9 (13 +) onwards.

Pupils across the School enjoy the benefits of being part of a small, supportive community based in an environment appropriate to their specific educational needs, yet with access to the state-of-the-art facilities of a large school; a 500-seat theatre, a six-lane 25m swimming pool and sports centre, and one of the best art departments in the country.

The School prides itself on offering outstanding levels of pastoral care and, in an echo of its boarding roots, the House system is a key feature of Berkhamsted. Senior School pupils are allocated to Houses and the Head of House, supported by House Tutors, has the primary responsibility for the academic and pastoral progress of each student in their House. Over and above the close academic supervision and support, this structure provides an excellent social base for pupils, allowing them to mix and get to know others across the year groups.

Berkhamsted offers scholarships – academic, art, drama, music and sport – and means-tested bursaries to talented pupils on entry to the school.

Parents are welcome to visit the School at any time: please call 01442 358001 for an appointment and a tour to appreciate what Berkhamsted can offer your child.

# Davenies School

Day Preparatory School for boys aged 4 to 13 years

(Founded 1940)

Station Road, Beaconsfield,

Buckinghamshire HP9 1AA

**Tel:** 01494 685400

**Fax:** 01494 685408

**Email:** office@davenies.co.uk

**Website:** www.davenies.co.uk

**Headmaster:** Mr Carl Rycroft BEd (Hons)

**Appointed:** September 2015

**School type:** Boys' Day

**Age range of boys:** 4–13

**No. of pupils enrolled as at 01/01/2018:** 335

**Fees per annum as at 01/01/2018:**

**Day:** £11,985–£16,800

**Average class size:** Max 20

Davenies is a thriving IAPS day school for boys aged 4–13. Our ethos and philosophy enable the boys to make the most of their preparatory years, supported by high-quality pastoral care, a broad and stimulating curriculum and numerous extra-curricular opportunities.

Davenies has its own distinct character and from their earliest years children are encouraged to relish the learning experience.

We are committed to an education both in and out of the classroom, thereby enabling the academic, artistic, musical, creative and physical potential of each child to flourish. This school is a warm, caring and happy one, where self-esteem is nurtured and grown; we believe that by fostering a wide range of interests and passions we provide the boys with every opportunity to develop in confidence. Our high-quality teachers have an excellent track record of preparing children for life at the country's leading senior schools and beyond.

Enterprises such as the unique Davenies Award Scheme and the permeation of technology in our teaching and learning ensure we offer a truly independent educational experience.

At Davenies, our outstanding facilities support us in providing a positive learning experience with our own language of learning that nurtures each boy's understanding of how he learns. Davenies' boys are polite and friendly with their own individual characters, personalities, passions and interests.

# Pangbourne College

(Founded 1917)

Pangbourne, Reading, Berkshire RG8 8LA
**Tel:** 0118 984 2101
**Fax:** 0118 984 1239
**Email:** registrar@pangbourne.com
**Website:** www.pangbourne.com
**Headmaster:** Thomas J C Garnier
**School type:** Coeducational Boarding & Day

**Age range of pupils:** 11–18
**No. of pupils enrolled as at 01/01/2018:** 426
**Boys:** 275 **Girls:** 151 **Sixth Form:** 133
**Fees per annum as at 01/01/2018:**
**Day:** £17,055–£24,036
**Full Boarding:** £24,021–£33,996
**Average class size:** 8-20
**Teacher/pupil ratio:** 1:7

Pangbourne College offers wide-ranging academic and co-curricular opportunities to girls and boys aged 11-18, with an emphasis on outstanding pastoral care and character development.

Pangbourne is a vibrant boarding and day school community, perfectly balancing strong Service values with a dynamic, modern outlook and unpretentious, inclusive attitude. The College is proud of its outstanding pastoral care, taking an integrated approach to caring for each pupil, and understanding the challenges young people face in order to improve the support it provides.

Headmaster, Mr Thomas Garnier, says: *"Above all, we are a 'people place'. We are committed to the personal development of our pupils in the fullest sense. They are encouraged to work hard towards academic success with a robust and comprehensive curriculum."*

*"Just as important is character development: confidence and values, creative and physical skills and an* appreciation of themselves and what they can contribute to the world."

The Flag Values of Kindness, Selflessness, Moral Courage, Initiative, Industry, Resilience, and Integrity underpin every aspect of life at the College. They are rooted in a Christian ethos and go a long way to preparing pupils for life's challenges and the responsibilities of adulthood. The aim is to equip Pangbournians with the strongest possible foundations for their future.

Pangbourne is set in 230 acres within an Area of Outstanding Natural Beauty, within easy reach of excellent transport connections. It is 10 minutes from Junction 12 of the M4 and served by London Paddington – Oxford Mainline rail network. Daily school transport services are available from Newbury, Basingstoke, Wantage and, as of January 2018, Henley, Twyford, Wargrave and the surrounding areas.

Entry is offered at 11+, 13+, and 16+, and occasionally into other year groups. The best way to experience Pangbourne is to come and visit, enjoy a tour of the College and speak to pupils and staff. To arrange a tour or to attend our next Open Morning, please email the Registrar.

*A distinctive school that puts huge emphasis on self-discipline, teamwork and leadership. Caring and supportive, Pangbourne buzzes with activity and encourages every pupil to have a go.* **– Good Schools Guide**

*The personal development of Pangbourne's students is outstanding, and supported by an excellent, broad curriculum which enables students to progress academically and supports the development of the whole individual.* **– ISI Inspection Report**

# LVS Ascot

(Founded 1803)

London Road, Ascot, Berkshire SL5 8DR

**Tel:** 01344 882770

**Fax:** 01344 890648

**Email:** enquiries@lvs.ascot.sch.uk

**Website:** www.lvs.ascot.sch.uk

**Headmistress:** Mrs Christine Cunniffe

BA (Hons), MMus, MBA

**Appointed:** September 2010

**School type:** Coeducational Day & Boarding

**Religious Denomination:**

Non-denominational

**Age range of pupils:** 4–18

**No. of pupils enrolled as at 01/01/2018:** 830

**Fees per annum as at 01/01/2018:**

*Day:* £9,708–£18,609

*Full Boarding:* £24,846–£32,694

**Average class size:** 18

LVS Ascot is a non-selective, co-educational day and boarding school of over 800 pupils aged 4-18. It is a through-school so pupils can begin their school career at LVS Ascot at age 4 and remain there until they complete Sixth Form.

Exam results in 2017 saw LVS Ascot achieve its highest ever pass rate of 99.5%. At GCSE level, Grade A and A* results rose to over 30%.

The school is located on a bright and spacious site amongst 25 acres of landscaped gardens and playing fields. As one of the most modern boarding and day schools in the UK, the purpose built campus provides excellent facilities in a safe and stimulating environment, including a sports centre with indoor swimming pool, fitness centre, sports hall and all-weather sports pitch, dance

studio, medical centre, a 250 seat theatre, drama studio and a music technology suite with recording studio, plus a Learning Resource Centre and over 500 networked computer workstations.

Both Junior and Senior school follow the National Curriculum, but with the added feature of a wide range of GCSE, A Level and Vocational options, catering for each individual pupil's strengths. An extensive range of activities and extra-curricular clubs and societies underpin academic studies by providing opportunities for pupils to extend their horizons in team sports, drama and music, visits, clubs, hobbies and interests.

Pastoral care is a great priority at LVS Ascot. In the Senior School each child is allocated to a house, and within that to a tutor group. House Masters and Mistresses, supported by teams of tutors, oversee the welfare and development of their pupils. In the Junior School, pastoral care is undertaken by the children's class teacher. Students are encouraged to give their best, whether the goal is university entrance, success at GCSE, honour on the sports field, artistic endeavour, or coping with the trials and tribulations of growing up. LVS Ascot aims to develop 'caring, confident citizens' for the future.

Academic Scholarships and Bursaries are available – please request further details. Our special arrangement with the HM Forces enables us to discount our fees by 10-20% to all HM Forces and UK Diplomatic personnel.

# Roedean School

ROEDEAN

(Founded 1885)
Roedean Way, Brighton, East Sussex
BN2 5RQ

**Tel:** 01273 667500
**Fax:** 01273 680791
**Email:** info@roedean.co.uk
**Website:** www.roedean.co.uk
**Headmaster:**
Mr. Oliver Bond BA(Essex), PGCE, NPQH
**Appointed:** 2013
**School type:** Girls' Boarding & Day
**Age range of girls:** 11–18

**No. of pupils enrolled as at 01/01/2018:** 568
*Sixth Form:* 171
**No. of boarders:** 296
**Fees per annum as at 01/01/2018:**
*Day:* £15,960–£20,865
*Weekly Boarding:* £28,230–£31,470
*Full Boarding:* £30,930–£37,440
**Average class size:** 18
**Teacher/pupil ratio:** 1:7

**Roedean – the Top Girls' School in Sussex**

A Roedean education is unique, combining academic excellence with space for the girls to grow up at their own pace and realise their full potential.

Roedean inspires curiosity and a love of learning without losing the enjoyment and delight of an all-round education. Following an outstanding ISI report in May 2016, which judged it to be excellent in every area, Roedean celebrated both its best ever A Level (62% A*-A) and GCSE (50% A*) results over the last two years. The DfE's new A Level league tables, published in the Telegraph in January, rank Roedean as the highest performing girls' school in Sussex. Away from London's academic pressure-cooker, 51.9% of Roedean girls

last year achieved A Level grades of AAB or higher in at least two facilitating subjects, which is what is required by the UK's Russell Group universities.

Girls are given the freedom to develop their talents and passions, and the school's holistic vision of education means that activities such as sport, art, drama, music, and dance complement academic achievement and make up an essential part of life at the school. It is precisely this rounded education which produces independent and creative young women who will make their mark in the world.

Roedean's exceptional facilities include our farm with chickens and sheep, a flood-lit all-weather pitch in the near future, and the recent impressive £1/2

million refurbishment of the Sixth Form facilities. Having grown by 70 students this academic year, Roedean now numbers 570 girls, and is expected to grow further next year. Weekly and flexi-boarders from London benefit from the weekend chaperoned service to and from London Victoria.

Roedean is one of the UK's leading girls' schools – the girls play sport with the sea's blue behind them and the green of the South Downs in front of them, the maths and humanities classrooms have perhaps the best view of any school in the country, and which other boarding houses have been likened to a boutique hotel? Roedean is simply unique.

www.roedean.co.uk

# St Neot's School

## ST NEOT'S
### PREPARATORY SCHOOL
(Founded 1888)

St Neot's Road, Eversley,
Hampshire RG27 0PN
**Tel:** 0118 9739650
**Email:** admissions@stneotsprep.co.uk
**Website:** www.stneotsprep.co.uk
**Head of School:** Mrs Deborah Henderson
**Appointed:** September 2015

**School type:** Co-educational Day,
Preparatory
**Age range of pupils:** 2–13 years
**No. of pupils enrolled as at 01/01/2018:** 327
**Fees per annum as at 01/01/2018:**
*Day:* £4,680–£14,994
**Average class size:** 18
**Teacher/pupil ratio:** 1:8

St Neot's, founded in 1888, is a happy, vibrant community for boys and girls from 2 to 13 years and is situated on the Hampshire/Berkshire border in 70 acres of beautiful grounds.

Our pupils develop a love of learning in a supportive and happy environment, where each individual is encouraged to achieve their full academic potential. Children are given the opportunity to embrace challenge, think creatively, develop self-confidence and foster empathy towards others, preparing them both intellectually and emotionally for success in the modern world. Forest School and Outdoor Education programmes encourage pupils to develop these attributes, which are so vital in today's world. The St Neot's journey culminates in the Years 7 and 8 leadership programme, which draws together a mix of skills through the core elements of the Prep Schools Baccalaureate (PSB).

We aim to provide the highest standards in teaching and learning, within a well rounded educational experience, and St Neot's has a very strong record of success in achieving Scholarships and Awards to numerous Senior Schools.

Physical Education is a strength of the school and our sports complex, comprising sports hall, 25m indoor pool, all-weather astro, cricket nets, hard tennis and netball courts, significantly supplements extensive playing fields. After school activities cover a wide range of interests and Holiday Clubs run in all school breaks offering a wealth of opportunities, both sporting and creative.

St Neot's holds a Gold Artsmark award, recognising our achievements in art, music, drama and dance. Plays, concerts and recitals take place throughout the school year for all age groups.

Open Mornings take place termly – details can be found on the school website www.stneotsprep.co.uk. We would also be delighted to arrange individual tours and meetings with the Head. Please contact Admissions on 0118 9739650 or e-mail admissions@stneotsprep.co.uk.

# St Swithun's School

**St Swithun's**
**WINCHESTER**

(Founded 1884)

Alresford Road, Winchester,
Hampshire SO21 1HA
**Tel:** 01962 835700
**Fax:** 01962 835779
**Email:** office@stswithuns.com
**Website:** www.stswithuns.com

**Head of School:**
Jane Gandee MA(Cantab)
**Appointed:** 2010
**School type:** Girls' Boarding & Day
**Age range of girls:** 11–18
**No. of pupils enrolled as at 01/01/2018:** 520
**No. of boarders:** 231

St Swithun's School is a renowned independent day, weekly and full-boarding school for girls set in 45 acres overlooking the Hampshire Downs on the outskirts of Winchester, yet only 50 minutes by train from central London. It offers excellent teaching, sporting and recreational facilities.

The school has a long-standing reputation for academic rigour and success. Girls are prepared for public examinations and higher education in a stimulating environment in which they develop intellectual curiosity, independence of mind and the ability to take responsibility for their own learning. They achieve almost one grade higher at GCSE than their already significant baseline ability would suggest, and approximately half a grade higher at A level. St Swithun's offers a comprehensive careers and higher education support service throughout the school years. Its Oxbridge preparation is part of a whole-school academic enrichment programme providing additional challenge and stimulation.

Whilst achieving academic excellence, girls also have the opportunity to do 'something else'. There is an extensive co-curricular programme of over 100 weekly and 50 weekend activities to choose from.

As well as academic classrooms and science laboratories, there is a magnificent performing arts centre with a 600-seat auditorium, a music school, an art and technology block, a sports hall and a full-size indoor swimming pool. There is an impressive library and ICT facility. The grounds are spacious and encompass sports fields, tennis courts and gardens.

With kindness and tolerance at the heart of its community, St Swithun's provides a civilised and caring environment in which all girls are valued for their individual gifts. By the time a girl leaves she will be courageous, compassionate, committed and self-confident with a love of learning, a moral compass and a sense of humour.

# Directory

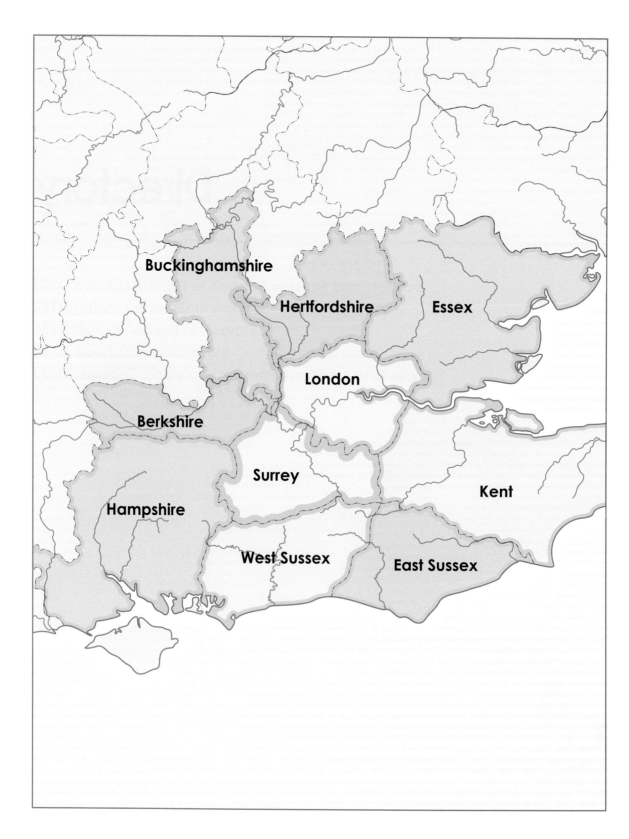

Buckinghamshire

Hertfordshire

Essex

London

Berkshire

Surrey

Kent

Hampshire

West Sussex

East Sussex

# Schools and Nursery Schools in Central London

## KEY TO SYMBOLS

- ⚲ Boys' school
- ⚲ Girls' school
- 🌐 International school
- ⑯ Tutorial or sixth form college
- Ⓐ A levels
- ⚘ Boarding accommodation
- £ Bursaries
- IB International Baccalaureate
- ✐ Learning support
- ⑯ Entrance at 16+
- ✺ Vocational qualifications
- IAPS Independent Association of Prep Schools
- HMC The Headmasters' & Headmistresses' Conference
- ISA Independent Schools Association
- GSA Girls' School Association
- BSA Boarding Schools' Association
- S Society of Heads

*Unless otherwise indicated, all schools are coeducational day schools. Single-sex and boarding schools will be indicated by the relevant icon.*

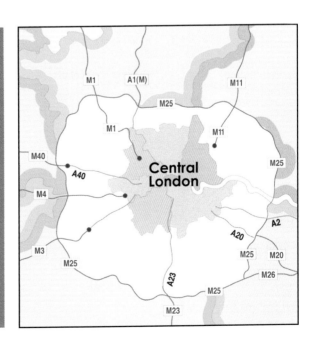

# London

## Central London

### Accent International Consortium for Academic Programs Abroad
99-103 Great Russell Street,
London WC1B 3LA
**Tel:** 020 7813 7723
**Head:** Natasa Blecic
16+

### Broadgate Day Nursery
21 Curtain Road, Hackney,
London EC2A 3LW
**Tel:** 020 7247 3491
**Principal:** Jacky Roberts NNEB
**Age range:** 0–5
**No. of pupils:** 50

### CATS London
43-45 Bloomsbury Square,
London WC1A 2RA
**Tel:** 02078 411580
**Principal:** Mario Di Clemente
**Age range:** 15–24
👤 🏫 £ 16+

### Cavendish College
35-37 Alfred Place,
London WC1E 7DP
**Tel:** 020 7580 6043
**Principal:** Dr J Sanders BSc, MBA, PhD
16+

### Charterhouse Square School
40 Charterhouse Square,
London EC1M 6EA
**Tel:** 020 7600 3805
**Head of School:** Mrs Caroline Lloyd BEd (Hons)
**Age range:** 3–11
**No. of pupils:** 196
**Fees:** Day £4,575

### City Lit Centre & Speech Therapy
Keeley House, Keeley Street,
London WC2B 4BA
**Tel:** 020 7492 2600
**Principal:** Mr G W Horgan
16+

### City of London School
Queen Victoria Street,
London EC4V 3AL
**Tel:** 020 3680 6300
**Head:** Mr A R Bird MSc
**Age range:** B10–18
**No. of pupils:** 930 VIth250
**Fees:** Day £16,731
🧍 £ ✏ 16+

### City of London School for Girls
St Giles' Terrace, Barbican,
London EC2Y 8BB
**Tel:** 020 7847 5500
**Headmistress:** Mrs E Harrop
**Age range:** G7–18
**No. of pupils:** 725
🧍 £ ✏ 16+

---

**DALLINGTON SCHOOL**
*For further details see p. 46*
8 Dallington Street, Islington,
London EC1V 0BW
**Tel:** 020 7251 2284
**Email:** hercules@
dallingtonschool.co.uk
**Website:**
www.dallingtonschool.co.uk
**Headteacher:** Mrs M C Hercules MBE
**Age range:** 3–11
**No. of pupils:** 134
**Fees:** Day £9,978–£12,630

---

**ÉCOLE JEANNINE MANUEL – LONDON**
*For further details see p. 50*
43-45 Bedford Square, ,
London WC1B 3DN
**Tel:** 020 3829 5970
**Email:** contact@jmanuel.uk.net
**Website:** www.ecole
jeanninemanuel.org.uk
**Head of School:** Pauline Prévot
**Age range:** 3–18 years
**No. of pupils:** 350
**Fees:** Day £17,460
🧍 £ IB

---

### eCollege London
1-3 Rivington Street,
London EC2A 3DT
**Tel:** 020 7729 9755
**Head:** Sheila Prendergast
16+

### Financial Training Academy
4 Frederick's Place, Old
Jewry, London EC2R 8AB
**Tel:** 0870 4232316/020
7397 1210
**Head:** Mr Rafi Ahmad
16+

### Guildhall School of Music & Drama
Barbican, London EC2Y 8DT
**Tel:** 020 7382 7192
**Principal:** Barry Ife CBE, FKC, HonFRAM
**Fees:** Day £0
16+

### Hansard Society
40-43 Chancery Lane,
London WC2A 1JA
**Tel:** 020 7438 1222
**Head:** Fiona Booth
16+

### Holborn School of Finance & Management
25 Old Gloucester Street, Queen
Square, London WC1N 3AN
**Tel:** 020 7404 2422
**Head:** Felix Orogun
16+

### Italia Conti Academy of Theatre Arts
Italia Conti House, 23 Goswell
Road, London EC1M 7AJ
**Tel:** 020 7608 0047
**Principal:** Anne Sheward
**Age range:** 10–21
16+ 16+

### Kensington College
23 Bloomsbury Square,
London WC1A 2PJ
**Tel:** 020 7580 1113
**Fees:** Day £0
16+

### Kidsunlimited Nurseries – Mango Tree
62-66 Farringdon Road,
London EC1R 3GA
**Tel:** 08458 500 222

### London College of English & Advanced Studies Ltd
178 Goswell Road,
London EC1V 7DT
**Tel:** 020 7250 0610
**Fees:** Day £0
16+

### London College of International Business Studies
14 Southampton Place,
London WC1A 2AJ
**Tel:** 020 7242 1004
**Heads:** Mr Philip Moore & Ms Irene Chong
16+

### London School of Accountancy & Management
3rd Floor, 12-20 Camomile
Street, London EC3A 7PT
**Tel:** 020 7623 8777
**Head:** Mr Dak Patel
16+

### London School of Business & Management
Central House, 14 Upper Woburn
Place, London WC1H 0NN
**Tel:** 020 7388 8877
**Head:** Mr Alistair Andrews
16+

### National Council for Drama Training
1-7 Woburn Walk, London WC1H 0JJ
**Tel:** 020 7387 3650
**Director:** Adele Bailey
16+

### Royal Academy of Dramatic Art
62-64 Gower Street,
London WC1E 6ED
**Tel:** 020 7636 7076
**Principal:** Nicholas Barter MA, FRSA
16+

### Smithfield House Children's Nursery
14 West Smithfield,
London EC1A 9HY
**Tel:** 020 7236 1000
**Manager:** Janet MacGregor
**Age range:** 0–5

---

**ST PAUL'S CATHEDRAL SCHOOL**
*For further details see p. 75*
2 New Change,
London EC4M 9AD
**Tel:** 020 7248 5156
**Email:** admissions@
spcs.london.sch.uk
**Website:** www.spcslondon.com
**Headmaster:** Simon Larter-Evans
BA (Hons), PGCE, FRSA
**Age range:** 4–13
**No. of pupils:** 247
**Fees:** Day £13,530–
£14,565 FB £8,424
🏫 £ ✏ 🧍

---

### The College of Central London
Tower Bridge Business Centre, 46-48
East Smithfield, London E1W 1AW
**Tel:** +44 (0) 20 3667 7607
**Principal:** Nicolas Kailides
**Fees:** Day £3,300
16+ 16+

### The Courtauld Institute of Art
Somerset House, Strand,
London WC2R 0RN
**Tel:** 020 7848 2777
**Director:** Dr Deborah Swallow
16+

### The London Film School
24 Shelton Street,
London WC2H 9UB
**Tel:** 020 7836 9642
**Director:** Ben Gibson
**Fees:** Day £0
16+

### The Lyceum
6 Paul Street, London EC2A 4JH
**Tel:** 020 7247 1588
**Joint Headteachers:** Mr Jeremy
Rowe & Mrs Lynn Hannay
**Age range:** 4–11
**No. of pupils:** 100
**Fees:** Day £8,700–£13,800

### The Method Studio London
Conway Hall, 25 Red Lion
Square, London WC1R 4RL
**Tel:** 020 7831 7335
16+

### The School of Computer Technology
73 Great Eastern Street,
London EC2A 3HR
**Tel:** 020 7739 9002
**Fees:** Day £0
16+

**Urdang Academy**
The Old Finsbury Town
Hall, Rosebery Avenue,
London EC1R 4RP
**Tel:** 020 7713 7710
**Principal:** Stephanie Pope ARAD
(dip PDTC)
**Age range:** 10–16

**Williams College**
Thavies Inn House, 5 Holborn
Circus, London EC1N 2HB
**Tel:** 020 7583 9222
**Head:** Mr Mujeeb Pathamanathan

# East London

**Al-Falah Primary School**
48 Kenninghall Road,
Clapton, London E5 8BY
**Tel:** 020 8985 1059
**Headteacher:** Mr M A Hussain
**Age range:** 5–11
**No. of pupils:** 83
**Fees:** Day £1,600

**Al-Mizan School**
46 Whitechapel Road,
London E1 1JX
**Tel:** 020 7650 3070
**Head:** Mr Ziaurr Ahman
**Age range:** B7–18
**No. of pupils:** 200 VIth13
**Fees:** Day £2,400

**Alphabet House Day
(Montessori) Nursery**
Methodist Church, Windmill
Lane, Stratford, London E15 1PG
**Tel:** 020 8519 2023
**Principal:** Ms Kemi Balogun

**Alphabet House
Nursery School**
23 Harold Road, Upton
Park, London E13 0SQ
**Tel:** 020 8548 9466
**Principal:** Ms Kemi Balogun

**Amhurst Nursery**
13, The Avenue, Waltham
Forest, London E4 9LB
**Tel:** 020 8527 1614
**Officer in Charge:** Mrs Mills

**Ann Tayler Children's
Centre Nurser**
1-13 Triangle Road (off Westgate
Street), Hackney, London E8 3RP
**Tel:** 020 7275 6022
**Fees:** Day £10

**Azhar Academy**
235A Romford Road, Forest
Gate, London E7 9HL
**Tel:** 020 8534 5959
**Headteacher:** Mrs R Rehman
**Age range:** G11–16
**No. of pupils:** 189

**Beis Trana Girls' School**
186 Upper Clapton Road,
London E5 9DH
**Tel:** 020 8815 8003
**Age range:** G3–16
**No. of pupils:** 270

**Bethnal Green
Montessori School**
68 Warner Place, Bethnal
Green, London E2 7DA
**Tel:** 020 7739 4343
**Head:** Sidonie Winter
**Age range:** 2–6

**Billet's Corner Day Nursery**
11 Walthamstow Avenue,
London E4 8ST
**Tel:** 020 8523 3823
**Principal:** B Harmsworth

**Building Crafts College**
Kennard Road, Stratford,
London E15 1AH
**Tel:** 020 8522 1705
**Principal:** Mr John Taylor

**Bushytails Day Nursery
and Nursery School**
591 Manchester Road,
Docklands, London E14 3NU
**Tel:** 020 7537 7776
**Headmistress:** Christine G Bush
NNEB
**Age range:** 0–5
**No. of pupils:** 15

**Busy Bees at Chingford**
2 Larkswood Leisure Park, 175 New
Road, Chingford, London E4 9EY
**Tel:** 020 8524 7063
**Nursery Manager:** Natalie Keyes
**Age range:** 3 months–5 years

**Busy Bees in London ExCel**
5 Western Gateway, Royal
Victoria Docks, London E16 1XL
**Tel:** 020 7474 7487
**Nursery Manager:** Rebecca Davy
**Age range:** 0–5

**Childsplay Day Nursery**
283 Hall Lane, Chingford,
London E4 8NU
**Tel:** 020 8529 6058
**Age range:** 0–5

**Chingford House School**
22 Marlborough Road, Waltham
Forest, London E4 9AL
**Tel:** 020 8527 2902; 07749
899 498
**Head teacher:** Helen McNulty
**Age range:** 0–5
**Fees:** Day £5,460–£8,320

**City of London College**
71 Whitechapel High
Street, London E1 7PL
**Tel:** 020 7247 2166
**Head:** Mr David Nixon

**City of London College**
80 Backchurch Lane, London E1 1LX
**Tel:** 020 7247 2166
**Head:** Mr David Nixon

**East End Computing
& Business College**
149 Commercial Road,
London E1 1PX
**Tel:** 020 7247 8447
**Head:** Anthony Wilkinson

**East London College**
Panther House, 647-661 High
Road, London E11 4RD
**Tel:** 020 8539 2224

**FARADAY SCHOOL**
*For further details see p. 52*
Old Gate House, 7 Trinity Buoy
Wharf, London E14 0JW
**Tel:** 020 8965 7374
**Email:** info@
newmodelschool.co.uk
**Website:**
www.faradayschool.co.uk
**Executive Head Teacher:** Mrs.
S. Gillam
**Age range:** 4–11
**No. of pupils:** 105
**Fees:** Day £3,284

**Forest Glade Nursery**
15 Dyson Road, London E11 1NA
**Tel:** 020 8989 9684
**Age range:** 0–5

**Forest School**
College Place, Snaresbrook,
London E17 3PY
**Tel:** 020 8520 1744
**Warden:** Mr Anthony Faccinello
**Age range:** 4–18
**No. of pupils:** 1355 VIth260
**Fees:** Day £11,049–£16,335

**Gatehouse School**
Sewardstone Road, Victoria
Park, London E2 9JG
**Tel:** 020 8980 2978
**Headmistress:** Mrs Belinda Canham
JP, BA(Hons), PGCE(Froebel)
**Age range:** 3–11
**No. of pupils:** 320
**Fees:** Day £6,920–£8,502

**Get Along Gang Playgroup**
St Mary of Eton Church Hall,
Eastway, Hackney, London E9 5JA
**Tel:** 020 8533 0926

**Grangewood
Independent School**
Chester Road, Forest
Gate, London E7 8QT
**Tel:** 020 8472 3552
**Headteacher:** Mrs B A Roberts B.Ed
(Hons); PG Cert (SEN)
**Age range:** 2–11
**No. of pupils:** 71
**Fees:** Day £5,157–£6,750

**Green Gables
Montessori School**
St George in the East Crypt
West, 14 Cannon Street
Road, London E1 0BH
**Tel:** 020 7488 2374
**Head:** Mrs V Hunt
**Age range:** 0–8
**No. of pupils:** 45
**Fees:** Day £740–£10,480

**Happy Child Day Nursery**
The Old Town Hall, 14B
Orford Road, Walthamstow
Village, London E17 9NL
**Tel:** 020 8520 8880
**Head:** Mrs Margaret Murphy

**Happy Faces at
Wisdom Kids Nursery**
524 High Street, London E12 6QN
**Tel:** 020 8478 2805

**Humpty Dumpty Nursery**
24 Fairlop Road, Waltham
Forest, London E11 1BL
**Tel:** 020 8539 3810
**Age range:** 1–5

**Hyland House School**
Holcombe Road, Tottenham,
, London N17 9AD
**Tel:** 020 8520 4186
**Head Teacher:** Mrs Gina
Abbequaye
**Age range:** 3–11
**Fees:** Day £2,520

**Independent
Place Nursery**
26/27 Independent Place,
Shacklewell Lane, Hackney,
London E8 2HD
**Tel:** 020 7275 7755
**Head:** Ms Dawn Pennington
**Age range:** 0–5
**No. of pupils:** 43

**Interlink College of
Technology & Business**
Interlink House, Unit 11, Unity
Works, 22 Sutherland Road,
Walthamstow, London E17 6JW
**Tel:** 0208 531 1118
**Head:** Mr Kanmi Alo

**Kaye Rowe Nursery School**
Osborne Road, London E7 0PH
**Tel:** 020 8534 4403

**Kids Inc Day Nursery
– Chingford**
3 Friday Hill West, Chingford
Hatch, London E4 6UP
**Tel:** 020 8524 6745

**Kids Inc Day Nursery
– South Woodford**
71 Cleveland Road, South
Woodford, London E18 2AE
**Tel:** 020 8518 8855
**Manager:** Sarah-Jane Smith NNEB
**Age range:** 3months–5

**Lanterns Nursery
and Pre-school**
F4-F6 Lanterns Court, 22
Millharbour, London E14 9TU
**Tel:** 020 7363 0951

**Leaview Community
Nursery Ltd**
Leaview House, Springfield,
London E5 9EJ
**Tel:** 020 8806 9012
**Co-ordinator:** Leticia Adu
AdvMontDip
**Age range:** 6months–5
**Fees:** Day £3,000–£6,250

**Little Green Man Nursery**
15 Lemna Road, Waltham
Forest, London E11 1HX
**Tel:** 020 8539 7228
**Age range:** 0–5
**No. of pupils:** 46

**London Crown College**
80-90 Mile End Road,
London E1 4UN
**Tel:** 020 7790 3330
**Head:** Mr Firoz Hasan
🔞

**London East Academy**
46-80 Whitechapel Road,
London E1 1JX
**Tel:** 020 7650 3070
**Headteacher:** Musleh Faradhi
**Age range:** B11–18
**No. of pupils:** VIth18
**Fees:** Day £3,000
🚹

**London Oriental Academy**
Suite B, 1-3 Kempton Road,
East Ham, London E6 2LD
**Tel:** 020 8470 9876
**Head:** Saraswathi Namasivayam
🔞

**London School of
Commerce & IT**
128 Commercial Road,
London E1 1NL
**Tel:** 020 7702 2509
**Head:** Dr Abul Kalam
🔞

**London School of
Computer Education**
Second Floor, 1-3 Norton
Folgate, London E1 6DB
**Tel:** 020 7392 9696
**Head:** Mr David Kohn
🔞

**London School of
Management &
Technology**
Queensway House, 109 High
Street, Stretford, London E15 2QQ
**Tel:** 020 8534 9996
🔞

**Low Hall Nursery**
Low Hall Lane, London E17 8BE
**Tel:** 020 8520 1689

**Lubavitch House
School (Junior Boys)**
135 Clapton Common,
London E5 9AE
**Tel:** 020 8800 1044
**Head:** Rabbi D Golomb
**Age range:** B5–11
**No. of pupils:** 101
**Fees:** Day £520–£3,100
🚹

**Madani Girls School**
Myrtle Street, London E1 1HL
**Tel:** 020 7377 1992
**Headteacher:** Mrs F Liyawdeen
**Age range:** G11–18
**No. of pupils:** 248 VIth11
**Fees:** Day £1,900
🚹

**Magic Roundabout
Nursery – Docklands**
Jack Dash House, 2 Lawn House
Close, Marsh Wall, London E14 9YQ
**Tel:** 020 7364 6028

**Magic Roundabout
Nursery – Walthamstow**
161 Wadham Road, Centre Way,
Walthamstow, London E17 4HU
**Tel:** 020 8523 5551

**Market Nursery**
Wilde Close, Off Pownall Road,
Hackney, London E8 4JS
**Tel:** 020 7241 0978
**Head:** Ms Hazel Babb
**No. of pupils:** 24
🖊

**Merryfield Montessori
Nursery**
76 Station Road, Waltham
Forest, London E4 7BA
**Tel:** 020 8524 7697
**No. of pupils:** 45

**Metropolitan College
of London**
22-27 The Oval, London E2 9DT
**Tel:** 020 7159 2601/7168 2024
**Head:** Mr Mazumdar Kumar
🔞

**Noah's Ark Nursery**
within Mildmay Hospital, Hackney
Road, London E2 7NA
**Tel:** 020 7613 6346

**Normanhurst School**
68-74 Station Road,
Chingford, London E4 7BA
**Tel:** 020 8529 4307
**Headmistress:** Mrs Claire Osborn
**Age range:** 2–16
**No. of pupils:** 250
**Fees:** Day £7,470–£11,235
🖊

**Oliver Thomas
Nursery School**
Mathews Avenue, East
Ham, London E6 6BU
**Tel:** 020 8552 1177
**Head Teacher:** Dianne Walls
**Age range:** 3–5

**Paragon Christian
Academy**
233-241 Glyn Road, London E5 0JP
**Tel:** 020 8985 1119
**Headteacher:** Mrs J A Lynch
**Age range:** 5–16
**No. of pupils:** 34

**Pillar Box Montessori
Nursery & Pre-Prep School**
107 Bow Road, London E3 2AN
**Tel:** 020 8980 0700
**Age range:** 0–7
**Fees:** Day £250–£500

**Promised Land Academy**
St Cedds Hall, Webb Gardens,
Plaistow, London E13 8SR
**Tel:** 0207 473 3229
**Head:** Mr A Coote
**Age range:** 4–16

**Quwwat-ul Islam
Girls School**
16 Chaucer Road, Forest
Gate, London E7 9NB
**Tel:** 020 8548 4736
**Headteacher:** Mrs B Khan
**Age range:** G4–11
**No. of pupils:** 150
🚹

**River House
Montessori School**
3-4 Shadwell Pierhead, Glamis
Road, London E1W 3TD
**Tel:** 020 7538 9886
**Headmistress:** Miss S Greenwood
**Age range:** 3–12
**Fees:** Day £2,700–£9,000
🖊

**Snaresbrook
Preparatory School**
75 Woodford Road, South
Woodford, London E18 2EA
**Tel:** 020 8989 2394
**Interim Head:** Mrs Linda Chiverrell
**Age range:** 3–11
**No. of pupils:** 164
**Fees:** Day £6,696–£8,952
🖊

**Spitalfields Nursery**
21 Lamb Street, London E1 6EA
**Tel:** 020 7375 0775
**Principal:** Angela Dorian

**St Joseph's Convent
School For Girls**
59 Cambridge Park,
Wanstead, London E11 2PR
**Tel:** 020 8989 4700
**Headteacher:** Ms C Glover
**Age range:** G3–11
**No. of pupils:** 171
**Fees:** Day £5,355
🚹 🖊

**Sunbeams Day Nursery**
10 Bushwood, Leytonstone,
London E11 3AY
**Tel:** 020 8530 2784

**Sunshine Day Nursery**
167 Wallwood Road,
Leytonstone, London E11 1AQ
**Tel:** 020 8556 6889

**Talmud Torah Machikei
Hadass School**
96-98 Clapton Common,
London E5 9AL
**Tel:** 020 8800 6599
**Headteacher:** Rabbi C Silbiger
**Age range:** B4–11
**No. of pupils:** 271
🚹

**The Happy Nest
Nursery Ltd**
Fellows Court Family
Centre, Weymouth Terrace,
Hackney, London E2 8LR
**Tel:** 020 7739 3193

**The Music School**
59a High Street, Wanstead,
London E11 2AE
**Tel:** 020 8502 0932
🔞

**Tinkerbells Nursery**
185 Coppermill Lane,
Walthamstow, London E17 7HU
**Tel:** 020 8520 8338
**Principal:** Sue Walker

**Tom Thumb Nursery**
1-7 Beulah Road, London E17 9LG
**Tel:** 020 8520 1329
**Age range:** 2–5
**No. of pupils:** 32

**Tree House Nursery
& After School**
35 Woodbine Place,
London E11 2RH
**Tel:** 020 8532 2535

**Western Governors
Graduate School**
27-33 Bethnal Green
Road, London E1 6LA
**Tel:** 020 7033 9596
**Principal:** Mark Chatlani
🔞

**Whitechapel College**
1-13 Adler Street, London E1 1EG
**Tel:** 020 8555 3355
**Principal:** Luke Julias Maughan-
Pawsey
🔞

**Winston House Preparatory School**
140 High Road, London E18 2QS
Tel: 020 8505 6565
**Head Teacher:** Mrs Marian Kemp
**Age range:** 3–11
**Fees:** Day £5,850–£7,050

# North London

**5 E College of London**
Selby Centre, Selby Road, London N17 8JL
Tel: 020 8885 3456/5454
**Head:** Mr Raj Doshi
16+

**Academy of the Science of Acting & Directing**
9-15 Elthorne Road, London N19 4AJ
Tel: 020 7272 0027
**Principal:** Helen Pierpoint BSc, PhD
16+

**Annemount School**
18 Holne Chase, Hampstead Garden Suburb, London N2 0QN
Tel: 020 8455 2132
**Principal:** Mrs G Maidment BA(Hons), MontDip
**Age range:** 2–7
**No. of pupils:** 100
**Fees:** Day £2,500–£4,500

**Appletree Nursery**
59A Osbaldeston Road, Hackney, London N16 7DL
Tel: 020 8806 3525

**Asquith Nursery – Crouch Hill**
33 Crouch Hill, London N4 4AP
Tel: 020 7561 1533
**Age range:** 3 months–5

**Asquith Nursery – Finsbury Park**
Dulas Street, Finsbury Park, Islington, London N4 3AF
Tel: 020 7263 3090
**Age range:** 3 months–5

**Asquith Nursery – Salcombe**
33 The Green, Southgate, London N14 6EN
Tel: 020 8882 2136

**Avenue Nursery & Pre-Preparatory School**
2 Highgate Avenue, London N6 5RX
Tel: 020 8348 6815
**Principal:** Mrs. Mary Fysh
**Age range:** 3 1/2–7 1/2
**No. of pupils:** 79

**Beatty Road Nursery**
162 Albion Road, Hackney, London N16 9JS
Tel: 020 7249 7404
**Principal:** Geraldine Sinnott

**Beis Chinuch Lebonos Girls School**
Woodberry Down Centre, Woodberry Down, London N4 2SH
Tel: 020 88097 737
**Headmistress:** Mrs Bertha Schneck
**Age range:** G2–16
**No. of pupils:** 421

**Beis Malka Girls School**
93 Alkham Road, London N16 6XD
Tel: 020 8806 2070
**Headmaster:** M Dresdner
**Age range:** G5–16
**No. of pupils:** 339

**Beis Rochel D'Satmar Girls School**
51-57 Amhurst Park, London N16 5DL
Tel: 020 8800 9060
**Headmistress:** Mrs A Scher
**Age range:** G2–17
**No. of pupils:** 788

**Bnois Jerusalem School**
79-81 Amhurst Park, London N16 5DL
Tel: 020 8802 7470
**Head:** Mrs Sonnenschein
**Age range:** G3–16

**Busy Bees at Enfield Highlands Village**
2 Florey Square, Highlands Village, London N21 1UJ
Tel: 020 8360 6610
**Nursery Manager:** Simone Prince
**Age range:** 3 months–5 years

**Busy Bees Nursery**
c/o David Lloyd Leisure Club, Leisure Way, High Road, Finchley, London N12 0QZ
Tel: 020 8343 8500
**Manager:** Toni Difonzo
**Age range:** 3months–5
**No. of pupils:** 18

**Channing School**
The Bank, Highgate, London N6 5HF
Tel: 020 8340 2328
**Head:** Mrs B M Elliott
**Age range:** G4–18
**No. of pupils:** 746 VIth108
**Fees:** Day £14,085–£15,255

**City of London Business College**
Ebenezer House, 726-728 Seven Sisters Road, London N15 5NH
Tel: 020 8800 6621
**Head:** Mr Kwateng
16+

**City of London Business College**
Gaunson House, Units 1 / 1A / 2, Markfield Road, London N15 4QQ
Tel: 020 8808 2810
**Head:** Mr Kwateng
16+

**Coconut Nursery**
133 Stoke Newington Church Street, London N16 0UH
Tel: 020 7923 0720

**Court Theatre Training Co**
55 East Road, London N1 6AH
Tel: 020 7739 6868
**Artistic Director:** June Abbott
16+

**Dwight School London**
6 Friern Barnet Lane, London N11 3LX
Tel: +44 (0)20 8920 0637
**Head:** Mrs Alison Cobbin BA, Dip Ed, MBA
**Age range:** 3–18

**Finchley & Acton Yochien School**
6 Hendon Avenue, Finchley, London N3 1UE
Tel: 020 8343 2191
**Headteacher:** Mr Katsumasa Kitagaki
**Age range:** 2–6
**No. of pupils:** 145

**Floral Place Day Nursery**
2 Floral Place, Northampton Grove, London N1 2PL
Tel: 020 7354 9945

**Getters Talmud Torah**
86 Amhurst Park, London N16 5AR
Tel: 020 8802 2512
**Headteacher:** Mr David Kahana
**Age range:** B4–11
**No. of pupils:** 171

**Grange Park Preparatory School**
13 The Chine, Grange Park, Winchmore Hill, London N21 2EA
Tel: 020 8360 1469
**Headteacher:** Miss F Rizzo
**Age range:** G4–11
**No. of pupils:** 90
**Fees:** Day £9,900

**Greek Secondary School of London**
Avenue Lodge, Bounds Green Road, London N22 7EU
Tel: 020 8881 9320
**Headteacher:** Antonia Valavani
**Age range:** 13–18
**No. of pupils:** 200
16+

**Hackney Care For Kids**
61 Evering Road, Hackney, London N16 7PR
Tel: 020 7923 3471

**Highgate**
North Road, Highgate, London N6 4AY
Tel: 020 8340 1524
**Head Master:** Mr A S Pettitt MA
**Age range:** 3–18
**No. of pupils:** 1541 VIth312
**Fees:** Day £15,135–£17,475
£ 16+

**Highgate Junior School**
Cholmeley House, 3 Bishopswood Road, London N6 4PL
Tel: 020 8340 9193
**Principal:** Mr S M James BA
**Age range:** 7–11
**Fees:** Day £10,695–£11,955

**Highgate Pre-Preparatory School**
7 Bishopswood Road, London N6 4PH
Tel: 020 8340 9196
**Principal:** Mrs Diane Hecht
**Age range:** 3–7
**No. of pupils:** 150
**Fees:** Day £17,640

**Impact Factory**
Suite 121, Business Design Centre, 52 Upper Street, London N1 0QH
Tel: 020 7226 1877
**Founding Partners:** Robin Chandler & Jo Ellen Grzyb
16+

**Keble Prep**
Wades Hill, Winchmore Hill, London N21 1BG
Tel: 020 8360 3359
**Headmaster:** Mr M J Mitchell
**Age range:** B4–13
**No. of pupils:** 228
**Fees:** Day £3,850–£4,930
£

**Kerem House**
18 Kingsley Way, London N2 0ER
Tel: 020 8455 7524
**Headmistress:** Mrs D Rose
**Age range:** 2–5
**No. of pupils:** 96
**Fees:** Day £2,025–£5,160

**Kerem School**
Norrice Lea, London N2 0RE
Tel: 020 8455 0909
**Head Teacher:** Miss Alyson Burns
**Age range:** 3–11
**Fees:** Day £8,250–£6,675

**Kidsunlimited Nurseries – Camden**
The Mary Seacole Nursery, Tollington Way, London N7 8QX
Tel: 01625 585222

**Laurel Way Playgroup**
Nansen Village, 21 Woodside Avenue, London N12 8AQ
Tel: 020 8445 7514
**Head:** Mrs Susan Farber
**Age range:** 3–5

## London School of Business & Computing
Business Design Centre, 52 Upper Street, London N1 0QH
**Tel:** 020 7288 6307/8
**Head:** Dr Viramouttou
16

## London Studio Centre
42-50 York Way, Kings Cross, London N1 9AB
**Tel:** 020 7837 7741
**Director & CEO:** Mr Nic Espinosa
**Age range:** 18+
16

## Lubavitch House School (Senior Girls)
107-115 Stamford Hill, Hackney, London N16 5RP
**Tel:** 020 8800 0022
**Headmaster:** Rabbi Shmuel Lew FRSA
**Age range:** G11–17
**No. of pupils:** 102
**Fees:** Day £3,900

## Lubavitch Orthodox Jewish Nursery – North London
107-115 Stamford Hill, Hackney, London N16 5RP
**Tel:** 020 8800 0022
**Head:** Mrs F Sudak

## MARS Montessori Islington Green Nursery
4 Collins Yard, Islington Green, London N1 2XU
**Tel:** 020 7704 2805
**Head:** Angela Euesden
**Age range:** 2–5
**No. of pupils:** 24

## Montessori House
5 Princes Avenue, Muswell Hill, London N10 3LS
**Tel:** 020 8444 4399
**Head:** Ms Lisa Christoforou
**Age range:** 6 months–7 years
**No. of pupils:** 100
**Fees:** Day £5,355–£9,450

## New Park Montessori School
67 Highbury New Park, Islington, London N5 2EU
**Tel:** 020 7226 1109

## Norfolk House School
10 Muswell Avenue, Muswell Hill, London N10 2EG
**Tel:** 020 8883 4584
**Head Teacher:** Ms Sam Habgood
**Age range:** 4–11
**No. of pupils:** 130
**Fees:** Day £9,855

## North London Grammar School
110 Colindeep Lane, Hendon, London NW9 6HB
**Tel:** 0208 205 0052
**Head Teacher:** Hakan Gokce
**Age range:** 11–18
**No. of pupils:** VIth20
**Fees:** Day £7,500
£

## North London Muslim School
131-133 Fore Street, Edmonton, London N18 2XF
**Tel:** 020 8345 7008
**Headteacher:** Mr W Abdulla
**Age range:** 4–10
**No. of pupils:** 21

## North London Rudolf Steiner School
1-3 The Campsbourne, London N8 7PN
**Tel:** 020 8341 3770
**Age range:** 2.5–7
**No. of pupils:** 40

## One-Tech (UK) Ltd
1st Floor, 12 Cheapside, High Road, London N22 6HH
**Tel:** 020 8889 0707
**Head:** Mr Len Sutherland
16

## Palmers Green High School
Hoppers Road, Winchmore Hill, London N21 3LJ
**Tel:** 020 8886 1135
**Headmistress:** Mrs Christine Edmundson BMus(Hons), MBA, PGCE, LRAM, ARCM
**Age range:** G3–16
**No. of pupils:** 300
**Fees:** Day £5,985–£10,785

## Pardes House Grammar School
Hendon Lane, Finchley, London N3 1SA
**Tel:** 020 8349 4222
**Headteacher:** Mr S Mallett
**No. of pupils:** B10–16
**No. of pupils:** 222

## Pentland Day Nursery
224 Squires Lane, Finchley, London N3 2QL
**Tel:** 020 8970 2441
**Principal:** Rachele Parker

## Phoenix Academy
85 Bounces Road, Edmonton, London N9 8LD
**Tel:** 020 8887 6888
**Headteacher:** Mr A Hawkes
**Age range:** 11–16
**No. of pupils:** 19

## Phoenix Montessori Nursery
27 Stamford Hill, London N16 5TN
**Tel:** 020 8880 2550
**Manageress:** Kelly Murphy
**Age range:** 0–5 years

## Rainbow Nursery
Yorkshire Grove Estate, 22-26 Nevill Road, London N16 8SP
**Tel:** 020 7254 7930
**Age range:** 3 months–5 years

## Rosemary Works Independent School
1 Branch Place, London N1 5PH
**Tel:** 020 7739 3950
**Head:** Dorothy Davey
**Age range:** 3–11
**No. of pupils:** 104
**Fees:** Day £6,195

## Salcombe Preparatory School
224-226 Chase Side, Southgate, , London N14 4PL
**Tel:** 020 8441 5356
**Headmistress:** Mrs Sarah-Jane Davies BA(Hons) QTS MEd
**Age range:** 3–11
**No. of pupils:** 250
**Fees:** Day £11,175
£

## Salcombe Pre-School
Green Road, Southgate, , London N14 4AD
**Tel:** 020 8441 5356
**Headmistress:** Mrs Sarah-Jane Davies BA(Hons) QTS MEd

## St Andrew's Montessori
St Andrew's Church, Thornhill Square, London N1 1BQ
**Tel:** 020 7700 2961
**Principal:** Samantha Rawson MontDip
**Age range:** 2–6
**No. of pupils:** 40
**Fees:** Day £4,200–£6,525

## St Paul's Steiner School
1 St Paul's Road, Islington, London N1 2QH
**Tel:** 020 7226 4454
**College of Teachers:** College of Teachers
**Age range:** 2–14
**No. of pupils:** 136
£

## Sunrise Nursery, Stoke Newington
1 Cazenove Road, Stoke Newington, Hackney, London N16 6PA
**Tel:** 020 8806 6279
**Principal:** Didi Ananda Manika

## Sunrise Primary School
55 Coniston Road, Tottenham, London N17 0EX
**Tel:** 020 8806 6279 (Office); 020 8885 3354 (School)
**Head:** Mrs Mary-Anne Lovage MontDipEd, BA
**Age range:** 2–11
**No. of pupils:** 30
**Fees:** Day £5,343

## Talmud Torah Bobov Primary School
87 Egerton Road, London N16 6UE
**Tel:** 020 8809 1025
**Headmaster:** Mr Eisen
**Age range:** B3–13
**No. of pupils:** 320

## Talmud Torah Chaim Meirim School
26 Lampard Grove, London N16 6XB
**Tel:** 020 8806 0017
**Principal:** Rabbi S Hoffman
**Age range:** B6–13

## Talmud Torah Yetev Lev School
111-115 Cazenove Road, London N16 6AX
**Tel:** 020 8806 3834
**Headteacher:** Mr J Stauber
**Age range:** B2–11
**No. of pupils:** 567

## Tawhid Boys School
21 Cazenove Road, London N16 6PA
**Tel:** 020 8806 2999
**Headteacher:** Mr Usman Mapara
**Age range:** B10–15
**No. of pupils:** 115
**Fees:** Day £2,000

## Tayyibah Girls School
88 Filey Avenue, Stamford Hill, London N16 6JJ
**Tel:** 020 8880 0085
**Headmistress:** Mrs N B Qureishi MSc
**Age range:** G5–15
**No. of pupils:** 270
**Fees:** Day £1,630

## Teddies Nurseries New Southgate
60 Beaconsfield Road, New Soutgate, London N11 3AE
**Tel:** 0333 920 4841
**Nursery Manager:** Ms Katerina Barotsaki
**Age range:** 3 months–5 years

## The Children's House School
77 Elmore Street, London N1 3AQ
**Tel:** 020 7354 2113
**Head:** Jill Rothwell
**Age range:** 2–4
**No. of pupils:** 73
**Fees:** Day £1,550–£1,675

## The Children's House Upper School
King Henry's Walk, London N1 4PB
**Tel:** 020 7249 6273
**Headteacher:** Mrs J Rothwell
**Age range:** 4–7
**No. of pupils:** 60
**Fees:** Day £3,250

## The City College
University House, 55 East Road, London N1 6AH
**Tel:** 020 7253 1133
**Principal:** A Andrews MCMI
**Age range:** 18–40
**Fees:** Day £0
16

**The Dance Studio**
843-845 Green Lanes,
London N21 2RX
**Tel:** 020 8360 5700
16⁺

**The Gower School
Montessori Nursery**
18 North Road, Islington,
London N7 9EY
**Tel:** 020 7700 2445
**Principal:** Miss Emma Gowers
**Age range:** 3 months–5 years
**No. of pupils:** 237

**The Gower School
Montessori Primary**
10 Cynthia Street, Barnsbury,
London N1 9JF
**Tel:** 020 7278 2020
**Principal:** Miss Emma Gowers
**Age range:** 4–11
**No. of pupils:** 237
**Fees:** Day £4,680–£19,129

**The Grove Nursery**
Shepperton House, 83-
93 Shepperton Road,
Islington, London N1 3DF
**Tel:** 020 7226 4037
**Owners:** Ms Rebecca Browne & Ms
Elaine Catchpole
**Age range:** 0–5

**The Highgate
Activity Nurseries**
1 Church Road, Highgate,
London N6 4QH
**Tel:** 020 8348 9248
**Head:** Helena Prior
**Age range:** 2–5
**Fees:** Day £5,460–£9,620

**The Institute – Hampstead
Garden Suburb**
The Institute Office, 11 High
Road, London N2 8LL
**Tel:** 020 8829 4141
**Institute Principal:** Fay Naylor
16⁺

**The London Academy
of Health & Beauty**
53 Alkham Road, Stoke
Newington, London N16 7AA
**Tel:** 020 8806 1135
**Fees:** Day £0
16⁺

**The Montessori House**
5 Princes Avenue, Muswell
Hill, London N10 3LS
**Tel:** 020 8444 4399

**The Sam Morris Centre**
Parkside Crescent, London N7 7JG
**Tel:** 020 7609 1735

**Tiny Tots Nursery School**
Walker Hall, Christchurch Parish
Centre, The Green, Waterfall Road,
Southgate, London N14 7EG
**Tel:** 020 8447 9098
**Age range:** 2–5

**TTTYY School**
14 Heathland Road,
London N16 5NH
**Tel:** 020 8802 1348
**Headmaster:** Mr S B Gluck
**Age range:** B2–13
**No. of pupils:** 187

**Twinkle Stars Day Nursery**
416 Seven Sisters Road,
Hackney, London N4 2LX
**Tel:** 020 8802 0550
**Admin Officer:** Noori Mohamed
**Age range:** 1–5

**Vista Training**
107-115 Stamford Hill,
London N16 5RP
**Tel:** 020 8802 8772
16⁺

**Vita et Pax School**
Priory Close, Southgate,
London N14 4AT
**Tel:** 020 8449 8336
**Headteacher:** Miss Gillian
Chumbley
**Age range:** 3–11
**Fees:** Day £6,150

**Woodberry Day Nursery**
63 Church Hill, Winchmore
Hill, London N21 1LE
**Tel:** 020 8882 6917
**Manager:** Michelle Miller
**Age range:** 6 weeks–5
**No. of pupils:** 62

**Yesodey Hatorah School**
2-4 Amhurst Park, London N16 5AE
**Tel:** 020 8826 5500
**Headteacher:** Rabbi Pinter
**Age range:** 3–16
**No. of pupils:** 920

# North-West London

**Abbey Nursery School**
Cricklewood Baptist Church,
Sneyd Road, Cricklewood,
London NW2 6AN
**Tel:** 020 8208 2202
**Head:** Mrs Ruby Azam

**Abercorn School**
38 Portland Place, London NW8 9XP
**Tel:** 020 7286 4785
**High Mistress:** Mrs Andrea
Greystoke BA(Hons)
**Age range:** 2–13
**No. of pupils:** 360
**Fees:** Day £7,245–£13,425

**Al-Sadiq & Al-
Zahra Schools**
134 Salusbury Road,
London NW6 6PF
**Tel:** 020 7372 7706
**Headteacher:** Dr M Movahedi
**Age range:** 4–16
**No. of pupils:** 389

**Arnold House School**
1 Loudoun Road, St John's
Wood, London NW8 0LH
**Tel:** 020 7266 4840
**Headmaster:** Mr Vivian Thomas
**Age range:** B5–13
**No. of pupils:** 270
**Fees:** Day £5,878

**Asquith Nursery –
Golders Green**
212 Golders Green Road, Golders
Green, London NW11 9AT
**Tel:** 020 8458 7388
**Age range:** 1–5
**No. of pupils:** 68

**Asquith Nursery – Hendon**
46 Allington Road, Hendon,
London NW4 3DE
**Tel:** 020 8203 9020
**Age range:** 3 months–5

**Asquith Nursery – Hill Park**
5 Sunningfields Road,
Hendon, London NW4 4QR
**Tel:** 020 8201 5816
**Age range:** 3 months–5

**Asquith Nursery –
West Hampstead**
11 Woodchurch Road, West
Hampstead, London NW6 3PL
**Tel:** 020 7328 4787
**Age range:** 3 months–5

**Ayesha Community School**
10A Montagu Road, Hendon,
London NW4 3ES
**Tel:** 02034112660
**Headteacher:** Mr Shakil Ahmed
**Age range:** G4–18
**Fees:** Day £3,000

**Beehive Montessori School**
Christchurch Hall, Christchurch
Avenue, Brondebury Park,
London NW6 7BJ
**Tel:** 020 8451 5477
**Headmistress:** Ms Lucilla Baj
**Age range:** 2–5
**Fees:** Day £2,550

**Beis Hamedrash Elyon**
211 Golders Green Road,
London NW11 9BY
**Tel:** 020 8201 8668
**Headteacher:** Mr C Steinhart
**Age range:** B11–14
**No. of pupils:** 45

**Beis Soroh Schneirer**
Arbiter House, Wilberforce
Road, London NW9 6AT
**Tel:** 020 8343 1190
**Head:** Mrs R Weiss
**Age range:** G2–11
**No. of pupils:** 150

**Belmont, Mill Hill
Preparatory School**
The Ridgeway, London NW7 4ED
**Tel:** 020 8906 7270
**Headmaster:** Mr Leon Roberts MA
**Age range:** 7–13
**No. of pupils:** 490
**Fees:** Day £5,685

**Beth Jacob Grammar
School for Girls**
Stratford Road, Hendon,
London NW4 2AT
**Tel:** 020 8203 4322
**Headteacher:** Mrs D Steinberg
**Age range:** G11–17
**No. of pupils:** 264

**Bluebells Nursery**
Our Lady Help of Christians
Church Hall, Lady Margaret
Road, London NW5 2NE
**Tel:** 020 7284 3952
**Principal:** Ms Anita Pearson
**Age range:** 2–5
**No. of pupils:** 20

**Brampton College**
Lodge House, Lodge Road,
Hendon, London NW4 4DQ
**Tel:** 020 8203 5025
**Principal:** B Canetti BA(Hons), MSc
**Age range:** 15–20
**Fees:** Day £2,735–£12,470
16⁺

**British American
Drama Academy**
14 Gloucester Gate,
London NW1 4HG
**Tel:** 020 7487 0730
**Head:** Paul Costello
16⁺

**Broadhurst School**
19 Greencroft Gardens,
London NW6 3LP
**Tel:** 020 7328 4280
**Headmistress:** Mrs Zoe Sylvester
**Age range:** 2–5
**No. of pupils:** 145
**Fees:** Day £6,480–£10,950

**Brondesbury
College for Boys**
8 Brondesbury Park,
London NW6 7BT
**Tel:** 020 8830 4522
**Headteacher:** Mr Dan Salahuddin
Clifton
**Age range:** B11–16
**No. of pupils:** 93

**Busy Bees at Mill Hill**
30 Mill Way, Mill Hill,
London NW7 3RB
**Tel:** 0208 906 9123
**Nursery Manager:** Danielle Baker
**Age range:** 0–5

## Camden Community Nurseries
99 Leighton Road, London NW5 2RB
**Tel:** 020 7485 2105

## Chaston Nursery & Pre-preparatory School
Chaston Place, Off Grafton Terrace, London NW5 4JH
**Tel:** 020 7482 0701
**Head:** Mrs Sandra Witten DipEd, DMS
**Age range:** 0–5
**No. of pupils:** 69
**Fees:** Day £7,020–£12,732

## Chaston Nursery School
30 Palmerston Road, London NW6 2JL
**Tel:** 020 7372 2120
**Head:** Mr Roger Witten
**Age range:** 0–5
**No. of pupils:** 48
**Fees:** Day £6,504–£12,216

## Cherryfields Nursery School
523 Finchley Road, Hampstead, London NW3 7BB
**Tel:** 020 8905 3350
**Head:** Mrs Pamela Stewart

## Church Row Nursery
Crypt Room, Hampstead Parish Church, Church Row, Hampstead, London NW3 6UU
**Tel:** 020 7431 2603
**Head:** Mrs Marianne Wilson

## City Mission Nursery
2 Scrub Lane, London NW10 6RB
**Tel:** 0208 960 0838
**Age range:** 6 months–5

## College Francais Bilingue De Londres
87 Holmes Road, Kentish Town, , London NW5 3AX
**Tel:** +44 (0) 20 7993 7400
**Principal:** Mr François-Xavier Gabet
**Age range:** 5–15
**No. of pupils:** 210
🌐

## DEVONSHIRE HOUSE PREPARATORY SCHOOL
**For further details see p. 47**
2 Arkwright Road, Hampstead, London NW3 6AE
**Tel:** 020 7435 1916
**Email:** enquiries@devonshire houseprepschool.co.uk
**Website:** www.devonshire houseschool.co.uk
**Headmistress:** Mrs S. Piper BA(Hons)
**Age range:** B2 1/2–13 G2 1/2–11
**No. of pupils:** 670
**Fees:** Day £9,750–£17,985
£

## Eton Nursery Montessori School
45 Buckland Crescent, London NW3 5DJ
**Tel:** 020 7722 1532
**Head:** Mrs H Smith

## Fine Arts College, Hampstead
24 Lambolle Place, Belsize Park, London NW3 4PG
**Tel:** 020 7586 0312
**Co Principals:** Candida Cave & Nicholas Cochrane
**Age range:** 13–19
**No. of pupils:** 115
**Fees:** Day £6,000–£15,600
16▸ £ 16▸

## Francis Holland School, Regent's Park, NW1
Clarence Gate, Ivor Place, Regent's Park, London NW1 6XR
**Tel:** 020 7723 0176
**Head:** Mr C B Fillingham MA (King's College London)
**Age range:** G11–18
**No. of pupils:** 495 VIth120
**Fees:** Day £19,260
🏃 £ 16▸

## Golders Hill School
666 Finchley Road, London NW11 7NT
**Tel:** 020 8455 2589
**Headmistress:** Mrs A T Eglash BA(Hons)
**Age range:** 2–7
**No. of pupils:** 180
**Fees:** Day £831–£6,870

## Goodwyn School
Hammers Lane, Mill Hill, London NW7 4DB
**Tel:** 020 8959 3756
**Principal:** Struan Robertson
**Age range:** 3–11
**No. of pupils:** 223
**Fees:** Day £9,645–£10,779

## Grimsdell, Mill Hill Pre-Preparatory School
Winterstoke House, Wills Grove, Mill Hill, London NW7 1QR
**Tel:** 020 8959 6884
**Head:** Mrs Kate Simon BA, PGCE
**Age range:** 3–7
**No. of pupils:** 182
**Fees:** Day £1,971–£4,285
🖋

## Hampstead Hill Pre-Prep & Nursery School
St Stephen's Hall, Pond Street, Hampstead, London NW3 2PP
**Tel:** 020 7435 6262
**Principal:** Mrs Andrea Taylor
**Age range:** B2–7+ G2–7+
**Fees:** Day £11,000–£14,000
🖋

## Happy Child Day Nursery
59 Longstone Avenue, Harlesdon, London NW10 3TY
**Tel:** 020 8961 3485
**Age range:** 3 months–5

## Happy Child Day Nursery
2 Victoria Road, Kilburn, London NW6 6QG
**Tel:** 020 7328 8791
**Age range:** 3 months–5

## Happy Child Day Nursery
St Anne's & St Andrew's Church Hall, 125 Salisbury Road, Queens Park, London NW6 6RG
**Tel:** 020 7625 1966
**Age range:** 2–5

## Heathside Preparatory School
16 New End, Hampstead, London NW3 1JA
**Tel:** +44 (0)20 7794 5857
**Headteacher:** Ms Melissa Remus Elliot MSc
**Age range:** 2–13
**No. of pupils:** 370
**Fees:** Day £9,300–£14,250
🖋

## Hendon Montessori School
7 Denehurst Gardens, London NW4 3QS
**Tel:** 020 8202 8516

## Hendon Prep School
20 Tenterden Grove, Hendon, London NW4 1TD
**Tel:** 020 8203 7727
**Head of School:** Mr M. Lloyd-Williams
**Age range:** 2–13 years
**No. of pupils:** 165
**Fees:** Day £6,345–£14,175
£ 🖋

## Hendon Secretarial College
15 Watford Way, Hendon, London NW4 3JL
**Tel:** 020 8202 3677
16▸

## Hereward House School
14 Strathray Gardens, London NW3 4NY
**Tel:** 020 7794 4820
**Headmaster:** Mr T W Burden
**Age range:** B4–13
**No. of pupils:** 170
**Fees:** Day £13,065–£14,205
🏃

## Highgate Children's Centre
Highgate Studios, 53-79 Highgate Road, London NW5 1TL
**Tel:** 020 7485 5252
**Principal:** Lorraine Thompson

## Hill Park Pre-School
5 Sunningfields Road, Hendon, London NW4 4QR
**Tel:** 020 8201 5816
**Age range:** 1–5
**No. of pupils:** 92

## International Community School
4 York Terrace East, Regents Park, London NW1 4PT
**Tel:** +44 20 7935 1206
**Head of School:** Ms Rose Threlfall
**Age range:** 3–18
**No. of pupils:** 260
**Fees:** Day £16,650–£22,100
🌐 IB 🖋 16▸

## Islamia Girls' High School
129 Salusbury Road, London NW6 6PE
**Tel:** 020 7372 3472
**Headteacher:** Ms S Jabeen
**Age range:** G11–16 years
**Fees:** Day £6,900
🏃

## Joel Nursery
214 Colindeep Lane, Colindale, London NW9 6DF
**Tel:** 020 8200 0189
**Age range:** 2–5
🖋

## Kentish Town Day Nursery
37 Ryland Road, London NW5 3EH
**Tel:** 020 7284 3600
**Manager:** Carol Kewley
**Age range:** 3 months–5 years
**No. of pupils:** 55

## Kentish Town Montessori School
34 Oakford Road, Kentish Town, London NW5 1AH
**Tel:** 020 7485 1056

## Kidsunlimited Nurseries – Regents Place
1 Triton Mall, Regents Place, Longford Street, London NW1 3FN
**Tel:** 01625 585222

## Kidsunlimited Nurseries – St Pancras
The Fig Tree Nursery, St Pancras Hospital, 4 St Pancras Way, London NW1 0PE
**Tel:** 01625 585222

## Kindercare Montessori Nursery
Bridge Park Business Centre, Harrow Road, London NW10 0RG
**Tel:** 020 8838 1688
**Age range:** 2–5
**Fees:** Day £4,420

## Lakefield Catering & Educational Centre
Maresfield Gardens, Hampstead, London NW3 5RY
**Tel:** 020 7794 5669
**Course Director:** Mrs Maria Brown
**Age range:** G16–24
**No. of pupils:** 16
**Fees:** FB £1,160
🏃 16▸ 🏛 £ 🖋 16▸ 🐾

## L'Ile Aux Enfants
22 Vicar's Road, London NW5 4NL
**Tel:** 020 7267 7119
**Headmistress:** Mrs Chailleux
**Age range:** 3–11
**No. of pupils:** 192
**Fees:** Day £3,270

## Little Cherubs Kindergarten
2 Belgrave Close, Mill Hill, London NW7 3QG
**Tel:** 020 8959 2420
**Head:** Mrs Pauline D Mitson
**No. of pupils:** 19

## London Academy of Dressmaking and Design
18 Dobree Avenue, Willesden,
London NW10 2AE
**Tel:** 020 8451 7174
**Principal:** Mrs P A Parkinson MA
**Age range:** 13+
**Fees:** Day £2,650

## London Jewish Girls' High School
18 Raleigh Close, Hendon,
London NW4 2TA
**Tel:** 020 8203 8618
**Headteacher:** Mr Joel Rabinowitz
**Age range:** G11–16

## London Thames College
Crown House, North Circular Road,
Park Royal, London NW10 7PN
**Tel:** 020 8961 9003
**Head:** Dr Archana Raheja

## LYNDHURST HOUSE PREP SCHOOL
*For further details see p. 58*
24 Lyndhurst Gardens,
Hampstead, London NW3 5NW
**Tel:** 020 7435 4936
**Email:** office@
lyndhursthouse.co.uk
**Website:**
www.lyndhursthouse.co.uk
**Head of School:** Mr Andrew Reid
MA (Oxon)
**Age range:** B4–13
**No. of pupils:** 165
**Fees:** Day £5,735–£6,410

## MAPLE WALK SCHOOL
*For further details see p. 59*
62A Crownhill Road,
London NW10 4EB
**Tel:** 020 8963 3890
**Email:** admin@
maplewalkschool.co.uk
**Website:**
www.maplewalkschool.co.uk
**Head Teacher:** Mrs S Gillam
**Age range:** 4–11
**No. of pupils:** 200
**Fees:** Day £3,190

## Maria Montessori Children's House – West Hampstead
St Mary's Community Hall, 134a
Abbey Road, London NW6 4SN
**Tel:** 020 7624 5917

## Maria Montessori Institute
26 Lyndhurst Gardens,
Hampstead, London NW3 5NW
**Tel:** 020 7435 3646
**Director of Training & School:** Mrs
Lynne Lawrence BA, Mont Int
Dip(AMI)
**Age range:** 18+
**No. of pupils:** 50
**Fees:** Day £7,100

## Maria Montessori School – Hampstead
26 Lyndhurst Gardens,
Hampstead, London NW3 5NW
**Tel:** +44 (0)20 7435 3646
**Director of School:** Miss L Kingston
**Age range:** 2–11
**No. of pupils:** 100
**Fees:** Day £5,400

## Mill Hill School
The Ridgeway, Mill Hill
Village, London NW7 1QS
**Tel:** 020 8959 1176
**Head:** Dr Dominic Luckett
**Age range:** 13–18
**No. of pupils:** 689 VIth259
**Fees:** Day £13,860 FB £21,900

## Naima Jewish Preparatory School
21 Andover Place, London NW6 5ED
**Tel:** 020 7328 2802
**Headteacher:** Mr Michael Cohen
MA, NPQH
**Age range:** 3–11
**Fees:** Day £5,997–£7,470

## Nancy Reuben Primary School
Finchley Lane, Hendon,
London NW4 1DJ
**Tel:** 020 82025646
**Head:** D A David
**Age range:** 3–11
**No. of pupils:** 207

## Neasden Montessori School
St Catherine's Church Hall, Dudden
Hill Lane, London NW2 7RX
**Tel:** 020 8208 1631
**Head:** Mrs J Sen Gupta BA,
MontDip(AMI)
**Age range:** 2–5

## Nicoll Road Nursery School
40 Nicoll Road, Harlesden,
London NW10 9AB
**Tel:** 020 8961 6648
**Age range:** 2–5
**No. of pupils:** 50

## NORTH BRIDGE HOUSE NURSERY AND PRE-PREP SCHOOLS
8 Netherhall Gardens,
London NW3 5RR
**Tel:** 020 7428 1520
**Head of School:** Mrs
C McLelland
**Age range:** 2 years 9
months–7 years
**No. of pupils:** 380
**Fees:** Day £15,975–£16,575

## NORTH BRIDGE HOUSE PREP SCHOOL REGENT'S PARK
1 Gloucester Avenue,
London NW1 7AB
**Tel:** 020 7428 1520
**Head of School:** Brodie Bibby
**Age range:** 7–13
**No. of pupils:** 460
**Fees:** Day £17,340

## NORTH BRIDGE HOUSE SENIOR CANONBURY
6-9 Canonbury Place,
Islington, London N1 2NQ
**Tel:** 020 7428 1520
**Head of School:** Mr
Jonathan Taylor
**Age range:** 11–18 years
**No. of pupils:** 180
**Fees:** Day £17,295–£18,555

## NORTH BRIDGE HOUSE SENIOR HAMPSTEAD
*For further details see p. 63*
65 Rosslyn Hill, London NW3 5UD
**Tel:** 020 7428 1520
**Email:** admissionsenquiries@
northbridgehouse.com
**Website:**
www.northbridgehouse.com
**Head of Senior Hampstead:** Mr.
Brendan Pavey
**Age range:** 2 years 9
months–18 years
**No. of pupils:** 1375

## NW5 Theatre School
14 Fortess Road, London NW5 2EU
**Tel:** 020 7482 3236
**Founder:** George O'Gorman
**Age range:** 16–30
**Fees:** Day £3,600

## Octagon Nursery School
St Saviour's Church Hall, Eton
Road, London NW3 4SU
**Tel:** 020 7586 3206

## OYH Primary School
Finchley Lane, Hendon,
London NW4 1DJ
**Tel:** 020 8202 5646
**Headteacher:** D A David
**Age range:** 3–11
**No. of pupils:** 180

## Rainbow Montessori School
13 Woodchurch Road,
Hampstead, London NW6 3PL
**Tel:** 020 7328 8986
**Head Mistress:** Maggy Miller
MontDip
**Age range:** 5–12
**Fees:** Day £3,250–£3,297

## Ready Steady Go – Camden
123 St Pancras Way,
London NW1 0SY
**Tel:** 020 7586 5862
**Age range:** 2–4

## Ready Steady Go – Fitzroy Road
Primrose Hill Community Centre,
29 Hopkinson's Place, Fitzroy
Road, London NW1 8TN
**Tel:** 020 7586 5862
**Age range:** 2–3

## Ready Steady Go – Primrose Hill
12a King Henry's Road,
London NW3 3RP
**Tel:** 020 7586 5862
**Age range:** 3–5

## Ready Steady Go – St John's Wood
21 Alexandra Road,
London NW8 0DP
**Tel:** 020 7586 5862
**Age range:** 2–5

## Saint Christina's R C Preparatory School
25 St Edmunds Terrace, Regent's
Park, London NW8 7PY
**Tel:** 020 7722 8784
**Headteacher:** Mrs P Mortimer
**Age range:** B3–G3–11
**No. of pupils:** 224
**Fees:** Day £11,076

## Sarum Hall
15 Eton Avenue, London NW3 3EL
**Tel:** 020 7794 2261
**Headmistress:** Mrs Christine Smith
**Age range:** G3–11
**No. of pupils:** 170
**Fees:** Day £6,048–£10,065

## South Hampstead High School GDST
3 Maresfield Gardens,
London NW3 5SS
**Tel:** 020 7435 2899
**Headmistress:** Mrs J E Stephen BSc
**Age range:** G4–18
**No. of pupils:** 852 VIth162
**Fees:** Day £9,342–£12,006

## Southbank International School – Hampstead
16 Netherhall Gardens,
London NW3 5TH
**Tel:** 020 7243 3803
**Principal:** Shirley Harwood
**Age range:** 3–11

## St Anthony's School for Boys
90 Fitzjohn's Avenue, Hampstead,
London NW3 6NP
**Tel:** 020 7431 1066
**Headmaster:** Mr Paul Keyte
**Age range:** B4–13
**No. of pupils:** 310

## St Christopher's School
32 Belsize Lane, Hampstead,
London NW3 5AE
**Tel:** 020 7435 1521
**Head:** Mrs S A West BA(Hons),
PGCE, MA
**Age range:** G4–11
**No. of pupils:** 235
**Fees:** Day £12,450

## ST JOHN'S WOOD PRE-PREPARATORY SCHOOL
*For further details see p. 73*
St Johns Hall, Lords Roundabout,
London NW8 7NE
**Tel:** 020 7722 7149
**Email:** info@sjwpre-prep.org.uk
**Website:**
www.sjwpre-prep.org.uk
**Principal:** Adrian Ellis
**Age range:** 3–7

## St Margaret's School
18 Kidderpore Gardens,
Hampstead, London NW3 7SR
**Tel:** 020 7435 2439
**Principal:** Mr M Webster BSc, PGCE
**Age range:** G4–16
**No. of pupils:** 156
**Fees:** Day £10,410–£12,060

## St Marks Square Nursery School
St Mark's Church, St Mark's
Square, Regents Park Road,
London NW1 7TN
**Tel:** +44 (0)20 7586 8383
**Head:** Dr Sheema Parsons B.Ed OBE
**Age range:** 2–6

## St Martin's School
22 Goodwyn Avenue, Mill
Hill, London NW7 3RG
**Tel:** 020 8959 1965
**Head:** Dr Jason Walak
**Age range:** 3–11
**No. of pupils:** 90
**Fees:** Day £6,750

## ST MARY'S SCHOOL HAMPSTEAD
*For further details see p. 74*
47 Fitzjohn's Avenue,
Hampstead, London NW3 6PG
**Tel:** 020 7435 1868
**Email:** enquiries@stmh.co.uk
**Website:** www.stmh.co.uk
**Head Teacher:** Mrs Harriet
Connor-Earl
**Age range:** B2 years 9
months–7 years G2 years
9 months–11 years
**No. of pupils:** 300
**Fees:** Day £7,305–£13,500

## St Nicholas School
22 Salmon Street, London NW9 8PN
**Tel:** 020 8205 7153
**Headmistress:** Mrs Alyce Gregory
CertEd
**Age range:** 5–11
**No. of pupils:** 80
**Fees:** Day £5,760

## Sue Nieto Theatre School
19 Parkside, London NW7 2LJ
**Tel:** 020 8201 1500
**Principal:** Sue Nieto
**Age range:** 3–18

## Swaminarayan School
260 Brentfield Road, Neasden,
London NW10 8HE
**Tel:** 020 8965 8381
**Headteacher:** Nilesh Manani
**Age range:** 2–18
**No. of pupils:** 452 VIth36
**Fees:** Day £7,818–£10,707

## The Academy School
3 Pilgrims Place, Rosslyn Hill,
Hampstead, London NW3 1NG
**Tel:** 020 7435 6621
**Headteacher:** Mr Garth Evans
**Age range:** 6–14

## The American School in London
One Waverley Place,
London NW8 0NP
**Tel:** 020 7449 1221
**Head:** Mrs Coreen Hester
**Age range:** 4–18
**No. of pupils:** 1350
**Fees:** Day £21,950–£25,650

## The Beehive Montessori on Queen's Park
147 Chevening Road,
London NW6 6DZ
**Tel:** 020 8969 2235
**Age range:** 2–5
**Fees:** Day £3,900–£4,300

## The Cavendish School
31 Inverness Street, Camden
Town, London NW1 7HB
**Tel:** 020 7485 1958
**Headmistress:** Mrs T Dunbar
BSc(Hons), PGCE, NPQH
**Age range:** G3–11
**No. of pupils:** 218
**Fees:** Day £11,550

## The Central School of Speech and Drama
Embassy Theatre, Eton
Avenue, London NW3 3HY
**Tel:** 020 7722 8183
**Principal & CEO:** Professor Gary
Crossley
**Fees:** Day £0

## The Childrens Centre
Christ Church, St Albans
Road, London NW10 8UG
**Tel:** 020 8961 9250
**Head:** Denise Lepore
**Age range:** 18 months–5
**No. of pupils:** 25

## The Hall School
23 Crossfield Road, Hampstead,
London NW3 4NU
**Tel:** 020 7722 1700
**Headmaster:** Mr Chris Godwin
**Age range:** B4–13
**No. of pupils:** 440
**Fees:** Day £9,300–£11,400

## The Interior Design School
22 Lonsdale Road, Queens
Park, London NW6 6RD
**Tel:** 020 7372 2811
**Principal:** Ms Iris Dunbar

## The Islamia Schools' Trust
129 Salusbury Road,
London NW6 6PE
**Tel:** 020 7372 3472

## The King Alfred School
Manor Wood, North End
Road, London NW11 7HY
**Tel:** 020 8457 5200
**Head:** Robert Lobatto MA (Oxon)
**Age range:** 4–18
**No. of pupils:** 650 VIth100
**Fees:** Day £14,862–£17,916

## The Little Ark Montessori
80 Westbere Road,
London NW2 3RU
**Tel:** 020 7794 6359
**Principal:** Angela Coyne MontDip
**Age range:** 2–5

## The Mount, Mill Hill International
Milespit Hill, London NW7 2RX
**Tel:** +44 (0)20 3826 33
**Head of School:** Ms Sarah Bellotti
**Age range:** 13–17
**No. of pupils:** 68
**Fees:** Day £23,799 WB
£33,618 FB £39,549

## The Mulberry House School
7 Minster Road, West
Hampstead, London NW2 3SD
**Tel:** 020 8452 7340
**Headteacher:** Ms Julie Kirwan
**Age range:** 2–8
**No. of pupils:** 184
**Fees:** Day £8,460–£15,698

## The Oak Tree Nursery
2 Arkwright Road, Hampstead,
London NW3 6AD
**Tel:** 020 7435 1916
**Head:** Mrs S Alexander
**Age range:** 2–3
**Fees:** Day £4,650

## The School of the Islamic Republic of Iran
100 Carlton Vale, London NW6 5HE
**Tel:** 020 7372 8051
**Headteacher:** Mr Farzad Farzan
**Age range:** 6–16
**No. of pupils:** 53

## The Village School
2 Parkhill Road, Belsize
Park, London NW3 2YN
**Tel:** 020 7485 4673
**Headmistress:** Miss C E F Gay
BSc(Hons), PGCE
**Age range:** G3–11
**No. of pupils:** 106
**Fees:** Day £15,525

## Theatretrain
69 Great North Way,
London NW4 1HS
**Tel:** 020 8202 2006
**Director:** Kevin Dowsett CertEd,
AdvDip(Drama in Education)
**Age range:** 6–18

## Toddlers Inn Nursery School
Cicely Davies Hall, Cochrane
Street, London NW8 7NX
**Tel:** 020 7586 0520
**Principal:** Ms Laura McCole

## Torah Vodaas
Julian Headon House,
West Hendon Broadway,
London NW9 7AL
**Tel:** 02036704670
**Head of School:** Mr Mark Shelton
**Age range:** B2–11

## Trevor-Roberts School
55-57 Eton Avenue,
London NW3 3ET
**Tel:** 020 7586 1444
**Headmaster:** Simon Trevor-Roberts
BA
**Age range:** 5–13
**Fees:** Day £12,270–£14,070

## UCS Phoenix School
36 College Crescent,
London NW3 5LF
**Tel:** 020 7722 4433
**Headmistress:** Dr Zoe Dunn
**Age range:** 3–7
**No. of pupils:** 100

## University College School
Frognal, Hampstead,
London NW3 6XH
**Tel:** 020 7435 2215
**Headmaster:** Mr M J Beard MA
**Age range:** B11–18
**No. of pupils:** 850 VIth300
**Fees:** Day £16,005

## University College School (Junior)
11 Holly Hill, London NW3 6QN
**Tel:** 020 7435 3068
**Headmaster:** Mr Lewis Hayward MA (Oxon Lit. Hum), MA (OU, ED. Management), PGCE
**Age range:** B7–11
**No. of pupils:** 250
**Fees:** Day £5,105

## Wentworth Tutorial College
6-10 Brentmead Place, London NW11 9LH
**Tel:** 020 8458 8524/5
**Principal:** Alan Davies BSc, MSc
**Age range:** 14–19
**No. of pupils:** 115

## York Rise Nursery
St Mary Brookfield Hall, York Rise, London NW5 1SB
**Tel:** 020 7485 7962
**Headmistress:** Miss Becca Coles
**Age range:** 2–5

# South-East London

## ABC Childrens Centre
48 Chapel Rd, West Norwood, London SE27 0UR
**Tel:** 020 8766 0246
**Principal:** Ms E Carr

## Alleyn's School
Townley Road, Dulwich, London SE22 8SU
**Tel:** 020 8557 1500
**Headmaster:** Dr G Savage MA, PhD, FRSA
**Age range:** 4–18
**No. of pupils:** 1252 VIth302
**Fees:** Day £16,395–£18,852

## Alpha Meridian Colleges
Meridian House, Greenwich High Road, Greenwich, London SE10 8TL
**Tel:** 020 8853 4111
**Head:** Mr Kudsi Tuluoglu

## Anerley Montessori Nursery
45 Anerley Park, London SE20 8NQ
**Tel:** 020 8778 2810
**Headmistress:** Mrs P Bhatia
**Age range:** 3 months–5
**Fees:** Day £2,750–£4,600

## Asquith Nursery – Elizabeth Terrace
18-22 Elizabeth Terrace, Eltham, London SE9 5DR
**Tel:** 020 8294 0377
**Age range:** 3 months–5

## Asquith Nursery – New Eltham
699 Sidcup Road, New Eltham, London SE9 3AQ
**Tel:** 020 8851 5057
**Age range:** 3 months–5

## Asquith Nursery – Peckham Rye
24 Waveney Avenue, Peckham Rye, London SE15 3UE
**Tel:** 020 7635 5501
**Age range:** 4 months–5

## Asquith Nursery – West Dulwich
Chancellor Grove, West Dulwich, London SE21 8EG
**Tel:** 020 8761 6750
**Age range:** 3 months–5

## Bellenden Day Nursery
Faith Chapel, 198 Bellenden Road, London SE15 4BW
**Tel:** 020 7639 4896
**Manager:** Jason Cranston

## Bellerbys College London
Bounty House, Greenwich, London SE8 3DE
**Tel:** +44 (0)208 694 7000
**Principal:** Ms Alison Baines
**Age range:** 15–19

## Blackheath & Bluecoats Day Nursery
Old Dover Road, Blackheath, London SE3 8SJ
**Tel:** 020 8858 8221 Ext:147
**Principal:** Tracy Malyon

## Blackheath Day Nursery
The Rectory Field, Charlton, London SE3 8SR
**Tel:** 020 8305 2526
**Headmistress:** Mrs Shipley
**Age range:** 0–5
**No. of pupils:** 61

## Blackheath High School GDST
Vanbrugh Park, Blackheath, London SE3 7AG
**Tel:** 020 8853 2929
**Head:** Mrs Carol Chandler-Thompson BA (Hons) Exeter, PGCE Exeter
**Age range:** G3–18
**No. of pupils:** 780

## Blackheath Montessori Centre
Independents Road, Blackheath, London SE3 9LF
**Tel:** 020 8852 6765
**Headmistress:** Mrs Jane Skillen MontDip
**Age range:** 3–5
**No. of pupils:** 36

## Blackheath Preparatory School
4 St Germans Place, Blackheath, London SE3 0NJ
**Tel:** 020 8858 0692
**Headmistress:** Mrs P J Thompson
**Age range:** 3–11
**No. of pupils:** 390
**Fees:** Day £7,305–£12,210

## Blake Hall College
10-11 Dock Offices, Surrey Quays Road, London SE16 2XU
**Tel:** 020 7252 2033
**Head:** Mr Brink Gardner

## Bright Horizons at Tabard Square
10-12 Empire Square, Tabard Street, London SE1 4NA
**Tel:** 020 7407 2068

## Broadfields Day Nursery
96 Broadfields Road, Catford, London SE6 1NG
**Tel:** 020 8697 1488
**Head:** Elainne Dalton
**Age range:** 4 months–5

## Clive Hall Day Nursery
rear of 54 Clive Road, London SE21 8BY
**Tel:** 020 8761 9000

## Colfe's Preparatory School
Horn Park Lane, Lee, London SE12 8AW
**Tel:** 020 8463 8240
**Head:** Mrs Sarah Marsh
**Age range:** 3–11
**No. of pupils:** 355
**Fees:** Day £8,730–£10,134

## Colfe's School
Horn Park Lane, Lee, London SE12 8AW
**Tel:** 020 8852 2283
**Head:** Mr R F Russell MA(Cantab)
**Age range:** 3–18
**No. of pupils:** 1120
**Fees:** Day £11,934–£16,110

## Dulwich College
London SE21 7LD
**Tel:** 020 8693 3601
**Master:** Dr J A F Spence
**Age range:** B7–18
**No. of pupils:** 1589 VIth470
**Fees:** Day £18,231 WB £35,679 FB £38,052

## Dulwich College Kindergarten & Infants School
Eller Bank, 87 College Road, London SE21 7HH
**Tel:** 020 8693 1538
**Head:** Mrs H M Friell
**Age range:** 3 months–7 years
**No. of pupils:** 251

## Dulwich College Preparatory School
42 Alleyn Park, Dulwich, London SE21 7AA
**Tel:** 020 8766 5500
**Headmaster:** Mr M W Roulston MBE, MEd
**Age range:** B3–13 G3–5
**No. of pupils:** 817
**Fees:** Day £4,350–£13,542 WB £18,213–£19,662

## Dulwich Nursery
adj Sainsbury's Dulwich Store, 80 Dog Kennel Hill, London SE22 8DB
**Tel:** 020 7738 4007
**Principal:** Amanda Shead

## Eltham College
Grove Park Road, Mottingham, London SE9 4QF
**Tel:** 0208 857 1455
**Headmaster:** Guy Sanderson
**Age range:** B7–18 G16–18
**No. of pupils:** 830 VIth220
**Fees:** Day £17,058

## Eltham Green Day Nursery
Eltham Green School, Queenscroft Road, London SE9 5EQ
**Tel:** 020 8850 4720
**Head:** Mrs Walker
**Age range:** 3months–5
**No. of pupils:** 30

## First Steps Montessori Day Nursery & Pre School
254 Upland Road, East Dulwich, London SE22 0DN
**Tel:** 020 8299 6897
**Principal:** Karime Dinkha
**Age range:** 2–5
**No. of pupils:** 43

## Five Steps Community Nursery
31-32 Alpine Road, London SE16 2RE
**Tel:** 020 7237 2376

## Goldsmith International Business School
N107 (North Building), Westminster Business Square, 45 Durham Street, London SE1 5JH
**Tel:** 020 7820 8212
**Head:** Mr Emman Aluko

## Greenwich School of Management
Meridian House, Royal Hill, Greenwich, London SE10 8RD
**Tel:** 020 8516 7800
**Head:** Dr W G Hunt

## Greenwich Steiner School
Woodlands, 90 Mycenae Road, Blackheath, London SE3 7SE
**Tel:** 020 8858 4404
**Head of School:** Mr Adrian Dow
**Age range:** 3–14
**No. of pupils:** 180
**Fees:** Day £6,930–£8,100

## Half Moon Montessori Nursery
Methodist Church Hall, 155 Half Moon Lane, London SE24 9HU
**Tel:** 020 7326 5300
**Age range:** 2–5
**No. of pupils:** 65

## Hamilton College
9 Albert Embankment, London SE1 7SP
**Tel:** 020 7820 1133/020 7793 9801
**Head:** Mr Zubair Ahmad
16.

## Happy Faces Montessori
35 West Park, London SE9 4RZ
**Tel:** 020 8857 9990
**Age range:** 18 months–5

## Happy Faces Nursery
161 Sumner Road, Peckham, London SE15 6JL
**Tel:** 020 7701 3320

## Heath House Preparatory School
37 Wemyss Road, Blackheath, London SE3 0TG
**Tel:** 020 8297 1900
**Head Teacher:** Mrs Sophia Laslett CertEd PGDE
**Age range:** 3–11
**No. of pupils:** 115
**Fees:** Day £10,185–£13,785
£.

## Herne Hill School
The Old Vicarage, 127 Herne Hill, London SE24 9LY
**Tel:** 020 7274 6336
**Headteacher:** Mrs Ngaire Telford
**Age range:** 2–7
**No. of pupils:** 296
**Fees:** Day £5,550–£13,755

## Hillyfields Day Nursery
41 Harcourt Road, Brockley, London SE4 2AJ
**Tel:** 020 8694 1069
**Head:** Ms Lisa Reeves

## Holborn College
Woolwich Road, London SE7 8LN
**Tel:** 020 8317 6000
**Principal:** Mr Mohamed Maladwala
16.

## James Allen's Girls' School
144 East Dulwich Grove, Dulwich, London SE22 8TE
**Tel:** 020 8693 1181
**Head of School:** Mrs Sally-Anne Huang MA, MSc
**Age range:** G4–18
**No. of pupils:** 1075

## Kaplan Financial (London)
179-191 Borough High Street, London SE1 1HR
**Tel:** 020 7407 5000
**Head:** Mr Vinod Siyani
16.

## Kings Kids Christian School
New Testament Church of God, Bawtree Road, New Cross, London SE14 6ET
**Tel:** 020 8691 5813
**Headteacher:** Mrs M Okenwa
**Age range:** 5–11
**No. of pupils:** 36

## Lingfield Day Nursery (Blackheath)
37 Kidbrooke Grove, Kidbrooke, London SE3 0LJ
**Tel:** 020 8858 1388
**Manager:** Sophie Campbell
**Age range:** 18 months–5
**No. of pupils:** 30
**Fees:** Day £9,350

## Lingfield Day Nursery (Grove Park)
155 Baring Road, London SE12 0LA
**Tel:** 020 8851 7800
**Manager:** Samantha Goodwright
**Age range:** 18 months–5
**No. of pupils:** 30
**Fees:** Day £8,700

## Little Cherubs Day Nursery
2a Bell Green Lane, London SE26 5TB
**Tel:** 020 8778 3232

## Lollipops Child Care Ltd
27 Southwood Road, London SE9 3QE
**Tel:** 020 8859 5832
**Principal:** Miss L Thompson

## London Bridge Business Academy
7-13 Melior Street, London SE1 3QP
**Tel:** 020 7378 1000
**Head:** Shmina Mandal
16.

## London Christian School
40 Tabard Street, London SE1 4JU
**Tel:** 020 3130 6430
**Headmistress:** Miss Georgina Hale
**Age range:** 3–11
**No. of pupils:** 105
**Fees:** Day £7,725
£.

## London College of Accountancy
200 Great Dover Street, London SE1 4YB
**Tel:** 020 7407 1119
**Head:** Mr Ravi Gill
16.

## London College of Computing & Management
Atrium Suite, The Hop Exchange, 24 Southwark Street, London SE1 1TY
**Tel:** 020 7378 6333
**Head:** Dr Waheed Iqbal
16.

## London College of Engineering & Management
18-36 Wellington Street, London SE18 6PF
**Tel:** 020 8854 6158
**Head:** Mr Shakhar Sharman
16.

## London Institute of Shipping and Transport
51-55 Waterloo Road, London SE1 8TX
**Tel:** 020 7928 0029
**Head:** Dr N Kyritsis
16.

## Magic Roundabout Nursery – Kennington
35 Sutherland House, Sutherland Square, London SE17 3EE
**Tel:** 020 7277 3643

## Marathon Science School
1-9 Evelyn Street, Surrey Quays, London SE8 5RQ
**Tel:** +44 (0)20 7231 3232
**Headteacher:** Mr Uzeyir Onur
**Age range:** B11–16
**No. of pupils:** 67

## Maritime Greenwich College
4th Floor, Royal Sovereign House, 40 Beresford Street, London SE18 6BF
**Tel:** 0208 305 8508
**Head:** Mr N Kandel
16.

## McAlpine Dance Studio
Longfield Hall, 50 Knatchbull Road, London SE5 9QY
**Tel:** 020 8673 4992
16.

## Mother Goose Nursery
248 Upland Road, East Dulwich, London SE22 0NU
**Tel:** 020 8693 9429
**Age range:** 1–5

## Mother Goose Nursery
34 Waveney Avenue, Nunhead, London SE15 3UE
**Tel:** 020 7277 5951
**Age range:** 1–5

## Mother Goose Nursery
The Pavilion, 65 Greendale Fields, off Wanley Road, London SE5 8JZ
**Tel:** 020 7738 7700
**Age range:** 0–5

## Mother Goose Nursery (Head Office)
133 Brookbank Road, Lewisham, London SE13 7DA
**Tel:** 020 8694 8700
**Age range:** 1–5

## Nell Gwynn Nursery
Meeting House Lane, London SE15 2TT
**Tel:** 020 7252 8265

## Oakfield Preparatory School
125-128 Thurlow Park Road, West Dulwich, London SE21 8HP
**Tel:** 020 8670 4206
**Head of School:** Ms. Jane Stevens
**Age range:** 2–11 years
**No. of pupils:** 420
**Fees:** Day £9,750

## Octavia House School, Kennington
214b Kennington Road, London SE11 6AU
**Tel:** 020 3651 4396 (Option:3)
**Executive Head:** Mr James Waite

## Octavia House School, Vauxhall
Vauxhall Primary School, Vauxhall Street, , London SE11 5LG
**Tel:** 02036 514396 (Option:1)
**Executive Head:** Mr James Waite
**Age range:** 5–14
**No. of pupils:** 65

## Octavia House School, Walworth
Larcom House, Larcom Street, , London SE17 1RT
**Tel:** 02036 514396 (Option:2)
**Executive Head:** Mr James Waite

## One World Day Nursery
11 Thurlby Road, London SE27 0RN
**Tel:** 020 8761 3308

## Riverston School
63-69 Eltham Road, Lee Green, London SE12 8UF
**Tel:** 020 8318 4327
**Headmistress:** Mrs S E Salathiel
**Age range:** 9 months–19 years
**No. of pupils:** 215
£.

## School of Technology & Management
Kingshead House, Kingshead Yard, London SE1 1NA
**Tel:** 020 7378 0052
16.

**Skallywags Nursery**
St Crispin Hall, Southwark
Park Road, Rotherhithe,
London SE16 2HU
**Tel:** 020 7252 3225
**Headmistress:** Miss Allison
Armstrong NVQ
**Age range:** 3 months–5 years

**St Dunstan's College**
Stanstead Road, London SE6 4TY
**Tel:** 020 8516 7200
**Headmistress:** Mrs J D Davies BSc
**Age range:** 3–18
**No. of pupils:** 870

**St Olave's Preparatory
School**
106 Southwood Road, New
Eltham, London SE9 3QS
**Tel:** 020 8294 8930
**Headteacher:** Miss Claire Holloway
BEd, QTS
**Age range:** 3–11
**No. of pupils:** 220
**Fees:** Day £7,264–£11,610

**St. Patrick's Montessori
Day Nursery**
91 Cornwall Road, London SE1 8TH
**Tel:** 020 7928 5557

**Sydenham High
School GDST**
19 Westwood Hill, London SE26 6BL
**Tel:** 020 8557 7000
**Headmistress:** Mrs Katharine
Woodcock
**Age range:** G4–18
**No. of pupils:** 600 VIth70
**Fees:** Day £12,780–£16,251

**Teddies Nurseries
Greenwich**
Chavening Road, Greenwich,
London SE10 0LB
**Tel:** 0333 305 3679
**Nursery Manager:** Ms Loraine
Thorpe
**Age range:** 3 months–5 years

**Teddies Nurseries
West Dulwich**
Old Church, 226c Gipsy
Road, London SE27 9RB
**Tel:** 0333 305 1189
**Nursery Manager:** Ms Nazmin
Uddin
**Age range:** 3 months–5 years

**The British School
of Osteopathy**
275 Borough High Street,
London SE1 1JE
**Tel:** 020 7407 0222
**Principal & Chief Executive:** Martin
Collins BSc(Hons), PhD, MSc, Cbiol,
MIBiol, FRSH, DO, ILTM
**Fees:** Day £0

**The Oak Tree Nursery**
Tell Grove, Southwark,
London SE22 8RH
**Tel:** 020 8693 0306

**The Pavilion Nursery**
Catford Cricket Club Pavilion,
Penerley Road, London SE6 2LQ
**Tel:** 020 8698 0878
**Head:** Mrs Karen Weller
**Age range:** 2–5

**The Pointer School**
19 Stratheden Road,
Blackheath, London SE3 7TH
**Tel:** 020 8293 1331
**Headmaster:** Mr R J S Higgins MA,
BEd, CertEd, FCollP
**Age range:** 3–11
**No. of pupils:** 370
**Fees:** Day £6,912–£13,782

**The Villa Pre-Preparatory
School & Nursery**
54 Lyndhurst Grove, Peckham,
London SE15 5AH
**Tel:** 020 7703 6216
**Head Teacher:** Emma Bryant
**Age range:** 2–7
**No. of pupils:** 210

**The Village
Montessori School**
Kingswood Hall, Kingswood
Place, London SE13 5BU
**Tel:** 020 8318 6720
**Director:** Catherine Westlake
MontDip
**Age range:** 3–5
**Fees:** Day £1,491

**The Village Nursery**
St Mary's Centre, 180 Ladywell
Road, Lewisham, London SE13 7HU
**Tel:** 020 8690 6766
**Principal:** Frances Rogers

**Thornsbeach Day Nursery**
10 Thornsbeach Road,
London SE6 1DX
**Tel:** 020 8697 7699
**Manager:** Mrs M James
**Age range:** 2–5

**Toad Hall Montessori
Nursery School**
37 St Mary's Gardens,
Kennington, London SE11 4UF
**Tel:** 020 7735 5087
**Principal:** Mrs V K Rees NNEB,
MontDip
**Age range:** 2–5
**No. of pupils:** 40
**Fees:** Day £6,300

**Trinity Child Care**
Holy Trinity Church Hall, Bryan
Road, London SE16 5HF
**Tel:** 020 7231 5842
**Manager:** Sharron Williams
**Age range:** 2–5
**No. of pupils:** 60
**Fees:** Day £6,240

**Waterloo Day Nursery**
The Chandlery, 50 Westminster
Bridge Road, London SE1 7QY
**Tel:** 020 7721 7432
**Principal:** Julie Ellis

**Willow Park**
19 Glenlyon Road, Eltham,
London SE9 1AL
**Tel:** 020 8850 8753
**Principal:** Mrs McMahon

# South-West
London

**345 Nursery School**
Fitzhugh Community Clubroom,
Fitzhugh Grove, Trinity Road,
London SW18 3SA
**Tel:** 020 8870 8441
**Principal:** Mrs Annabel Dixon
**Age range:** 3–5
**No. of pupils:** 42
**Fees:** Day £3,555

**Abacus Day Care Nursery**
United Reform Church, Grafton
Square, London SW4 0DE
**Tel:** 020 7720 7290
**Headmistress:** Mrs Cynthia Clarke

**ABACUS Early Learning
Nursery School –
Balham Day Nursery**
135 Laitwood Road, Balham,
London SW12 9QH
**Tel:** 020 8675 8093

**ABACUS Early Learning
Nursery School –
Stretham Day Nursery**
7 Drewstead Road, Streatham
Hill, London SW16 1LY
**Tel:** 020 8677 9117
**Principals:** Mrs M Taylor BEd & Ms S
Petgrave
**Age range:** 12 mths–5 years
**No. of pupils:** 40

**Abbey College – London**
22 Grosvenor Gardens,
Belgravia, London SW1W 0DH
**Tel:** 020 7824 7300
**Principal:** Mr Mark Love BEd
**Age range:** 14–19
**No. of pupils:** 150 VIth150
**Fees:** Day £5,950–£16,400
FB £30,200

**Academy of Live &
Recorded Arts**
Studio1, Royal Victoria
Patriotic Building, John Archer
Way, London SW18 3SX
**Tel:** 020 8870 6475
**Principal:** Anthony Castro
**Age range:** 18+
**No. of pupils:** 108
**Fees:** Day £3,000–£9,888

**Al-Muntada Islamic School**
7 Bridges Place, Parsons
Green, London SW6 4HW
**Tel:** 020 7471 8283
**Headteacher:** Salma Ullah
**Age range:** 4–11
**No. of pupils:** 165
**Fees:** Day £2,500

**Alphabet Nursery School**
Chatham Hall, Northcote Road,
Battersea, London SW11 6DY
**Tel:** 020 8871 7473
**Principal:** Mrs A McKenzie-Lewis
**No. of pupils:** 40
**Fees:** Day £1,500–£1,800

**Al-Risalah Nursery**
10A Gatton Road, Tooting,
London SW17 0EE
**Tel:** 020 8767 0716
**Head of School:** Nasir Qurashi

**Al-Risalah Secondary
School**
145 Upper Tooting Road,
London SW17 7TJ
**Tel:** 020 8767 6057
**Headmaster:** Nasir Qurashi
**Age range:** 3–16
**No. of pupils:** 250

**Asquith Nursery – Balham**
36 Radbourne Road, Balham,
London SW12 0EF
**Tel:** 020 8673 1405

**Asquith Nursery
– Battersea**
18/30 Latchmere Road,
Battersea, London SW11 2DX
**Tel:** 020 7228 7008
**Age range:** 3 months–5

**Asquith Nursery – Lambeth**
50 Groveway, Stockwell,
London SW9 0AR
**Tel:** 020 7793 9922
**Age range:** 0–5
**No. of pupils:** 25

**Asquith Nursery – Putney**
107-109 Norroy Road, Putney,
London SW15 1PH
**Tel:** 020 8246 5611
**Age range:** 3 months–5

**Asquith Nursery –
Raynes Park**
c/o David Lloyd Leisure
Club, Bushey Road, Raynes
Park, London SW20 8TE
**Tel:** 020 8543 9005
**Age range:** 3 months–5

**Battersea Pre-
School & Nursery**
18/30 Latchmere Road,
Battersea, London SW11 2DX
**Tel:** 020 7228 4722
**Head:** Miss Sharon Nelson
**Age range:** 0–5
**No. of pupils:** 86

**Beechwood School**
55 Leigham Court Road,
Streatham, London SW16 2NJ
**Tel:** 020 8677 8778
**Headmistress:** Mrs M Marshall
**Age range:** 0–11
**No. of pupils:** 100
**Fees:** Day £6,726–£7,875

**Beehive Nursery School**
St Margarets Church Hall, Putney
Park Lane, London SW15 5HU
**Tel:** 020 8780 5333
**Headmistress:** Lindsay Deans
**Age range:** 2–5
**No. of pupils:** 16
**Fees:** Day £1,140

**Bees Knees Nursery School**
within Brookside Community Hall,
12 Priory Lane, London SW15 5JL
**Tel:** 020 8876 8252
**Headmistress:** Jo Wood
**Age range:** 2–5

**Bertrum House School**
290 Balham High Road,
London SW17 7AL
**Tel:** 020 8767 4051
**Principal:** Miss. Kirsty Pirrie
**Age range:** 2–7
**No. of pupils:** 94
**Fees:** Day £1,630–£4,090
🖉

**Blundells Day Nursery**
The Old Court, 194-196 Sheepcote
Lane, Battersea, London SW11 5BW
**Tel:** 020 7924 4204
**Headmistress:** Susan Stevens
**Age range:** 18 months–5
**No. of pupils:** 66
**Fees:** Day £4,655–£8,575
🖉

**Bobby's Playhouse**
16 Lettice Street, London SW6 4EH
**Tel:** 020 7384 1190
**Principal:** Mrs Emma Hannay
**Age range:** 3 months–5 years
**Fees:** Day £11,000

**Broomwood Hall School**
68-74 Nightingale Lane,
London SW12 8NR
**Tel:** 020 8682 8830
**Headmistress:** Mrs Carole
Jenkinson
**Age range:** B4–8 G4–13
**No. of pupils:** 670
**Fees:** Day £14,790–£18,165
🖉

**Busy Bee Nursery School**
19 Lytton Grove, Putney,
London SW15 2EZ
**Tel:** 020 8789 0132
**Headmistress:** Dr Sally Corbett
**Age range:** 2–5

**Cameron House**
4 The Vale, Chelsea,
London SW3 6AH
**Tel:** 020 7352 4040
**Acting Headmistress:** Miss Mary-
Anne Malloy BE (HDE)
**Age range:** 4–11
**No. of pupils:** 118
**Fees:** Day £17,925
£ 🖉

**Carmena Christian
Day Nurseries**
47 Thrale Road, Streatham,
London SW16 1NT
**Tel:** 020 8677 8231
**Head:** Mrs S Allen

**Centre Academy London**
92 St John's Hill, Battersea,
London SW11 1SH
**Tel:** 020 7738 2344
**Principal:** Dr. Duncan Rollo BA,
MA, PhD
**Age range:** 9–19
**Fees:** Day £27,600–£40,100
🌐 £ 🖉 16⁺

**Chelsea Independent
College**
517-523 Fulham Road,
London SW6 1HD
**Tel:** +44 (0) 20 7610 1114
**Principal:** Dr Martin Meenagh
**Age range:** 14–19
**No. of pupils:** 164
16⁺ 🏠

**Chelsea Kindergarten**
St Andrews Church, Park Walk,
Chelsea, London SW10 0AU
**Tel:** 020 7352 4856
**Headmistress:** Miss Lulu Tindall
MontDip
**Age range:** 2–5
**Fees:** Day £3,900–£6,120
🖉

**Clapham Day Nursery**
3 Peardon Street, London SW8 3BW
**Tel:** 020 7498 3165
**Manager:** Nicolette Warnes NNEB,
NVQ4
**Age range:** 3 months–5
**No. of pupils:** 72

**Clapham Montessori**
St Paul's Community Centre,
St Paul's Church, Rectory
Grove, London SW4 0DX
**Tel:** 020 7498 8324
**Head:** Mrs R Bowles BSc, IntMontDip
**Age range:** 2–5

**Clapham Park Montessori**
St James' Church House, 10 West
Road, Clapham, London SW4 7DN
**Tel:** 020 7627 0352
**Head:** Mrs R Bowles BSc, IntMontDip
**Age range:** 2–5

**Collingham**
23 Collingham Gardens,
London SW5 0HL
**Tel:** 020 7244 7414
**Principal:** Mr G Hattee MA(Oxon),
DipEd
**Age range:** 14–19
**No. of pupils:** VIth200
**Fees:** Day £4,140–£11,850
16⁺ £ 🖉

**Cresset Kindergarten**
The Waldorf School of South
West London, 12 Ballam Park
Road, London SW12 8DR
**Tel:** 020 8673 4881
**Principal:** Pat Hague

**Crown Kindergartens**
Coronation House, Ashcombe
Road, Wimbledon,
London SW19 8JP
**Tel:** 020 8540 8820
**Principal:** Mrs Acres
**Age range:** 1–5
**No. of pupils:** 28
🖉

**Dawmouse Montessori
Nursery School**
34 Haldane Road, Fulham,
London SW6 7EU
**Tel:** 020 7381 9385
**Principal:** Mrs Emma V Woodcock
NNEB, MontDip
**Age range:** 2–5
**No. of pupils:** 72

**DOLPHIN SCHOOL**
*For further details see p. 49*
106 Northcote Road,
London SW11 6QW
**Tel:** 020 7924 3472
**Email:** admissions@
dolphinschool.org.uk
**Website:**
www.dolphinschool.org.uk
**Principal:** Mrs. N. Baldwin
**Age range:** 2.5–11
**No. of pupils:** 301
**Fees:** Day £5,640–£12,885
🖉

**Donhead**
33 Edge Hill, London SW19 4NP
**Tel:** 020 8946 7000
**Headmaster:** Mr G C McGrath
BA(Hons), PGCE, MBA(Ed)
**Age range:** B4–11
**No. of pupils:** 280
**Fees:** Day £7,800–£8,325
🧍 £ 🖉

**Eaton House Belgravia**
3-5 Eaton Gate, London SW1W 9BA
**Tel:** 020 7730 9343
**Head of School:** Mrs Annabel
Abbott
**Age range:** B4–8
**Fees:** Day £15,390
🧍 🧍 🖉

**Eaton House The
Manor Girls School**
58 Clapham Common
Northside, London SW4 9RU
**Tel:** 020 7924 6000
**Head:** Mrs Sarah Segrave
**Age range:** G4–11
**Fees:** Day £14,244
🧍 £ 🖉

**Eaton House The Manor
Pre Prep School**
58 Clapham Common
Northside, London SW4 9RU
**Tel:** 020 7924 6000
**Head of School:** Mr Huw May
**Age range:** B2–8
🧍

**Eaton House The
Manor Prep School**
58 Clapham Common
Northside, London SW4 9RU
**Tel:** 020 7924 6000
**Head:** Mrs Sarah Segrave
**Age range:** B8–13
🧍 £ 🖉

**Eaton House The Vale**
2 Elvaston Place, London SW7 5QH
**Tel:** 020 7924 6000
**Head:** Mr Robin Greenwood
**Age range:** 3–11
**Fees:** Day £7,416–£14,670
🖉

**Eaton Square Nursery
School Pimlico**
32a Lupus Street, London SW1V 3DZ
**Age range:** 2–5

**Eaton Square School**
79 Eccleston Square,
London SW1V 1PP
**Tel:** 020 7931 9469
**Headmaster:** Mr Sebastian Hepher
BEd(Hons)
**Age range:** 2–13
**No. of pupils:** 529
**Fees:** Day £4,080–£19,785
🌐 £ 🖉

**Ecole Charles De
Gaulle – Wix**
Clapham Common North
Side, London SW4 0AJ
**Tel:** +44 20 7738 0287
**Headteacher:** Mr Blanchard
**Age range:** 5–11
**No. of pupils:** 100
🌐

**Ecole Marie D'Orliac**
60 Clancarty Road,
London SW6 3AA
**Tel:** +44 7736 020 58 63
**Principal:** Mr Olivier Rauch
**Age range:** 4–11
**No. of pupils:** 50
🌐

**Elm Park Nursery School**
90 Clarence Avenue,
Clapham, London SW4 8JR
**Tel:** 020 8678 1990
**Head:** Ms Jacqueline Brooks
**No. of pupils:** 113

## Emanuel School
Battersea Rise, London SW11 1HS
**Tel:** 020 8870 4171
**Headmaster:** Mr Mark Hanley-Browne
**Age range:** 10–18
**No. of pupils:** 890
**Fees:** Day £17,574
£ ✎ 16+

## Eveline Day & Nursery Schools
14 Trinity Crescent, Upper Tooting, London SW17 7AE
**Tel:** 020 8672 4673
**Headmistress:** Ms Eveline Drut
**Age range:** 3 months–11 years
**No. of pupils:** 80
**Fees:** Day £11,059
✎

## Falkner House
19 Brechin Place, South Kensington, London SW7 4QB
**Tel:** 020 7373 4501
**Headteacher:** Mrs Anita Griggs BA(Hons), PGCE
**Age range:** B3–4 G3–11
**Fees:** Day £8,025–£16,050
♦

## Finton House School
171 Trinity Road, London SW17 7HL
**Tel:** 020 8682 0921
**Head of School:** Mr Ben Freeman
**Age range:** 4–11
**No. of pupils:** 321
**Fees:** Day £4,630–£4,850
£ ✎

## First Steps School of Dance & Drama
234 Lillie Road, London SW6 7QA
**Tel:** 020 7381 5224
**Age range:** 3–17
**Fees:** Day £2,700
16+ £ ❀

## Francis Holland School, Sloane Square, SW1
39 Graham Terrace, London SW1W 8JF
**Tel:** 020 7730 2971
**Head:** Mrs Lucy Elphinstone MA(Cantab)
**Age range:** G4–18
**No. of pupils:** 520 VIth70
**Fees:** Day £17,760–£20,085
♦ £ ✎ 16+

## Garden House School
Boys' School & Girls' School, Turk's Row, London SW3 4TW
**Tel:** 020 7730 1652
**Boys' Head:** Mr Christian Warland BA(Hons), LLB.
**Age range:** 3–11
**No. of pupils:** 490
**Fees:** Day £12,600–£22,000
£ ✎

## Gateway House Nursery School
St Judes Church Hall, Heslop Road, London SW12 8EG
**Tel:** 020 8675 8258
**Principal:** Miss Elizabeth Marshall
**Age range:** 2–4
**No. of pupils:** 30
**Fees:** Day £1,010–£1,060
✎

## Glendower School
86/87 Queen's Gate, London SW7 5JX
**Tel:** 020 7370 1927
**Headmistress:** Mrs Sarah Knollys BA, PGCE
**Age range:** G4–11+
**No. of pupils:** 206
**Fees:** Day £14,280
♦ £ ✎

## Hall School Wimbledon
Beavers Holt, Stroud Crescent, Putney Vale, London SW15 3EQ
**Tel:** 020 8788 2370
**Headmaster:** Timothy J Hobbs MA
**Age range:** 4–16
**No. of pupils:** 520
**Fees:** Day £9,999–£13,224
✎

## Hall School Wimbledon Senior School
17 The Downs, Wimbledon, London SW20 8HF
**Tel:** 020 8879 9200
**Headmaster:** Timothy J Hobbs MA
**Age range:** 11–16
**No. of pupils:** 520
**Fees:** Day £10,698–£14,151
✎

## Happy Nursery Days
Valens House, 132a Uppertulse Hill, London SW2 2RX
**Tel:** 020 8674 7804
**Age range:** 3 months–5

## Happy Times Nursery
40 Parkgate Road, London SW11 4NP
**Tel:** 020 7350 5959

## Happy Times Nursery
The Limes, 123 Mortlake High Street, London SW14 8SN
**Tel:** 0800 652 2424

## Hornsby House School
Hearnville Road, Balham, London SW12 8RS
**Tel:** 020 8673 7573
**Headmaster:** Mr Edward Rees
**Age range:** 4–11
**Fees:** Day £12,375–£13,305
£ ✎

## Hurlingham School
122 Putney Bridge Road, Putney, London SW15 2NQ
**Tel:** 020 8874 7186
**Headteacher:** Mr Jonathan Brough
**Age range:** 4–11
**No. of pupils:** 343
**Fees:** Day £15,540–£16,185
£ ✎

## Ibstock Place School
Clarence Lane, London SW15 5PY
**Tel:** 020 8876 9991
**Head:** Mrs Anna Sylvester-Johnson BA(Hons), PGCE
**Age range:** 4–18
**No. of pupils:** 970
**Fees:** Day £5,220–£6,690
£ 16+

## Inchbald School of Design
Interior Design Faculty, 7 Eaton Gate, London SW1W 9BA
**Tel:** 020 7730 5508
**Principal:** Mrs Jacqueline Duncan FIIDA, FIDDA
**Age range:** 18–50
**No. of pupils:** 120
16+

## JJAADA Interior Design Academy
28 Abbeville Mews, 88 Clapham Park Road, London SW4 7BX
**Tel:** 020 7494 3363
16+

## Judith Blacklock Flower School
4/5 Kinnerton Place South, London SW1X 8EH
**Tel:** 020 7235 6235
**Head:** Judith Blacklock
16+

## Kensington Prep School GDST
596 Fulham Road, London SW6 5PA
**Tel:** 0207 731 9300
**Head:** Mrs P Lynch MA (St Andrews) PGCE
**Age range:** G4–11
**No. of pupils:** 289
**Fees:** Day £11,103
♦

## Kids Inc Day Nursery – East Sheen
459b Upper Richmond Road West, East Sheen, London SW14 7PR
**Tel:** 020 8876 8144

## King's College Junior School
Southside, Wimbledon Common, London SW19 4TT
**Tel:** 020 8255 5335
**Headmaster:** Dr. G A Silverlock
**Age range:** B7–13
**No. of pupils:** 437
♦ £

## King's College School
Southside, Wimbledon Common, London SW19 4TT
**Tel:** 020 8255 5300
**Head Master:** A D Halls MA
**Age range:** B11–18 G16–18
**No. of pupils:** 967
**Fees:** Day £18,975–£20,985
♦ ♦ £ IB 16+

## Knightsbridge School
67 Pont Street, Knightsbridge, London SW1X 0BD
**Tel:** 020 7590 9000
**Head:** Ms Shona Colaco MA, PGCE, MSB, CBiol
**Age range:** 3–13
**No. of pupils:** 400
**Fees:** Day £16,224–£17,265
£ ✎

## Ladybird Nursery School
9 Knowle Close, London SW9 0TQ
**Tel:** 020 7924 9505

## L'Ecole du Parc
12 Rodenhurst Road, London SW4 8AR
**Tel:** 020 8671 5287
**Headteacher:** Mrs E Sicking-Bressler
**Age range:** 1–5
**No. of pupils:** 55
**Fees:** Day £4,000–£7,500

## Lion House School
The Old Methodist Hall, Gwendolen Avenue, London SW15 6EH
**Tel:** 020 8780 9446
**Head:** Miss H J Luard MontDip
**Age range:** 2 –7
**No. of pupils:** 115

## Little Acorns Nursery School
Church of St James The Less, Moreton Street, London SW1V 2PT
**Tel:** 020 7931 0898

## Little People of Fulham
250a Lillie Road, Fulham, London SW6 7PX
**Tel:** 020 7386 0006
**Owner:** Miss Jane Gleasure
**Age range:** 4 months–5

## Little Red Hen Nursery School
Church of the Nazarene, 2 Grant Road, Battersea, London SW11 2NU
**Tel:** 020 7738 0321
**Age range:** 2–5
**Fees:** Day £1,470–£1,740

## London College of Business & Computer Studies
219 Clapham Road, London SW9 9BE
**Tel:** 020 7733 4868
**Principal:** Mr T Olarewaju

## London College Wimbledon
LCW House, 2A Mansel Road, London SW19 4AA
**Tel:** 020 8944 1134

## London Electronics College
20 Penywern Road, Earls Court, London SW5 9SU
**Tel:** 020 7373 8721
**Principal:** M D Spalding BSc(Hons), MSc,CEng,MIEE,PGCE,MCybSoc,F RSA,MIOD
**Age range:** 21–65
**Fees:** Day £5,100

## London Film Academy
The Old Church, 52a Walham Grove, London SW6 1QR
**Tel:** 020 7386 7711
**Founders & Joint Principals:** Daisy Gili & Anna Macdonald

## London Study Centre
Munster House, 676 Fulham Road, London SW6 5SA
**Tel:** 020 7731 3549/736 4990
**Principal:** Margaret McLeod
**Age range:** 16

## Lowther Nursery Unit
Stillingfleet Road, Barnes, London SW13 9AE
**Tel:** 020 8563 7769
**Age range:** 3–5

## Lycée Français Charles de Gaulle
35 Cromwell Road, London SW7 2DG
**Tel:** 020 7584 6322
**Head of School:** Mr Olivier Rauch
**Age range:** 5 –19
**No. of pupils:** 4000

## Magic Roundabout Nursery – Stockwell
Surrey Hall, Binfield Road, Stockwell, London SW4 6TB
**Tel:** 020 7498 1194

## MANDER PORTMAN WOODWARD – LONDON
*For further details see p. 60*
90-92 Queen's Gate, London SW7 5AB
**Tel:** 020 7835 1355
**Email:** london@mpw.ac.uk
**Website:** www.mpw.ac.uk
**Principal:** Mr John Southworth BSc MSc
**Age range:** 14–19
**No. of pupils:** 724
**Fees:** Day £9,075–£9,833

## Melrose House Nursery School
39 Melrose Road, London SW18 1LX
**Tel:** 020 8874 7769
**Age range:** 2–5

## Melrose House Nursery School
55 Finlay Street, London SW6 6HF
**Tel:** 020 7736 9296

## Mini Stars Day Nursery
St Margarets Church, Barcombe Avenue, London SW2 3HH
**Tel:** 020 8678 8600
**Age range:** 6 months–5
**No. of pupils:** 26

## Miss Daisy's Nursery School
Fountain Court Club Room, Ebury Square, London SW1W 9SU
**Tel:** 020 7730 5797
**Head:** Daisy Harrison
**Age range:** 2–5
**No. of pupils:** 30
**Fees:** Day £1,050–£5,550

## Modern Montessori International Ltd (London)
MMI House, 142 Micham Lane London, London SW16 6SN
**Tel:** 020 8769 5555
**Head:** Mrs Marianne Burke

## Montessori School
St Paul's Community Centre, Rectory Grove, Clapham, London SW4 0DX
**Tel:** 020 7498 8324
**Age range:** 6 months–6

## MORE HOUSE SCHOOL
*For further details see p. 62*
22-24 Pont Street, Knightsbridge, London SW1X 0AA
**Tel:** 020 7235 2855
**Email:** office@morehouse.org.uk
**Website:** www.morehouse.org.uk
**Co-Heads:** Mrs. Amanda Leach & Mr. Michael Keeley
**Age range:** G11–18
**No. of pupils:** 206
**Fees:** Day £18,930

## Newton Prep
149 Battersea Park Road, London SW8 4BX
**Tel:** 020 7720 4091
**Headmistress:** Mrs Alison Fleming BA, MA Ed, PGCE
**Age range:** 3–13
**No. of pupils:** 647
**Fees:** Day £6,840–£18,930

## Nightingale Montessori Nursery
St Lukes Community Hall, 194 Ramsden Road, London SW12 8RQ
**Tel:** 020 8675 8070
**Principal:** Mrs Tejas Earp
**Age range:** 2–5

## Noah's Ark Nursery Schools (Dolphin School Trust)
St Michael's Church Hall, Cobham Close, London SW11 6SP
**Tel:** 020 7924 3472 opt 2
**Head:** Miss Annette Miller
**Age range:** 2–5
**No. of pupils:** 40
**Fees:** Day £4,725

## Noah's Ark Nursery Schools (Dolphin School Trust)
Endlesham Church Hall, 48 Endlesham Road, London SW12 8JL
**Tel:** 020 924 3472 opt 2
**Head:** Miss Annette Miller
**Age range:** 2–5
**No. of pupils:** 32
**Fees:** Day £4,725

## Noddy's Nursery School
Trinity Church Hall, Beaumont Road, Wimbledon, London SW19 6SP
**Tel:** 020 8785 9191
**Principal:** Mrs Sarah Edwards NNEB, Mont Dip
**Age range:** 2–5

## Northcote Lodge School
26 Bolingbroke Grove, London SW11 6EL
**Tel:** 020 8682 8888
**Headmaster:** Mr Mark Smith
**Age range:** B8–13
**No. of pupils:** 244
**Fees:** Day £18,265

## Oliver House Preparatory School
7 Nightingale Lane, London SW4 9AH
**Tel:** 020 8772 1911
**Headteacher:** Ms Maureen Fields
**Age range:** 2 –13
**No. of pupils:** 144
**Fees:** Day £4,200–£9,300

## Paint Pots Montessori School – The Boltons
St Mary The Boltons Church Hall, The Boltons, London SW10 9TB
**Tel:** 07794 678 537
**Head Teacher:** Georgie Scully
**Age range:** 2 years 6 months–5 years

## Parkgate House School
80 Clapham Common North Side, London SW4 9SD
**Tel:** +44 (0)20 7350 2461
**Principal:** Miss Catherine Shanley
**Age range:** 2.5–11 years
**No. of pupils:** 220
**Fees:** Day £5,550–£14,550

## Parsons Green Prep School
1 Fulham Park Road, Fulham, London SW6 4LJ
**Tel:** 020 7371 9009
**Headteacher:** Ms. Helen Stavert
**Age range:** 4–11
**No. of pupils:** 200
**Fees:** Day £4,995–£5,395

## Peques Anglo-Spanish School
St John's Church, North End Road, Fulham, London SW6 1PB
**Tel:** 020 7385 0055
**Managing Director:** Margarita Morro Beltran
**Age range:** 3 months–5

## Playdays Nursery School Wimbledon
58 Queens Road, Wimbledon, London SW19 8LR
**Tel:** 020 8946 8139
**Nursery Manager:** Charline Baker

## Pooh Corner Kindergarten
St Stephen's Church Hall, 48 Emperor Gate, , London SW7 4HJ
**Tel:** 020 7373 6111
**Headmistress:** Sarah Crowther

**PROSPECT HOUSE SCHOOL**
*For further details see p. 66*
75 Putney Hill, London SW15 3NT
**Tel:** 020 8246 4897
**Email:** info@prospecths.org.uk
**Website:** www.prospecths.org.uk
**Headmaster:** Mr Michael Hodge BPED(Rhodes) QTS
**Age range:** 3–11
**No. of pupils:** 300
**Fees:** Day £8,520–£17,760

**Putney High School GDST**
35 Putney Hill, London SW15 6BH
**Tel:** 020 8788 4886
**Headmistress:** Mrs Suzie Longstaff BA, MA, PGCE
**Age range:** G4–18
**No. of pupils:** 976 VIth150

**Queen's Gate School**
133 Queen's Gate, London SW7 5LE
**Tel:** 020 7589 3587
**Principal:** Mrs R M Kamaryc BA, MSc, PGCE
**Age range:** G4–18
**No. of pupils:** 533

**Ravenstone Preparatory School**
24 Elvaston Place, South Kensington, London SW7 5NL
**Tel:** 020 7225 3131
**Head of School:** Dr Ronald Pritchard
**Age range:** 2–11
**No. of pupils:** 110
**Fees:** Day £11,280–£16,875

**Redcliffe School Trust Ltd**
47 Redcliffe Gardens, Chelsea, London SW10 9JH
**Tel:** 020 7352 9247
**Head:** Mrs Susan Bourne BSc, PGCE
**Age range:** B3–8 G3–11
**Fees:** Day £14,610–£14,610

**Ringrose Kindergarten Chelsea**
St Lukes Church Hall, St Lukes Street, London SW3 3RP
**Tel:** 020 7352 8784
**Age range:** 2–5

**Royal Academy of Dance**
36 Battersea Square, , London SW11 3RA
**Tel:** 020 7326 8000
**Chief Executive:** Luke Rittner
**Fees:** Day £0

**Royal College of Art**
Kensington Gore, London SW7 2EU
**Tel:** 020 7590 4444
**Rector & Vice-Provost:** Professor Christopher Frayling

**Sinclair House Preparatory School**
59 Fulham High Street, Fulham, London SW6 3JJ
**Tel:** 0207 736 9182
**Principal:** Mrs Carlotta T M O'Sullivan
**Age range:** 2–13
**No. of pupils:** 120
**Fees:** Day £10,950

**Square One Nursery School**
Lady North Hall, 12 Ravenna Road, Putney, London SW15 6AW
**Tel:** 020 8788 1546
**Principal:** Mrs King

**St Mary Magdalen Montessori Nursery School**
61 North Worple Way, London SW14 8PR
**Tel:** 020 8878 0756
**Head:** Liz Maitland NNEB, RSH, MontDip
**Age range:** 2–5

**St Mary's Summerstown Montessori**
46 Wimbledon Road, Tooting, London SW17 0UQ
**Tel:** 020 8947 7359
**Head:** Liz Maitland NNEB, RSH, MontDip
**Age range:** 18 months–5 years
**No. of pupils:** 30
**Fees:** Day £1,300

**St Michael's Montessori Nursery School**
St Michael's Church, Elm Bank Gardens, Barnes, London SW13 0NX
**Tel:** 020 8878 0116
**Head Teacher:** Debbie Goldberg
**Age range:** 2 1/2–5

**St Nicholas Preparatory School**
23 Princes Gate, Kensington, London SW7 1PT
**Tel:** 020 7225 1277
**Headmistress:** Jill Walker
**Age range:** 3–11
**No. of pupils:** 280
**Fees:** Day £11,475–£13,110

**St Paul's Juniors**
St Paul's School, Lonsdale Road, London SW13 9JT
**Tel:** 020 8748 3461
**Head of School:** Maxine Shaw
**Age range:** B7–13
**No. of pupils:** 436
**Fees:** Day £18,771

**St Paul's School**
Lonsdale Road, Barnes, London SW13 9JT
**Tel:** 020 8748 9162
**High Master:** Prof Mark Bailey
**Age range:** B13–18
**No. of pupils:** 897
**Fees:** Day £19,674 FB £29,466

**St Philip's School**
6 Wetherby Place, London SW7 4NE
**Tel:** 020 7373 3944
**Headmaster:** H J Biggs-Davison MA(Cantab)
**Age range:** B7–13
**No. of pupils:** 110
**Fees:** Day £12,750

**Streatham & Clapham High School GDST**
42 Abbotswood Road, London SW16 1AW
**Tel:** 020 8677 8400
**Headmaster:** Dr Millan Sachania
**Age range:** B3–5 G3–18
**No. of pupils:** 603 VIth70
**Fees:** Day £5,886–£9,810

**Streatham Montessori Nursery & Day Care**
66 Blairderry Road, Streatham Hill, London SW2 4SB
**Tel:** 020 8674 2208
**Nursery Manager:** Mrs Fehmida Gangji
**Age range:** 1–5

**Sussex House School**
68 Cadogan Square, London SW1X 0EA
**Tel:** 020 7584 1741
**Headmaster:** Mr N P Kaye MA(Cantab), ACP, FRSA, FRGS
**Age range:** B8–13
**No. of pupils:** 182
**Fees:** Day £19,770

**Swedish School**
82 Lonsdale Road, London SW13 9JS
**Tel:** 020 8741 1751
**Head of School:** Ms. Annika Simonsson Bergqvist
**Age range:** 3–18
**No. of pupils:** 300 VIth145
**Fees:** Day £8,650–£9,200–£6,900

**Teddies Nurseries Raynes Park**
3 Spencer Road, Raynes Park, Wimbledon, London SW20 0QN
**Tel:** 0333 920 1909
**Nursery Manager:** Ms Leanne Eustace
**Age range:** 3 months–5 years

**Teddies Nurseries Southfields**
Duntshill Mill, 21 Riverdale Drive, London SW18 4UR
**Tel:** 0330 057 6434
**Nursery Manager:** Ms Lydia Howards
**Age range:** 3 months–5 years

**Teddies Nurseries Streatham**
113 Blegborough Road, Streatham, London SW16 6DL
**Tel:** 0330 057 6267
**Nursery Manager:** Ms Nadia Kiani
**Age range:** 3 months–5 years

**Telten Montessori Nursery School**
Norbury Park Lawn Tennis Club, Ederline Avenue, London SW16 4RZ
**Tel:** 020 8764 2531/07974 249726
**Proprietress:** Mrs A Oke
**Age range:** 2–5
**Fees:** Day £562–£3,693

**Thames Christian College**
Wye Street, Battersea, London SW11 2HB
**Tel:** 020 7228 3933
**Executive Head:** Stephen Holsgrove PhD
**Age range:** 11–16
**No. of pupils:** 120
**Fees:** Day £9,660

**The Boltons Nursery School**
262b Fulham Road, Chelsea, London SW10 9EL
**Tel:** 020 7351 6993
**Age range:** 2–5
**No. of pupils:** 60
**Fees:** Day £2,370–£4,200

**The Bumble Bee Nursery School**
Church of Ascension, Pountney Road, , London SW11 5TU
**Headmistress:** Deepti Bansal

**The Castle Kindergarten**
20 Henfield Road, London SW19 3HU
**Tel:** 020 8544 0089
**Headmistress:** Mrs Beverley Davis DipEd
**Age range:** 2–5

**The Crescent I Kindergarten**
Flat 1, No 10 Trinity Crescent, , London SW17 7AE
**Tel:** 020 8767 5882
**Principal:** Philip Evelegh

**The Crescent II Kindergarten**
Holy Trinity Church Hall, Trinity Road, , London SW17 7SQ
**Tel:** 020 8682 3020

**The Crescent III Kindergarten**
Grafton Tennis Club, 70A Thornton Road, , London SW12 0LF
**Tel:** 020 8675 9659

**The Eveline Day Nursery Schools, Furzedown**
Seeley Hall, Chillerton Road, Furzedown, London SW17 9BE
**Tel:** 020 8672 0501

**The Eveline Day Nursery Schools, Tooting**
30 Ritherdon Road, Upper Tooting, London SW17 8QD
**Tel:** 020 8672 7549
**Principal:** Mrs T Larche

**The Eveline Day Nursery Schools, Wandsworth**
East Hill United Reformed Church Hall, Geraldine Road, Wandsworth, London SW18 2NR
**Tel:** 020 8870 0966

**The Eveline Day Nursery Schools, Wimbledon**
89a Quicks Road, Wimbledon, London SW19 1EX
**Tel:** 020 8545 0699

**The Hampshire School, Chelsea**
15 Manresa Road, Chelsea, London SW3 6NB
**Tel:** 020 7352 7077
**Principal:** Mr Donal Brennan
**Age range:** 3–13
**No. of pupils:** 300
**Fees:** Day £16,155–£17,100
£ ✎

**The Harrodian School**
Lonsdale Road, London SW13 9QN
**Tel:** 020 8748 6117
**Headmaster:** James R Hooke
**Age range:** 5–18
**No. of pupils:** 890 VIth95
**Fees:** Day £10,407–£15,219
✎ 16

**The Knightsbridge Kindergarten**
St Peter's Church, 119 Eaton Square, London SW1W 0HQ
**Tel:** 020 7235 5305
**Headmistress:** Mrs P Powell-Harper
**Age range:** 2–5
**Fees:** Day £4,000

**The Laurels School**
126 Atkins Road, Clapham, London SW12 0AN
**Tel:** 020 8674 7229
**Headmistress:** Linda Sanders BA Hons (Bristol), MA (Madrid)
🏃

**The Maria Montessori Children's House**
St John's Ambulance Hall, 122-124 Kingston Road, London SW19 1LY
**Tel:** 020 8543 6353
**Age range:** 2–5

**The Marmalade Bear Nursery School**
St. Magdalene Church Hall, Trinity Road, Tooting, London SW17 7HP
**Tel:** 0208 265 5224
**Principal:** Ms Rozzy Hyslop
**Age range:** 2–5
**Fees:** Day £3,270–£3,450
✎

**The Merlin School**
4 Carlton Drive, Putney Hill, London SW15 2BZ
**Tel:** 020 8788 2769
**Principal:** Mrs Kate Prest
**Age range:** 4–8
**No. of pupils:** 170

**The Moat School**
Bishops Avenue, Fulham, London SW6 6EG
**Tel:** 020 7610 9018
**Head:** Ms Clare King
**Age range:** 9–16
**Fees:** Day £28,800
✎

**The Montessori Childrens House Ltd**
St John's Church, 1 Spencer Hill, London SW19 4NZ
**Tel:** 020 8971 9135
**Age range:** 2–5

**The Montessori Pavilion – The Kindergarten School**
Vine Road, Barnes, London SW13 0NE
**Tel:** 020 8878 9695
**Age range:** 3–8
**No. of pupils:** 50
**Fees:** Day £1,950–£3,600
✎

**The Mouse House Nursery School**
27 Mallinson Road, , London SW11 1BW
**Tel:** 020 7924 1893
**Headmistress:** Amanda White-Spunner
**Age range:** 2–5
**Fees:** Day £1,650–£4,125
✎

**The Norwegian School**
28 Arterberry Road, Wimbledon, London SW20 8AH
**Tel:** 020 8947 6617
**Head:** Mr Geir Johansen
**Age range:** 3–16

**The Oval Montessori Nursery School**
within Vauxhall Park, Fentiman Road, London SW8 1LA
**Tel:** 020 7735 4816
**Head:** Ms Louise Norwood
**Age range:** 2–5
**Fees:** Day £3,000
✎

**The Park Kindergarten**
St Saviours Church Hall, 351 Battersea Park Road, , London SW11 4LH
**Tel:** 020 7627 5125
**Principal:** Miss Lisa Neilsen MontDip
**Age range:** 2–5
**Fees:** Day £2,370
✎

**The Rainbow Playgroup**
St Luke's Church Hall, St Luke's Street, London SW3 3RR
**Tel:** 020 7352 8156
**Age range:** 2–5

**THE ROCHE SCHOOL**
*For further details see p. 76*
11 Frogmore, London SW18 1HW
**Tel:** 020 8877 0823
**Email:** office@ therocheschool.co.uk
**Website:** www.therocheschool.com
**Headmistress:** Mrs V Adams BA(Hons), PGCE, MA
**Age range:** 2–11 years
**No. of pupils:** 305
**Fees:** Day £14,280–£14,970
£ ✎

**The Rowans School**
19 Drax Avenue, Wimbledon, London SW20 0EG
**Tel:** 020 8946 8220
**Head Teacher:** Mrs S Wingrove
**Age range:** 3–8
**Fees:** Day £5,460–£10,725

**The Study Preparatory School**
Wilberforce House, Camp Road, Wimbledon Common, London SW19 4UN
**Tel:** 020 8947 6969
**Headmistress:** Mrs Susan Pepper MA Oxon, PGCE
**Age range:** G4–11
**No. of pupils:** 315
🏃 £ ✎

**The Waldorf School of South West London**
PO Box 8541, London SW16 1ZB
**Tel:** 0208 772 3504
**Age range:** 3–14
**No. of pupils:** 80
**Fees:** Day £4,515–£6,217
£

**The White House Preparatory School & Woodentops Kindergarten**
24 Thornton Road, London SW12 0LF
**Tel:** 020 8674 9514
**Principal:** Mrs. Mary McCahery
**Age range:** 2–11
**Fees:** Day £4,436–£4,740
£

**The Willow Nursery School**
c/o Clapham Baptist Church, 823-825 Wandsworth Road, London SW8 3JX
**Tel:** 020 7498 0319
**Head:** Mrs Harriet Baring MontDip
**Age range:** 2–5
**Fees:** Day £3,000–£3,100
✎

**The Wimbledon Village Montessori School**
26 Lingfield Road, London SW19 4QD
**Tel:** 020 8944 0772

**The Zebedee Nursery School**
4 Parsons Green, London SW6 4TN
**Tel:** 020 7371 9224
**Headmistress:** Miss Su Gahan NNEB, RSH
**Age range:** 2–5
**No. of pupils:** 32
**Fees:** Day £3,900
✎

**Thomas's Kindergarten – Battersea**
St Mary's Church, Battersea Church Road, London SW11 3NA
**Tel:** 020 7738 0400
**Headmistress:** Miss Iona Jennings
**Age range:** 2–5
**Fees:** Day £1,365–£2,100

**Thomas's Kindergarten – Pimlico**
14 Ranelagh Grove, London SW1W 8PD
**Tel:** 020 7730 3596
**Headmistress:** Miss Tamara Spierenburg HBO

**Thomas's Preparatory School – Battersea**
28-40 Battersea High Street, London SW11 3JB
**Tel:** 020 7978 0900
**Head:** Ben V R Thomas MA
**Age range:** 4–13
**No. of pupils:** 547
**Fees:** Day £12,510–£18,330
✎

**Thomas's Preparatory School – Clapham**
Broomwood Road, London SW11 6JZ
**Tel:** 020 7326 9300
**Headmaster:** Mr Philip Ward BEd(Hons)
**Age range:** 4–13
**No. of pupils:** 647
**Fees:** Day £15,846–£17,916
£ ✎

**Thomas's Preparatory School – Fulham**
Hugon Road, London SW6 3ES
**Tel:** 020 7751 8200
**Head:** Miss Annette Dobson BEd(Hons), PGCertDys
**Age range:** 4–11

**Tiggers Nursery School**
87 Putney Bridge Road, London SW15 2PA
**Tel:** 020 8874 4668
**Headmistress:** Natasha Green MontDip
**Age range:** 2–5
**Fees:** Day £1,425–£1,725

**Toots Day Nursery**
214 Totterdown Street, Tooting, London SW17 8TD
**Tel:** 020 8767 7017
**Principal:** Angela Duffell
**Age range:** 1–5

## Tower House School
188 Sheen Lane, London SW14 8LF
**Tel:** 020 8876 3323
**Head:** Mr Gregory Evans
**Age range:** B4–13
**No. of pupils:** 180
**Fees:** Day £11,073–£12,558

## Twice Times Nursery School
The Cricket Pavilion in South Park, Clancarty Road, London SW6 3AF
**Tel:** 020 7731 4929
**Heads:** Mrs A Welch MontDip & Mrs S Henderson MontDip
**Age range:** 2–5
**No. of pupils:** 50

## Ursuline Preparatory School
18 The Downs, London SW20 8HR
**Tel:** 020 8947 0859
**Headmistress:** Mrs Anne Farnish BA (Hons) MA, NPQH, PGCE
**Age range:** B3–4 G3–11
**Fees:** Day £5,886–£9,600

## Wandsworth Nursery & Pre-School Academy
Dolphin House, Riverside West, Smugglers Way, Wandsworth, London SW18 1DE
**Tel:** 020 8877 1135
**Nursery Manager:** Evelyn Herrera
**Age range:** 0–5

## Wandsworth Preparatory School
The Old Library, 2 Allfarthing Lane, London SW18 2PQ
**Tel:** 0208 870 4133
**Head of School:** Miss Bridget Saul
**No. of pupils:** 90
**Fees:** Day £4,458

## Westminster Abbey Choir School
Dean's Yard, London SW1P 3NY
**Tel:** 0207 654 4918
**Headmaster:** Jonathan Milton BEd
**Age range:** B8–13
**No. of pupils:** 35
**Fees:** FB £8,240

## Westminster Cathedral Choir School
Ambrosden Avenue, London SW1P 1QH
**Tel:** 020 7798 9081
**Headmaster:** Mr Neil McLaughlan
**Age range:** B8–13
**No. of pupils:** 150
**Fees:** Day £13,656 FB £6,945

## Westminster School
Little Dean's Yard, Westminster, London SW1P 3PF
**Tel:** 020 7963 1003
**Headmaster:** Mr Patrick Derham
**Age range:** B13–18 G16–18
**No. of pupils:** 744
**Fees:** Day £26,130–£28,566 FB £37,740

## Westminster Tutors
86 Old Brompton Road, South Kensington, London SW7 3LQ
**Tel:** 020 7584 1288
**Principal:** Virginia Maguire BA, MA, MLitt
**Age range:** 14–mature
**No. of pupils:** VIth40
**Fees:** Day £7,700–£23,500

## Westminster Under School
Adrian House, 27 Vincent Square, London SW1P 2NN
**Tel:** 020 7821 5788
**Headteacher:** Mrs E A Hill MA
**Age range:** B7–13
**No. of pupils:** 265
**Fees:** Day £14,676

## Willington School
Worcester Road, Wimbledon, London SW19 7QQ
**Tel:** 020 8944 7020
**Head:** Mr Michael Chanter
**Age range:** B4–13
**No. of pupils:** 250
**Fees:** Day £9,345–£11,385

## Wiltshire Nursery
85 Wiltshire Road, Brixton, London SW9 7NZ
**Tel:** 020 7274 4446

## Wimbledon Common Preparatory
113 Ridgway, Wimbledon, London SW19 4TA
**Tel:** 020 8946 1001
**Head Teacher:** Mrs Tracey Buck
**Age range:** B4–8
**No. of pupils:** 160
**Fees:** Day £10,725

## Wimbledon High School GDST
Mansel Road, Wimbledon, London SW19 4AB
**Tel:** 020 8971 0900
**Headmistress:** Mrs Jane Lunnon
**Age range:** G4–18
**No. of pupils:** 900 VIth155
**Fees:** Day £11,445–£15,024

## Wimbledon Park Montessori School
206 Heythorp Street, Southfields, London SW18 5BU
**Tel:** 020 8944 8584
**Head:** Ms Clare Collins
**Age range:** 2–5
**Fees:** Day £830–£950

## Wimbledon School of Art
Merton Hall Road, London SW19 3QA
**Tel:** 020 8408 5000
**Principal:** Professor Roderick Bugg

## Young England Kindergarten
St Saviour's Hall, St George's Square, London SW1V 3QW
**Tel:** 020 7834 3171
**Principal:** Mrs Kay C King MontDip
**Age range:** 2.5–5
**Fees:** Day £3,300–£4,950

# West London

## Acorn Nursery School
2 Lansdowne Crescent, London W11 2NH
**Tel:** 020 7727 2122
**Principal:** Mrs Jane Cameron BEd(Hons)
**Age range:** 2–5
**Fees:** Day £2,400

## Acton Training Centre
296 High Street, Acton, London W3 9BJ
**Tel:** 020 8992 4144
**Head:** Mr Sukhev Virdi

## Acton Yochien Nursery School
The Pavilion, Queens Drive Playing Fields, Acton, London W3 0HT
**Tel:** 020 8343 2192

## Alan D Education
61-62 East Castle Street, London W1W 8NQ
**Tel:** 020 7580 1030
**Director of Education:** Alan Hemmings
**Fees:** Day £200 FB £12,400

## Albemarle Independent College
18 Dunraven Street, London W1K 7FE
**Tel:** 020 7409 7273
**Co-Principals:** Beverley Mellon & James Eytle
**Age range:** 16–19
**No. of pupils:** 160
**Fees:** Day £15,000–£18,000

## Arts Educational Schools London Sixth Form
Cone Ripman House, 14 Bath Road, Chiswick, London W4 1LY
**Tel:** 020 8987 6666
**Head Teacher:** Mr Adrian Blake
**Age range:** 16–18
**No. of pupils:** 85
**Fees:** Day £14,190

## Arts Educational Schools London Years 7-11
Cone Ripman House, 14 Bath Road, Chiswick, , London W4 1LY
**Tel:** 020 8987 6666
**Head Teacher:** Mr Adrian Blake
**Age range:** 11–16
**No. of pupils:** 141
**Fees:** Day £13,350

## Ashbourne Independent Sixth Form College
17 Old Court Place, Kensington, London W8 4PL
**Tel:** 020 7937 3858
**Principal:** M J Kirby MSc, BApSc
**Age range:** 16–19
**No. of pupils:** 170
**Fees:** Day £19,725 FB £21,500

## Ashbourne Middle School
17 Old Court Place, Kensington, London W8 4PL
**Tel:** 020 7937 3858
**Principal:** M J Kirby MSc, BApSc
**Age range:** 13–16
**No. of pupils:** VIth150
**Fees:** Day £14,725 FB £21,500

## Avenue House School
70 The Avenue, Ealing, London W13 8LS
**Tel:** 020 8998 9981
**Headteacher:** Mr Sheppard
**Age range:** 3–11
**No. of pupils:** 135
**Fees:** Day £5,070–£8,670

## Bales College
742 Harrow Road, Kensal Town, London W10 4AA
**Tel:** 020 8960 5899
**Principal:** William Moore
**Age range:** 11–19
**No. of pupils:** 90
**Fees:** Day £7,950–£8,550 FB £16,050

## Barbara Speake Stage School
East Acton Lane, East Acton, London W3 7EG
**Tel:** 020 8743 1306
**Headteacher:** Mr David Speake BA (Hons)
**Age range:** 3–16
**Fees:** Day £8,700–£9,000

## Blake College
162 New Cavendish Street,
London W1W 6YS
**Tel:** 020 7636 0658
**Course Director:** D A J Cluckie
BA, BSc
**Fees:** Day £4,720–£5,310
🔞 🔞 🐾

## BPP University
Aldine Place, 142-144 Uxbridge
Road, , London W12 8AA
**Tel:** (+44) 03331 226478
**Head:** Martin Taylor
**Fees:** Day £0
🔞

## Bright Futures
63-65 Portland Place,
Westminster, , London W1B 1QR
**Tel:** 020 7580 8096
**Principal:** Dawn Savage
🔞 ✏

## Bright Sparks
## Montessori School
25 Minford Gardens,
London W14 0AP
**Tel:** 020 7371 4697
**Headmistress:** Matilda D'Angelo
**Age range:** 2–5
**No. of pupils:** 16

## Busy Bees at Hammersmith
3a Bute Gardens, Hammersmith,
London W6 7DR
**Tel:** 020 8741 9445
**Nursery Manager:** Becky
**Age range:** 3 months–5 years

## Bute House Preparatory
## School for Girls
Bute House, Luxemburg
Gardens, London W6 7EA
**Tel:** 020 7603 7381
**Head:** Mrs Helen Lowe
**Age range:** G4–11
**No. of pupils:** 306
**Fees:** Day £13,317
🧍 £

## Buttercups Day Nursery
38 Grange Road, Chiswick,
London W4 4DD
**Tel:** 020 8995 6750

## Buttercups Day Nursery
9 Florence Road, Ealing,
London W5 3TU
**Tel:** 020 8840 4838

## Buttercups Day Nursery
St Lukes, Drayton Grove,
Ealing, London W13 0LA
**Tel:** 020 8997 8965

## Buttercups Nursery School
Ealing Dance Centre, 96 Pitshanger
Lane, Ealing, London W5 1QX
**Tel:** 020 8998 2774
**Principal:** Mrs C Whitehouse

## Buttons Day
## Nursery School
99 Oaklands Road, London W7 2DT
**Tel:** 020 8840 3355
**Head:** Julie Parhar BSc, NVQ3
**Age range:** 3 months–5
**No. of pupils:** 62
✏

## Campbell Harris Tutors
185 Kensington High Street,
London W8 6SH
**Tel:** 020 7937 0032
**Principals:** Mr Mark Harris & Ms
Claire Campbell
**Age range:** 13+
**Fees:** Day £4,000–£9,000
🔞 £ ✏

## Caterpillar Montessori
## Nursery School
St Albans Church Hall, South
Parade, Chiswick, London W4 3HY
**Tel:** 020 8747 8531
**Head:** Mrs Alison Scott
**Age range:** 2–5
**Fees:** Day £2,700

## Chepstow House School
19 Pembridge Villas,
London W11 3EP
**Tel:** 0207 243 0243
**Headteacher:** Angela Barr
**Age range:** 4–7

## Chiswick & Bedford
## Park Prep School
Priory House, Priory Avenue,
London W4 1TX
**Tel:** 020 8994 1804
**Headmistress:** Mrs C A Sunderland
**Age range:** B4–7+ G4–11
**No. of pupils:** 180
**Fees:** Day £8,850

## Chiswick Nursery
## and Pre-School
4 Marlborough Road,
Chiswick, London W4 4ET
**Tel:** 020 8742 0011
**Nursery Manager:** Roxane Lovell
**Age range:** 0–5

## Christie's Education
153 Great Titchfield Street,
London W1W 5BD
**Tel:** 020 7665 4350
**Academic Director:** Jon Waldon
🔞

## Clifton Lodge
8 Mattock Lane, Ealing,
London W5 5BG
**Tel:** 020 8579 3662
**Head:** Mr. Floyd Steadman
**Age range:** 3–13
**No. of pupils:** 146
**Fees:** Day £11,340–£12,405
£ ✏

## College of Naturopathic
## & Complementary
## Medicine Ltd
41 Riding House Street,
London W1W 7BE
**Tel:** 01342 410 505
**Head:** Hermann Keppler
🔞

## Connaught House School
47 Connaught Square,
London W2 2HL
**Tel:** 020 7262 8830
**Principals:** Mrs J A Hampton & Mr F
Hampton MA, RCA
**Age range:** B4–8 G4–11
**No. of pupils:** 75
**Fees:** Day £13,200–£14,700
£

## David Game College
31 Jewry Street, London EC3N 2ET
**Tel:** 020 7221 6665
**Principal:** D T P Game MA, MPhil
**Age range:** 14–19
**No. of pupils:** 200 VIth150
**Fees:** Day £12,000–£13,000
🔞 £ 🔞

## Devonshire Day Nursery
The Vicarage, Bennet Street,
Chiswick, London W4 2AH
**Tel:** 020 8995 9538
**Manager:** Dawn Freeman
**Age range:** 6 weeks–5
**No. of pupils:** 70

**DLD COLLEGE LONDON**
*For further details see p. 48*
199 Westminster Bridge
Road, London SE1 7FX
**Tel:** +44 (0)20 7935 8411
**Email:** dld@dld.org
**Website:** www.dldcollege.co.uk
**Principal:** Irfan H Latif BSc (Hons)
PGCE FRSA FRSC
**No. of pupils:** 440
**Fees:** Day £19,000–£23,000
FB £16,500–£24,000
🌐 🔞 🧍 £ ✏

## Durston House
12-14 Castlebar Road,
Ealing, London W5 2DR
**Tel:** 020 8991 6530
**Headmaster:** Mr Ian Kendrick MA,
BEd(Hons)
**Age range:** B4–13
**No. of pupils:** 390
**Fees:** Day £9,810–£12,570
🧍 £ ✏

## Ealing Independent
## College
83 New Broadway, Ealing,
London W5 5AL
**Tel:** 020 8579 6668
**Principal:** Dr Ian Moores
**Age range:** 13–22
**No. of pupils:** 100 VIth70
**Fees:** Day £3,865–£12,600
🔞 🔞

## Ealing Montessori School
St Martin's Church Hall, Hale
Gardens, London W3 9SQ
**Tel:** 020 8992 4513
**Head:** Mrs Soin
**No. of pupils:** 36

## Ecole Francaise
## Jacques Prevert
59 Brook Green, London W6 7BE
**Tel:** 020 7602 6871
**Principal:** P Possenti
**Age range:** 4–11
🌐

## Elmwood Montessori
## School
St Michaels Centre, Elmwood
Road, London W4 3DY
**Tel:** 020 8994 8177/995 2621
**Headmistress:** Mrs S Herbert BA
**Age range:** 2–5
**Fees:** Day £3,480–£4,440
✏

## Fulham Prep School
200 Greyhound Road,
London W14 9SD
**Tel:** 020 7386 2444
**Head of School:** Mr Neil Brooks
**Age range:** 4–18
**No. of pupils:** 647
**Fees:** Day £16,335–£19,200
🌐 ✏

## Great Beginnings
## Montessori School
The Welsh Church Hall, 82a
Chiltern Street, Marylebone,
London W1H 5JE
**Tel:** 020 7486 2276
**Age range:** 2–6
**Fees:** Day £1,095–£1,650
✏

## Greek Primary
## School of London
3 Pierrepoint Road, Acton,
London W3 9JR
**Tel:** 020 8992 6156
**Age range:** 1–11

## Halcyon London
## International School
33 Seymour Place, ,
London W1H 5AU
**Tel:** +44 (0)20 7258 1169
**Director:** Mr Barry Mansfield
**Age range:** 11–18
**No. of pupils:** 160
🌐 £ IB

## Hammersmith Day
## Nursery & Pre-School
50 Richford Gate, 61-69 Richford
Street, London W6 7HZ
**Tel:** 0207 622 0484
**Manager:** Marion Bones NVQ
**Age range:** 3 months–5 years
**No. of pupils:** 70

## Hammersmith Management College
80-90 King Street, Hammersmith, London W6 0QW
**Tel:** 020 8748 7481
**Head:** Mr J Nizami
16+

## Happy Child Day Nursery
St Gabriel's Church, Noel Road, Acton, London W3 0JE
**Tel:** 020 8992 0855
**Age range:** 6 months–5

## Happy Child Day Nursery
2A The Grove, Ealing, London W5 5LH
**Tel:** 020 8566 1546
**Age range:** 1–5

## Happy Child Day Nursery
Woodgrange Avenue, Ealing Common, London W5 3NY
**Tel:** 020 8992 0209
**Age range:** 3 months–5

## Happy Child Day Nursery
283-287 Windmill Road, Ealing, London W5 4DP
**Tel:** 020 8567 2244
**Age range:** 3 months–5

## Happy Child Day Nursery
Green Man Passage, Ealing, London W13 0TG
**Tel:** 020 8566 5515
**Age range:** 3 months–5

## Happy Child Training Centre
109 Uxbridge Road, Ealing, London W5 5TL
**Tel:** 020 8579 3955
16+

## Harvington School
20 Castlebar Road, Ealing, London W5 2DS
**Tel:** 020 8997 1583
**Headmistress:** Mrs Anna Evans
**Age range:** B3–4 G3–11
**No. of pupils:** 140
**Fees:** Day £9,300–£12,120

## HAWKESDOWN HOUSE SCHOOL KENSINGTON
**For further details see p. 53**
27 Edge Street, Kensington, London W8 7PN
**Tel:** 020 7727 9090
**Email:** admin@hawkesdown.co.uk
**Website:** www.hawkesdown.co.uk
**Headmistress:** Mrs. J. A. K. Mackay B.Ed (Hons)
**Age range:** 3–11
**No. of pupils:** 130
**Fees:** Day £16,020–£18,435

## Heathfield House School
Heathfield Gardens, Chiswick, London, London W4 4JU
**Tel:** 020 8994 3385
**Headteacher:** Mrs Goodsman
**Age range:** 4–11
**No. of pupils:** 197
**Fees:** Day £2,471–£3,676

## Holland Park Nursery School
St Johns Church, Lansdowne Crescent, London W11 2NN
**Tel:** 020 7221 2194
**Age range:** 3–5
**Fees:** Day £3,900

## Holland Park Pre Prep School and Day Nursery
5, Holland Road, Kensington, London W14 8HJ
**Tel:** 020 7602 9066/020 7602 9266
**Head Mistress:** Mrs Kitty Mason
**Age range:** 3 months–5 years
**No. of pupils:** 39
**Fees:** Day £3,627–£17,520

## Hotel and Catering Training Company
2nd Floor, South Wing, 26-28 Hammersmith Grove, London W6 7HT
**Tel:** 020 8735 9700
16+

## House Schools Group
42 Hartington Road, London W4 3TX
**Tel:** 020 8580 9626

## Instituto Español Vicente Cañada Blanch
317 Portobello Road, London W10 5SZ
**Tel:** +44 (0) 20 8969 2664
**Principal:** Mr A Vitria
**Age range:** 4–19
**No. of pupils:** 405

## International School of London (ISL) London
139 Gunnersbury Avenue, Ealing, London W3 8LG
**Tel:** +44 (0)20 8992 5823
**Middle & Lower School Principal:** Andrew Mitchell
**Age range:** 3–18 years
**No. of pupils:** 480
**Fees:** Day £18,000–£24,600

## James Lee Nursery School
Gliddon Road, London W14 9BH
**Tel:** 020 8741 8877

## Jigsaw Nursery & Montessori School
1 Courtfield Gardens, London W13 0EY
**Tel:** 020 8997 8330

## Jumbo Montessori Nursery School
22 George Street, London W1H 3QY
**Tel:** 020 7935 2441
**Age range:** 2–5
**No. of pupils:** 35
**Fees:** Day £1,785

## Kidsunlimited Nurseries – Ladbroke Grove
34 Ladbroke Grove, London W11 3BQ
**Tel:** 0845 850 0222

## King Fahad Academy
Bromyard Avenue, Acton, London W3 7HD
**Tel:** 020 8743 0131
**Director General:** Dr Abdulghani Alharbi
**Age range:** 3–19
**No. of pupils:** 550
**Fees:** Day £3,300–£4,300

## La Petite Ecole Francais
73 Saint Charles Square, London W10 6EJ
**Tel:** +44 208 960 1278
**Principal:** Ms A Stones
**Age range:** 2–6

## Ladbroke Square Montessori School
43 Ladbroke Square, London W11 3ND
**Tel:** 020 7229 0125
**Principal:** Mrs Sophia Russell-Cobb MontDip
**Age range:** 3–5
**Fees:** Day £850–£1,350

## Latymer Prep School
36 Upper Mall, Hammersmith, London W6 9TA
**Tel:** 020 7993 0061
**Principal:** Ms Andrea Rutterford B.Ed (Hons)
**Age range:** 7–11
**No. of pupils:** 165
**Fees:** Day £16,860

## Latymer Upper School
King Street, Hammersmith, London W6 9LR
**Tel:** 020862 92024
**Head:** Mr D Goodhew MA(Oxon)
**Age range:** 11–18
**No. of pupils:** 1200
**Fees:** Day £18,510

## Le Herisson
River Court Methodist Church, Rover Court Road, Hammersmith, London W6 9JT
**Tel:** 020 8563 7664
**Head Teacher:** C Behroozi
**Age range:** 2–6
**Fees:** Day £8,730–£8,970

## L'Ecole Bilingue
St David's Welsh Church, St Mary's Terrace, London W2 1SJ
**Tel:** 020 7224 8427
**Headteacher:** Ms Veronique Ferreira
**Age range:** 3–11
**No. of pupils:** 68
**Fees:** Day £6,000–£6,600

## Leiths School of Food & Wine
16-20 Wendell Road, Shepherd's Bush, London W12 9RT
**Tel:** 020 8749 6400
**Managing Director:** Camilla Schneideman
**Age range:** 17–99
**No. of pupils:** 96
16+

## Little Cherubs Nursery School
Our Lady of Victories Church Hall, 16 Abingdon Road, Kensington, London W8 6AF
**Tel:** 020 7376 4460/07810 712241
**Principal:** Mrs M Colvin MontDip
**Age range:** 2–5
**No. of pupils:** 42
**Fees:** Day £5,970–£10,170

## Little People of Shepherds Bush
61 Hadyn Park Road, Shepherds Bush, London W12 9AQ
**Tel:** 020 8749 5080
**Owner:** Miss Jane Gleasure
**Age range:** 4 months–5

## Little People of Willow Vale
9 Willow Vale, London W12 0PA
**Tel:** 020 8749 2877
**Head:** Miss Jane Gleasure
**Age range:** 4 months–5

## Little Sweethearts Montessori
St Saviours Church Hall, Warwick Avenue, London W9 2PT
**Tel:** 020 7266 1616

## LLOYD WILLIAMSON SCHOOLS
**For further details see p. 55**
12 Telford Road, London W10 5SH
**Tel:** 020 8962 0345
**Email:** admin@lws.org.uk
**Website:** www.lloydwilliamson.co.uk
**Co-Principals:** Ms Lucy Meyer & Mr Aaron Williams
**Age range:** 4 months–16 years (18 in 2019)
**Fees:** Day £13,950

## London Academy of Music & Dramatic Art
155 Talgarth Road, London W14 9DA
**Tel:** 020 8834 0500
**Head of Examinations:** Dawn Postans
**Age range:** 17+
16+ £

## London College
1st Floor, 23-25 Eastcastle Street, London W1W 8DF
**Tel:** 020 7580 7552
**Head:** Mr David Kohn
16+

## London College of Professional Training Ltd
The Opportunities Centre, 370-376 Uxbridge Road, London W12 7LL
**Tel:** 020 8746 2120
**Head:** Mrs Margaret Arokiasamy
16+

## London Hotel School
Springvale Terrace, West Kensington, London W14 0AE
**Tel:** 020 7665 0000
**Head:** Mr Rod Hardingham
16+

## London International College
147 Oxford Street, London W1D 2JE
**Tel:** 020 7734 6420
**Principal:** Mr T Ktorides
16+

## London School of Management Ltd
43-47 New Broadway, Ealing, London W5 5AH
**Tel:** 020 8567 4355
**Head:** Mr R S Rupal
16+

## London Skills Academy
123 Godolphin Road, London W12 8JN
**Tel:** 020 8749 6711
**Head:** Dr Tunde Idowu
16+

## Maria Montessori Children's House – Notting Hill
28 Powis Gardens, London W11 1JG
**Tel:** 020 7221 4141
**Head:** Mrs L Lawrence
**Age range:** 2–6
**No. of pupils:** 20
**Fees:** Day £4,500

## Maria Montessori Nursery School
Church of the Ascension Hall, Beaufort Road, Ealing, London W5 3EB
**Tel:** 07717 050761

## Maria Montessori School – Bayswater
St Matthew's Church, St Petersburgh Place, London W2 4LA
**Tel:** +44 (0)20 7435 3646

## Montessori Centre International
18 Balderton Street, London W1K 6TG
**Tel:** 020 7493 0165
**Director:** Ms Barbara Isaacs
**Age range:** 17–60
16+

## Montessori Neighbourhood Nursery School
St Andrew's Church, Star Road, London W14 9QE
**Tel:** 020 7386 5818
**Head:** Anita Grebot
**Age range:** 18 mths–5 yrs

## Norland Place School
162-166 Holland Park Avenue, London W11 4UH
**Tel:** 020 7603 9103
**Headmaster:** Mr Patrick Mattar MA
**Age range:** B4–8 years G4–11 years
**Fees:** Day £13,590–£16,389

## Notting Hill & Ealing High School GDST
2 Cleveland Road, West Ealing, London W13 8AX
**Tel:** (020) 8799 8400
**Headmistress:** Ms Lucinda Hunt
**Age range:** G4–18
**No. of pupils:** 903 VIth150
**Fees:** Day £12,849–£16,521

## Notting Hill Preparatory School
95 Lancaster Road, London W11 1QQ
**Tel:** 020 7221 0727
**Headmistress:** Mrs Jane Cameron
**Age range:** 4–13
**No. of pupils:** 325
**Fees:** Day £6,100

## One World Montessori Nursery & Pre-Prep
69-71 Brock Green, Hammersmith, London W6 7BE
**Tel:** 020 7603 6065
**Headteacher:** Ms N Greer
**Age range:** 2–8
**No. of pupils:** 21

## One World Preparatory School
10 Stanley Gardens, Acton, London W3 7SZ
**Tel:** 020 87433300
**Head:** Ms Lisa Manser
**Age range:** 3–11
**No. of pupils:** 52
**Fees:** Day £3,000

### ORCHARD HOUSE SCHOOL
*For further details see p. 64*
16 Newton Grove, Bedford Park, London W4 1LB
**Tel:** 020 8742 8544
**Email:** info@orchardhs.org.uk
**Website:** www.orchardhs.org.uk
**Headmistress:** Mrs Maria Edwards BEd(Beds) PGCE(Man) Mont Cert
**Age range:** 3–11
**No. of pupils:** 290
**Fees:** Day £8,520–£17,760

## Oxford House College – London
30 Oxford Street, London W1W 8AW
**Tel:** 020 7580 9785
**Principal:** Ms Muberra Orme
16+

## Paint Pots Montessori School – Bayswater
St Stephens Church, Westbourne Park Road, London W2 5QT
**Tel:** 07527 100534
**Head Teacher:** Vinni Lewis
**Age range:** 2 years 6 months–5 years

## Pembridge Hall
18 Pembridge Square, London W2 4EH
**Tel:** 020 7229 0121
**Headteacher:** Mr Henry Keighley-Elstub
**Age range:** G4–11
**No. of pupils:** 413

## Playhouse Day Nursery
Leighton Hall, Elthorne Park Road, London W7 2JJ
**Tel:** 020 8840 2851
**Head of Nursery:** Mrs Priti Patel

## Portland Place School
56-58 Portland Place, London W1B 1NJ
**Tel:** 0207 307 8700
**Head:** Mr Tim Cook
**Age range:** 11–18
**No. of pupils:** 300 VIth50
**Fees:** Day £12,522–£16,425

## Queen's College
43-49 Harley Street, London W1G 8BT
**Tel:** 020 7291 7000
**Head:** Dr F M R Ramsey MA, DPhil(Oxon)
**Age range:** G11–18
**No. of pupils:** 360 VIth90

## Queen's College Preparatory School
61 Portland Place, , London W1B 1QP
**Tel:** 020 7291 0660
**Headmistress:** Mrs Emma Webb
**Age range:** G4–11

### RAVENSCOURT PARK PREPARATORY SCHOOL
*For further details see p. 68*
16 Ravenscourt Avenue, London W6 0SL
**Tel:** 020 8846 9153
**Email:** secretary@rpps.co.uk
**Website:** www.rpps.co.uk
**Headmaster:** Mr Carl Howes MA (Cantab), PGCE (Exeter)
**Age range:** 4–11
**No. of pupils:** 419
**Fees:** Day £5,626

## Ravenstone Pre-Preparatory School
The Long Garden, St George's Fields, Albion Street, London W2 2AX
**Tel:** 020 7262 1190
**Head of School:** Mrs Karen Dapson
**Age range:** 2–7
**No. of pupils:** 74
**Fees:** Day £11,280–£16,875

## Ray Cochrane Beauty School
118 Baker Street, London W1U 6TT
**Tel:** 02033224738
**Age range:** 16–50
**No. of pupils:** 30
**Fees:** Day £2,195–£8,995
16+ 16+

## Rolfe's Nursery School
34A Oxford Gardens, London W10 5UG
**Tel:** 020 7727 8300
**Headteacher:** Mrs Victoria O'Brien
**Age range:** 2–5
**Fees:** Day £4,950–£8,595

## Sassoon Academy
56 Davies Mews, London W1K 5AA
**Tel:** 020 7399 6902
**Education Manager:** Peter Crossfield
**Age range:** 16–45
**Fees:** Day £13,500
16+

## Southbank International School – Fitzrovia
17 Conway Street, London W1T 6BN
**Tel:** +44 2076 312600

## Southbank International School – Kensington
36-38 Kensington Park Road, London W11 3BU
**Tel:** +44 (0)20 7243 3803
**Interim Principal:** Jonathan Coward
**Age range:** 3–18
IB

## Southbank International School – Westminster
63-65 Portland Place, London W1B 1QR
**Tel:** 020 7243 3803
**Interim Principal:** Siobhan McGrath
**Age range:** 11–18/19
IB 16+

### ST AUGUSTINE'S PRIORY
*For further details see p. 72*
Hillcrest Road, Ealing, London W5 2JL
**Tel:** 020 8997 2022
**Email:** office@sapriory.com
**Website:** www.sapriory.com
**Headteacher:** Mrs Sarah Raffray M.A., N.P.Q.H
**Age range:** B3–4 G3–18
**No. of pupils:** 456
**Fees:** Day £10,656–£15,162
16+

**ST BENEDICT'S SCHOOL**
*For further details see p. 70*
54 Eaton Rise, Ealing,
London W5 2ES
**Tel:** 020 8862 2000
**Email:** admissions@
stbenedicts.org.uk
**Website:**
www.stbenedicts.org.uk
**Headmaster:** Mr A Johnson BA
**Age range:** 3–18
**No. of pupils:** 1073 VIth219
**Fees:** Day £12,500–£16,104

## St James Junior School
Earsby Street, London W14 8SH
**Tel:** 020 7348 1777
**Headmistress:** Mrs Catherine
Thomlinson BA(Hons)
**Age range:** B4–11 G4–10
**Fees:** Day £10,650

## St James Senior Girls' School
Earsby Street, London W14 8SH
**Tel:** 020 7348 1777
**Headmistress:** Mrs Sarah Labram BA
**Age range:** G11–18
**No. of pupils:** 295 VIth67
**Fees:** Day £18,330

## St Matthews Montessori School
St Matthews Church Hall, North
Common Road, London W5 2QA
**Tel:** 07495 898 760
**Head Teacher:** Mrs Farah Virani
M.A, B.A., PGCE – Primary, Mont.
Dip.Adv.
**Age range:** 2–5

## St Patrick's International College
24 Great Chapel Street,
London W1F 8FS
**Tel:** 020 7287 6664
**Principal:** Mr Girish Chandra

## St Paul's Girls' School
Brook Green, London W6 7BS
**Tel:** 020 7603 2288
**High Mistress:** Mrs Sarah Fletcher
**Age range:** G11–18 years
**No. of pupils:** 740 VIth200
**Fees:** Day £23,934–£25,731

## St Peter's Nursery
59a Portobello Road,
London W11 3DB
**Tel:** 020 7243 2617
**Head of Nursery:** Tracey Lloyd

## Sylvia Young Theatre School
1 Nutford Place, London W1H 5YZ
**Tel:** 020 7258 2330
**Headteacher:** Ms Frances Chave
BSc, PGCE, NPQH
**Age range:** 10–16
**Fees:** Day £13,500–£13,800 WB
£18,060–£18,360 FB £21,060–£21,360

## Tabernacle School
32 St Anns Villas, Holland
Park, London W11 4RS
**Tel:** 020 7602 6232
**Headteacher:** Mrs P Wilson
**Age range:** 3–16
**Fees:** Day £4,500

## Teddies Nurseries Chiswick Park
Evershed Walk, London W4 5BW
**Tel:** 0333 920 0404
**Nursery Manager:** Ms Rebecca
Fergus
**Age range:** 3 months–5 years

## The Ark Montessori Nursery
All Saints Church, Bollo Bridge
Road, Acton, London W3 8AX
**Tel:** 020 8993 3540

## The Ark Montessori School
The Scout Hall, Rugby Road,
Chiswick, London W4 1AL
**Tel:** 020 8932 4766

## The Falcons School for Boys
2 Burnaby Gardens,
Chiswick, London W4 3DT
**Tel:** 020 8747 8393
**Headmaster:** Mr Gordon Milne
**Age range:** B3–7
**No. of pupils:** 225
**Fees:** Day £3,875–£11,625

## The Falcons School for Girls
15 Gunnersbury Avenue,
Ealing, London W5 3XD
**Tel:** 020 8992 5189
**Headteacher:** Miss Joan
McGillewie
**Age range:** G4–11
**No. of pupils:** 102
**Fees:** Day £3,625

## The Godolphin and Latymer School
Iffley Road, Hammersmith,
London W6 0PG
**Tel:** +44 (0)20 8741 1936
**Head Mistress:** Dr Frances Ramsey
**Age range:** G11–18
**No. of pupils:** 800

## The Japanese School
87 Creffield Road, Acton,
London W3 9PU
**Tel:** 020 8993 7145
**Headteacher:** Mrs Kiyoe Tsuruoka
**Age range:** 6–16
**No. of pupils:** 500

## The Jordans Montessori Nursery School
Holy Innocents Church,
Paddenswick Road,
London W6 0UB
**Tel:** 0208 741 3230
**Principal:** Ms Sara Green
**Age range:** 2–5
**Fees:** Day £1,356–£3,270

## The Meadows Montessori School
Dukes Meadows Community
Centre, Alexandra Gardens,
London W4 2TD
**Tel:** 020 8742 1327/8995 2621
**Headmistress:** Mrs S Herbert BA
**Age range:** 2–5
**Fees:** Day £3,030–£3,870

## The Minors Nursery School
10 Pembridge Square,
London W2 4ED
**Tel:** 020 7727 7253
**Headteacher:** Ms Jane Ritchie
**Age range:** 2–5

## The Sinclair Montessori Nursery School
The Garden Flat, 142 Sinclair
Road, London W14 0NL
**Tel:** 020 7602 3745
**Headmistress:** Miss C Burnaby-
Atkins MontDipEd, SENDip, NVQ
**Age range:** 2–5
**No. of pupils:** 24

## The Square Montessori School
18 Holland Park Avenue,
London W11 3QU
**Tel:** 020 7221 6004
**Principal:** Mrs V Lawson-Tancred
**No. of pupils:** 20
**Fees:** Day £2,220

## Thomas's Preparatory School – Kensington
17-19 Cottesmore Gardens,
London W8 5PR
**Tel:** 020 7361 6500
**Headmistress:** Miss Joanna Ebner
MA, BEd(Hons)(Cantab), NPQH
**Age range:** 4–11
**Fees:** Day £14,505–£15,795

## West London College
Parliament House, 35 North Row,
Mayfair, London W1K 6DB
**Tel:** 020 7491 1841
**Principal:** Paul S Smith BA(Hons),
FRSA
**Fees:** Day £0

## West London School of Management & Technology
99-103 St James Annexe,
The Broadway, West Ealing,
London W13 9BP
**Tel:** 020 8840 1177
**Principal:** Mr Syed Raza Gilani

## Wetherby Preparatory School
48 Bryanston Square,
London W1H 2EA
**Tel:** 020 7535 3520
**Headteacher:** Mr Nick Baker
**Age range:** B8–13
**No. of pupils:** 192
**Fees:** Day £4,665

## Wetherby Pre-Preparatory School
11 Pembridge Square,
London W2 4ED
**Tel:** 020 7727 9581
**Headmaster:** Mr Mark Snell
**Age range:** B2 1/2–8
**No. of pupils:** 350
**Fees:** Day £21,600

## Wetherby Senior School
100 Marylebone Lane,
London W1U 2QU
**Tel:** 020 7535 3530
**Headmaster:** Mr Seth Bolderow
**Age range:** B11–18

## Windmill Montessori Nursery School
62 Shirland Road, London W9 2EH
**Tel:** 020 7289 3410
**Principal:** Miss M H Leoni & Miss J
Davidson
**No. of pupils:** 48
**Fees:** Day £3,600

## World of Children
Log Cabin Childrens Centre,
259 Northfield Avenue,
, London W5 4UA
**Tel:** 020 8840 3400

## Young Dancers Academy
25 Bulwer Street, London W12 8AR
**Tel:** 020 8743 3856
**Head:** Mrs K Williams
**Age range:** 11–16
**Fees:** Day £10,500–£11,100

## Ysgol Gymraeg Llundain London Welsh School
Hanwell Community Centre,
Westcott Crescent, London W7 1PD
**Tel:** 020 8575 0237
**Leadteacher:** Miss Rachel Rawlins
**Age range:** 3–11
**No. of pupils:** 30
**Fees:** Day £1,950

# Schools in Greater London

## KEY TO SYMBOLS

- (♂) **Boys' school**
- (♀) **Girls' school**
- (🌐) **International school**
- (16) **Tutorial or sixth form college**
- (A) **A levels**
- (⚖) **Boarding accommodation**
- (£) **Bursaries**
- (IB) **International Baccalaureate**
- (✐) **Learning support**
- (16+) **Entrance at 16+**
- (🎓) **Vocational qualifications**
- (APS) **Independent Association of Prep Schools**
- (HMC) **The Headmasters' & Headmistresses' Conference**
- (ISA) **Independent Schools Association**
- (GSA) **Girls' School Association**
- (BSA) **Boarding Schools' Association**
- (S) **Society of Heads**

*Unless otherwise indicated, all schools are coeducational day schools. Single-sex and boarding schools will be indicated by the relevant icon.*

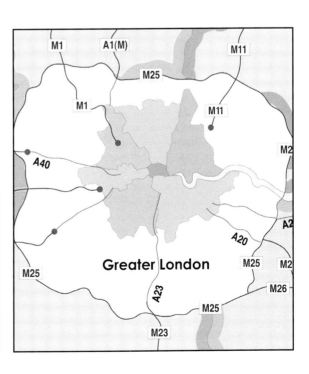

# Essex

### Al-Noor Primary School
Newton Industrial Estate, Eastern Avenue, Chadwell Heath, Romford, Essex RM6 5SD
**Tel:** 020 8597 7576
**Head:** Mrs Someera Butt
**Age range:** 4–10
**No. of pupils:** 175
**Fees:** Day £2,550–£2,750

### Avon House Preparatory School
490 High Road, Woodford Green, Essex IG8 0PN
**Tel:** 020 8504 1749
**Headteacher:** Mrs Amanda Campbell
**Age range:** 3–11
**No. of pupils:** 230
**Fees:** Day £9,375–£10,290

### BANCROFT'S SCHOOL
*For further details see p. 79*
High Road, Woodford Green, Essex IG8 0RF
**Tel:** 020 8505 4821
**Email:** office@bancrofts.org
**Website:** www.bancrofts.org
**Head:** Mr Simon Marshall MA, PGCE (Cantab), MA, MPhil (Oxon)
**Age range:** 7–18
**No. of pupils:** 1143 VIth245

### Beehive Preparatory School
233 Beehive Lane, Redbridge, Ilford, Essex IG4 5ED
**Tel:** 020 8550 3224
**Headmaster:** Mr C J Beasant BEd
**Age range:** 4–11
**Fees:** Day £4,900

### Braeside School for Girls
130 High Road, Buckhurst Hill, Essex IG9 5SD
**Tel:** 020 8504 1133
**Head Teacher:** Mrs G Haddon BA(Hons), PGCE
**Age range:** G3–16
**No. of pupils:** 199
**Fees:** Day £5,175–£10,875

### Chigwell School
High Road, Chigwell, Essex IG7 6QF
**Tel:** 020 8501 5700
**Headmaster:** Mr M E Punt MA, MSc
**Age range:** 4–18
**No. of pupils:** 915 VIth185
**Fees:** Day £10,200–£16,020
FB £26,730–£26,730

### Eastcourt Independent School
1 Eastwood Road, Goodmayes, Ilford, Essex IG3 8UW
**Tel:** 020 8590 5472
**Headmistress:** Mrs Christine Redgrave BSc(Hons), DipEd, MEd
**Age range:** 3–11
**Fees:** Day £6,300

### Gidea Park College
2 Balgores Lane, Gidea Park, Romford, Essex RM2 5JR
**Tel:** 01708 740381
**Headmistress:** Mrs Susan-Jayne Gooding BA
**Age range:** 3–11
**No. of pupils:** 177
**Fees:** Day £1,275–£2,500

### Goodrington School
17 Walden Road, Hornchurch, Essex RM11 2JT
**Tel:** 01708 448349
**Head Teacher:** Mrs J R Ellenby
**Age range:** 3–11
**Fees:** Day £6,600

### Guru Gobind Singh Khalsa College
Roding Lane, Chigwell, Essex IG7 6BQ
**Tel:** 020 8559 9160
**Principal:** Mr Amarjit Singh Toor BSc(Hons), BSc, BT
**Age range:** 3–17
**Fees:** Day £3,900

### Immanuel School
Havering Grange Centre, Havering Road North, Romford, Essex RM1 4HR
**Tel:** 01708 764449
**Principal:** Miss Norcross
**Age range:** 3–16

### Loyola Preparatory School
103 Palmerston Road, Buckhurst Hill, Essex IG9 5NH
**Tel:** 020 8504 7372
**Headmaster:** Mr P G M Nicholson CertEd, BEd(Hons)
**Age range:** B3–11
**No. of pupils:** 183
**Fees:** Day £9,330

### Maytime Montessori Nursery – Cranbrook Road
341 Cranbrook Road, Ilford, Essex IG1 4UF
**Tel:** 020 8554 3079

### Maytime Montessori Nursery – Eastwood Road
2 Eastwood Road, Goodmayes, Essex IG3 8XB
**Tel:** 020 8599 3744

### Maytime Montessori Nursery – York Road
87 York Road, Ilford, Essex IG1 3AF
**Tel:** 020 8553 1524
**Age range:** 0–6

### Oakfields Montessori School
Harwood Hall, Harwood Hall Lane, Corbets Tey, Essex RM14 2YG
**Tel:** 01708 220117
**Headmistress:** Mrs K Malandreniotis
**Age range:** 2–11
**Fees:** Day £2,508–£4,260

### Oaklands School
8 Albion Hill, Loughton, Essex IG10 4RA
**Tel:** 020 8508 3517
**Headmistress:** Mrs Cheryl Macnair
**Age range:** B2–7 G2–11
**No. of pupils:** 243
**Fees:** Day £3,795–£7,650

### Park School for Girls
20 Park Avenue, Ilford, Essex IG1 4RS
**Tel:** 020 8554 2466
**Headmistress:** Mrs N O'Brien BA
**Age range:** G7–18
**No. of pupils:** 230 VIth19
**Fees:** Day £4,755–£6,285

### Raphael Independent School
Park Lane, Hornchurch, Essex RM11 1XY
**Tel:** 01708 744735
**Head of School:** Mrs C Salmon
**Age range:** 4–16
**No. of pupils:** 135
**Fees:** Day £5,200–£7,800

### St Aubyn's School
Bunces Lane, Woodford Green, Essex IG8 9DU
**Tel:** 020 8504 1577
**Headmaster:** Mr Leonard Blom BEd(Hons) BA NPQH
**Age range:** 3–13
**No. of pupils:** 525
**Fees:** Day £5,190–£11,670

### St Mary's Hare Park School & Nursery
South Drive, Gidea Park, Romford, Essex RM2 6HH
**Tel:** 01708 761220
**Head Teacher:** Mrs K Karwacinski
**Age range:** 2–11
**No. of pupils:** 180
**Fees:** Day £4,485

### Stratford College of Management
1-7 Hainault Street, Ilford, Essex IG1 4EL
**Tel:** 020 8553 0205
**Head:** Dr Raza

### The Daiglen School
68 Palmerston Road, Buckhurst Hill, Essex IG9 5LG
**Tel:** 020 8504 7108
**Headteacher:** Mrs M Bradfield
**Age range:** 3–11
**No. of pupils:** 130
**Fees:** Day £6,360

### The Ursuline Preparatory School Ilford
2-8 Coventry Road, Ilford, Essex IG1 4QR
**Tel:** 020 8518 4050
**Headteacher:** Mrs Lisa McCoy
**Age range:** G3–11
**No. of pupils:** 159
**Fees:** Day £5,697

### Woodford Green Preparatory School
Glengall Road, Woodford Green, Essex IG8 0BZ
**Tel:** 020 8504 5045
**Headmaster:** Mr J P Wadge
**Age range:** 3–11
**No. of pupils:** 383
**Fees:** Day £3,270

# Hertfordshire

**Lyonsdown School**
3 Richmond Road, New Barnet,
Barnet, Hertfordshire EN5 1SA
**Tel:** 020 8449 0225
**Head:** Mr C Hammond BA (Hons)
PGCE
**Age range:** B3–7 G3–11
**No. of pupils:** 185
**Fees:** Day £4,080–£10,200

**MOUNT HOUSE SCHOOL**
*For further details see p. 88*
Camlet Way, Hadley Wood,
Barnet, Hertfordshire EN4 0NJ
**Tel:** 020 8449 6889
**Email:** admissions@
mounthouse.org.uk
**Website:**
www.mounthouse.org.uk
**Headmaster:** Mr Matthew Burke
**Age range:** 11–18
**No. of pupils:** 180
**Fees:** Day £14,820

**Norfolk Lodge Montessori
Nursery & Pre-Prep School**
Dancers Hill Road, Barnet,
Hertfordshire EN5 4RP
**Tel:** 020 8447 1565
**Head Teacher:** Mrs Mary Wales
**Age range:** 6 months–7 years
**No. of pupils:** 140
**Fees:** Day £2,200–£2,400

**Susi Earnshaw
Theatre School**
68 High Street, Barnet,
Hertfordshire EN5 5SJ
**Tel:** 020 8441 5010
**Headteacher:** Mr David Earnshaw
**Age range:** 11–16
**No. of pupils:** 60
**Fees:** Day £10,500

**The Royal Masonic
School for Girls**
Rickmansworth Park,
Rickmansworth,
Hertfordshire WD3 4HF
**Tel:** 01923 773168
**Headmaster:** Mr Kevin Carson
M.Phil (Cambridge)
**Age range:** G4–18
**No. of pupils:** 930 VIth165
**Fees:** Day £10,455–£15,915 WB
£18,345–£25,935 FB £19,350–£28,140

# Kent

**Ashgrove School**
116 Widmore Road,
Bromley, Kent BR1 3BE
**Tel:** 020 8460 4143
**Principal:** Patricia Ash CertEd,
BSc(Hons), PhD, CMath, FIMA
**Age range:** 4–11
**No. of pupils:** 106
**Fees:** Day £8,730

**BABINGTON HOUSE
SCHOOL**
*For further details see p. 78*
Grange Drive, Chislehurst,
Kent BR7 5ES
**Tel:** 020 8467 5537
**Email:** enquiries@
babingtonhouse.com
**Website:**
www.babingtonhouse.com
**Headmaster:** Mr Tim Lello MA,
FRSA, NPQH
**Age range:** B3–11 & 16–18 G3–18
**No. of pupils:** 364

**Beckenham College**
The Clockhouse Business Centre,
Unit 2, Thayers Farm Road,
Beckenham, Kent BR3 4LZ
**Tel:** 020 8650 3321
**Principal:** Mrs E Wakeling
**Age range:** 16+
**Fees:** Day £100–£3,500

**Benedict House
Preparatory School**
1-5 Victoria Road, Sidcup,
Kent DA15 7HD
**Tel:** 020 8300 7206
**Headmistress:** Mrs Gemma Chikola
**Age range:** 3–11
**Fees:** Day £2,145–£2,395

**Bickley Park School**
24 Page Heath Lane, Bickley,
Bromley, Kent BR1 2DS
**Tel:** 020 8467 2195
**Headmaster:** Mr Paul Ashley
**Age range:** B3–13 G3–4
**No. of pupils:** 370
**Fees:** Day £6,525–£11,925

**Bird College**
The Centre, 27 Station Road,
Sidcup, Kent DA15 7EB
**Tel:** 020 8300 6004/3031
**Principal & Chief Executive:** Ms
Shirley Coen BA(Hons), FSRA
**Fees:** Day £0

**Bishop Challoner School**
228 Bromley Road, Shortlands,
Bromley, Kent BR2 0BS
**Tel:** 020 8460 3546
**Headteacher:** Ms Paula Anderson
**Age range:** 3–18
**No. of pupils:** 412 VIth32
**Fees:** Day £6,441–£9,036

**Breaside Preparatory
School**
41-43 Orchard Road,
Bromley, Kent BR1 2PR
**Tel:** 020 8460 0916
**Executive Principal:** Mrs Karen A
Nicholson B.Ed, NPQH, Dip EYs
**Age range:** 2.5–11
**No. of pupils:** 365
**Fees:** Day £10,545–£12,285

**BROMLEY HIGH
SCHOOL GDST**
*For further details see p. 80*
Blackbrook Lane, Bickley,
Bromley, Kent BR1 2TW
**Tel:** 020 8781 7000/1
**Email:** bhs@bro.gdst.net
**Website:**
www.bromleyhigh.gdst.net
**Head:** Mrs A M Drew BA(Hons),
MBA (Dunelm)
**Age range:** G4–18
**No. of pupils:** 912 VIth120
**Fees:** Day £13,356–£16,563

**Darul Uloom London**
Foxbury Avenue, Perry Street,
Chislehurst, Kent BR7 6SD
**Tel:** 020 8295 0637
**Principal:** Mufti Mustafa
**Age range:** B11–18
**No. of pupils:** 160
**Fees:** FB £2,400

**Farringtons School**
Perry Street, Chislehurst,
Kent BR7 6LR
**Tel:** 020 8467 0256
**Head:** Mrs Dorothy Nancekievill
**Age range:** 3–18
**No. of pupils:** 681 VIth94
**Fees:** Day £14,610 WB
£28,830 FB £30,600

**Merton Court
Preparatory School**
38 Knoll Road, Sidcup,
Kent DA14 4QU
**Tel:** 020 8300 2112
**Headmaster:** Mr Dominic Price
BEd, MBA
**Age range:** 3–11
**Fees:** Day £8,115–£8,910

**St Christopher's
The Hall School**
49 Bromley Road,
Beckenham, Kent BR3 5PA
**Tel:** 020 8650 2200
**Headmaster:** Mr A Velasco MEd,
BH(Hons), PGCE
**Age range:** 3–11
**No. of pupils:** 305
**Fees:** Day £2,250–£6,630

**St. David's Prep**
Justin Hall,, Beckenham Road,
West Wickham, Kent BR4 0QS
**Tel:** 020 8777 5852
**Principal:** Mrs J Foulger
**Age range:** 4–11
**No. of pupils:** 155
**Fees:** Day £6,015–£6,165

**West Lodge School**
36 Station Road, Sidcup,
Kent DA15 7DU
**Tel:** 020 8300 2489
**Head Teacher:** Mrs Susan Webb
**Age range:** 3–11
**No. of pupils:** 163
**Fees:** Day £5,205–£8,700

**Wickham Court School**
Schiller International,
Layhams Road, West
Wickham, Kent BR4 9HW
**Tel:** 020 8777 2942
**Head:** Mrs Barbara Hunter
**Age range:** 2–16
**No. of pupils:** 121
**Fees:** Day £4,481–£6,900

# Middlesex

## 360 GSP College
6th Floor, Wembley Point,
1 Harrow Road, Wembley,
Middlesex HA9 6DE
**Tel:** 020 8672 4151/0845
6034709
**Head:** Mr Yassin Sayfoo

## Acorn House College
39-47 High Street, Southall,
Middlesex UB1 3HF
**Tel:** 020 8571 9900
**Principal:** Mr John Wilson
**Age range:** 13–19
**No. of pupils:** 121 VIth85
**Fees:** Day £5,200–£14,600

## ACS Hillingdon
## International School
Hillingdon Court, 108 Vine
Lane, Hillingdon, Uxbridge,
Middlesex UB10 0BE
**Tel:** +44 (0) 1895 259 771
**Head of School:** Linda LaPine
**Age range:** 4–18
**No. of pupils:** 520
**Fees:** Day £17,260–£23,110

## Alpha Preparatory School
21 Hindes Road, Harrow,
Middlesex HA1 1SH
**Head:** C.J.W Trinidad BSc(Hons),
PGCE
**Age range:** 3–11
**No. of pupils:** 170
**Fees:** Day £3,300–£10,590

## Ashton House School
50-52 Eversley Crescent,
Isleworth, Middlesex TW7 4LW
**Tel:** 020 8560 3902
**Headteacher:** Mrs M Grundberg
MA, PGCE
**Age range:** 3–11
**Fees:** Day £9,300–£10,200

## Buckingham
## Preparatory School
458 Rayners Lane, Pinner,
Harrow, Middlesex HA5 5DT
**Tel:** 020 8866 2737
**Head of School:** Mrs Sarah Hollis
**Age range:** B3–11
**Fees:** Day £9,321–£11,838

## Buxlow Preparatory School
5/6 Castleton Gardens,
Wembley, Middlesex HA9 7QJ
**Tel:** 020 8904 3615
**Headmistress:** Mrs Ann Baines
**Age range:** 4–11
**Fees:** Day £6,885

## Edgware Jewish Girls
## – Beis Chinuch
Yeshurun Synagogue,
Fernhurst Gardens, Edgware,
Middlesex HA8 7PH
**Tel:** 020 8951 0239
**Headteacher:** Mr M Cohen
**Age range:** G3–7

## Halliford School
Russell Road, Shepperton,
Middlesex TW17 9HX
**Tel:** 01932 223593
**Headmaster:** Mr James Davies
BMus
**Age range:** B11–18 G16–18
**No. of pupils:** 400
**Fees:** Day £15,285

## Hampton Prep and
## Pre-Prep School
Gloucester Road, Hampton,
Middlesex TW12 2UQ
**Tel:** 020 8979 1844
**Headmaster:** Mr Tim Smith
**Age range:** 3–11
**Fees:** Day £4,995–£11,580

## Hampton School
Hanworth Road, Hampton,
Middlesex TW12 3HD
**Tel:** 020 8979 9273
**Headmaster:** Mr Kevin Knibbs MA
(Oxon)
**Age range:** B11–18
**No. of pupils:** 1200
**Fees:** Day £6,125

## Harrow School
5 High Street, Harrow on the
Hill, Middlesex HA1 3HT
**Tel:** 020 8872 8000
**Head Master:** Mr Jim Hawkins
**Age range:** B13–18
**No. of pupils:** 830 VIth320
**Fees:** FB £33,285

## Harrow Secretarial
## College & Computer
## Training Centre
68 Station Road, Harrow,
Middlesex HA1 2SQ
**Tel:** 020 8424 9900
**Fees:** Day £0

## Holland House School
1 Broadhurst Avenue, Edgware,
Middlesex HA8 8TP
**Tel:** 020 8958 6979
**Headmistress:** Mrs Irinia Tyk
BA(Hons)
**Age range:** 4–11
**Fees:** Day £7,308

## International School
## of Business Studies
204-226 Imperial Drive, Rayners
Lane, Harrow, Middlesex HA2 7HH
**Tel:** 020 8872 4103
**Head:** Mr Dawar Aziz

## Jack and Jill School
30 Nightingale Road, Hampton,
Middlesex TW12 3HX
**Tel:** 020 8979 3195
**Principal:** Miss K Papirnik BEd(Hons)
**Age range:** B2–5 G2–7
**No. of pupils:** 155
**Fees:** Day £2,409–£9,597

**KEW HOUSE SCHOOL**
*For further details see p. 86*
Kew House, 6 Capital
Interchange Way, London,
Middlesex TW8 0EX
**Tel:** 0208 742 2038
**Email:** info@
kewhouseschool.com
**Website:**
www.kewhouseschool.com
**Headmaster:** Mr Mark Hudson
**Age range:** 11–18
**No. of pupils:** 450
**Fees:** Day £6,849

## Kids Inc Day
## Nursery – Enfield
8 Glyn Road, Southbury,
Enfield, Middlesex EN3 4JL
**Tel:** 020 8805 1144

## Lady Nafisa Independent
## Secondary School for Girls
83A Sunbury Road, Feltham,
Middlesex TW13 4PH
**Tel:** 020 8751 5610
**Headteacher:** Ms Fouzia Butt
**Age range:** G11–16

## Menorah Grammar School
Abbots Road, Edgware,
Middlesex HA8 0QS
**Tel:** 020 8906 9756
**Headteacher:** Rabbi A M Goldblatt
**Age range:** B11–17
**No. of pupils:** 203

## Merchant Taylors' School
Sandy Lodge, Northwood,
Middlesex HA6 2HT
**Tel:** 01923 820644
**Head:** Mr S J Everson MA (Cantab)
**Age range:** B11–18
**No. of pupils:** 865 VIth282
**Fees:** Day £16,660

## Newland House School
Waldegrave Park, Twickenham,
Middlesex TW1 4TQ
**Tel:** 020 8865 1305
**Headmaster:** Mr D A Alexander
**Age range:** B4–13 G4–11
**No. of pupils:** 425
**Fees:** Day £3,625–£4,055

## North London
## Collegiate School
Canons, Canons Drive,
Edgware, Middlesex HA8 7RJ
**Tel:** +44 (0)20 8952 0912
**Headmistress:** Mrs Sarah Clark
**Age range:** G4–18
**No. of pupils:** 1080
**Fees:** Day £5,530–£6,545

## Northwood College
## for Girls GDST
Maxwell Road, Northwood,
Middlesex HA6 2YE
**Tel:** 01923 825446
**Head Mistress:** Miss Jacqualyn Pain
MA, MA, MBA
**Age range:** G3–18
**No. of pupils:** 840 VIth100

## Oak Heights
3 Red Lion Court, Alexandra Road,
Hounslow, Middlesex TW3 1JS
**Tel:** 020 8577 1827
**Head:** Mr S Dhillon
**Age range:** 11–16
**No. of pupils:** 48
**Fees:** Day £6,000

## Orley Farm School
South Hill Avenue, Harrow,
Middlesex HA1 3NU
**Tel:** 020 8869 7600
**Headmaster:** Mr Tim Calvey
**Age range:** 4–13
**No. of pupils:** 497
**Fees:** Day £13,749–£15,861

## Quainton Hall
## School & Nursery
91 Hindes Road, Harrow,
Middlesex HA1 1RX
**Tel:** 020 8861 8861
**Headmaster:** S Ford BEd (Hons),
UWE Bristol
**Age range:** B2–13 G2–11
**Fees:** Day £9,075–£9,975

## Radnor House
Pope's Villa, Cross Deep,
Twickenham, Middlesex TW1 4QG
**Tel:** 020 8891 6264
**Head of School:** Mr. David Paton
MA

## Rambert School of Ballet & Contemporary Dance
Clifton Lodge, St Margaret's Drive, Twickenham, Middlesex TW1 1QN
**Tel:** 020 8892 9960
**Principal:** R McKim
**Age range:** 16+
16+

## Reddiford School
36-38 Cecil Park, Pinner, Middlesex HA5 5HH
**Tel:** 020 8866 0660
**Headteacher:** Mrs J Batt CertEd, NPQH
**Age range:** 3–11
**No. of pupils:** 320
**Fees:** Day £3,480–£8,340
£

## Regent College
Sai House, 167 Imperial Drive, Harrow, Middlesex HA2 7HD
**Tel:** 020 8966 9900
**Principal:** Mr Selva Pankaj MBA, FCMA
**Age range:** 11–19
**No. of pupils:** 167
**Fees:** Day £2,745–£12,995
16+ 16+

## Roxeth Mead School
Buckholt House, 25 Middle Road, Harrow, Middlesex HA2 0HW
**Tel:** 020 8422 2092
**Headmistress:** Mrs A Isaacs
**Age range:** 3–7
**No. of pupils:** 54
**Fees:** Day £9,450

## St Catherine's School
Cross Deep, Twickenham, Middlesex TW1 4QJ
**Tel:** 020 8891 2898
**Headmistress:** Sister Paula Thomas BEd(Hons), MA
**Age range:** G3–18
**No. of pupils:** 430
**Fees:** Day £10,509–£14,517
♦ £ ✎ 16+

## St Christopher's School
71 Wembley Park Drive, Wembley, Middlesex HA9 8HE
**Tel:** 020 8902 5069
**Headteacher:** Mr G. P. Musetti
**Age range:** 4–11
**Fees:** Day £8,400–£9,225

## St Helen's College
Parkway, Hillingdon, Uxbridge, Middlesex UB10 9JX
**Tel:** 01895 234371
**Joint Headteachers:** Mr D A Crehan & Mrs G R Crehan
**Age range:** 3–11
**No. of pupils:** 351
**Fees:** Day £5,850–£10,695
✎

## St Helen's School
Eastbury Road, Northwood, Middlesex HA6 3AS
**Tel:** +44 (0)1923 843210
**Headmistress:** Dr Mary Short BA, PhD
**Age range:** G3–18
**No. of pupils:** VIth165
♦ ✿ £ 16+

## St John's School
Potter Street Hill, Northwood, Middlesex HA6 3QY
**Tel:** 020 8866 0067
**Headmaster:** Mr M S Robinson BSc
**Age range:** B3–13 years
**No. of pupils:** 350
**Fees:** Day £10,070–£14,600
♦ £

## St John's Senior School
North Lodge, The Ridgeway, Enfield, Middlesex EN2 8BE
**Tel:** 020 8366 0035
**Headmaster:** Mr Andrew Tardios LLB(Hons), BA(Hons), CertEd
**Age range:** 11–18 years
**No. of pupils:** 309 VIth95
**Fees:** Day £13,170
16+

## St Martin's School
40 Moor Park Road, Northwood, Middlesex HA6 2DJ
**Tel:** 01923 825740
**Headmaster:** Mr D T Tidmarsh BSc(Wales)
**Age range:** B3–13
**No. of pupils:** 400
**Fees:** Day £1,450–£4,066
♦ £ ✎

## Tashbar of Edgeware
47-49 Mowbray Road, Edgware, Middlesex HA8 8JL
**Tel:** 020 8958 5162
**Headteacher:** Mr N Jaffe
**Age range:** B3–11
**No. of pupils:** 88
♦

## The Hall Pre-Preparatory School & Nursery
The Grange Country House, Rickmansworth Road, Northwood, Middlesex HA6 2RB
**Tel:** 01923 822807
**Headmistress:** Mrs S M Goodwin
**Age range:** 1–7
**Fees:** Day £3,120–£10,350
£ ✎

## The John Lyon School
Middle Road, Harrow on the Hill, Middlesex HA2 0HN
**Tel:** 020 8515 9400
**Head:** Miss Katherine Haynes BA, MEd, NPQH
**Age range:** B11–18
**No. of pupils:** 600
**Fees:** Day £5,710–£5,928
♦ £ ✎ 16+

## The Lady Eleanor Holles School
Hanworth Road, Hampton, Middlesex TW12 3HF
**Tel:** 020 8979 1601
**Head of School:** Mrs Heather Hanbury
**Age range:** G7–18
**No. of pupils:** 875
**Fees:** Day £18,945
♦ £ ✎ 16+

## The Mall School
185 Hampton Road, Twickenham, Middlesex TW2 5NQ
**Tel:** 0208 977 2523
**Headmaster:** Mr D C Price BSc, MA
**Age range:** B4–13
**No. of pupils:** 320
**Fees:** Day £10,281–£11,934
♦ £ ✎

## The Noam Primary School
8-10 Forty Avenue, Wembley, Middlesex HA9 8JW
**Tel:** 020 8908 9491
**Headteacher:** Mrs Sarah Simmonds
**Age range:** 3–11
**No. of pupils:** 154

## The St Michael Steiner School
Park Road, Hanworth Park, London, Middlesex TW13 6PN
**Tel:** 0208 893 1299
**Age range:** 3–16 (17 from Jul 2014)
**No. of pupils:** 101
**Fees:** Day £5,800–£8,900
£ ✎

## Twickenham Preparatory School
Beveree, 43 High Street, Hampton, Middlesex TW12 2SA
**Tel:** 020 8979 6216
**Head:** Mr David Malam BA(Hons) (Southampton), PGCE(Winchester)
**Age range:** B4–13 G4–11
**No. of pupils:** 273
**Fees:** Day £10,470–£11,340
£ ✎

# Surrey

## Al-Khair School
109-117 Cherry Orchard Road, Croydon, Surrey CR0 6BE
**Tel:** 020 8662 8664
**Headteacher:** Mr Usman Qureshi
**Age range:** 5–16
**No. of pupils:** 126

## Broomfield House School
Broomfield Road, Kew Gardens, Richmond, Surrey TW9 3HS
**Tel:** 020 8940 3884
**Head Teacher:** Mr N O York BA(Hons), MA, MPhil, FRSA
**Age range:** 3–11
**No. of pupils:** 160
**Fees:** Day £6,510–£13,140
✎

## Cambridge Tutors College
Water Tower Hill, Croydon, Surrey CR0 5SX
**Tel:** 020 8688 5284/7363
**Principal:** Mr M Eagers
**Age range:** 15–19
**No. of pupils:** 215 VIth200
**Fees:** Day £19,800
16+ ♦ £ 16+

## Canbury School
Kingston Hill, Kingston upon Thames, Surrey KT2 7LN
**Tel:** 020 8549 8622
**Headmistress:** Ms Louise Clancy
**Age range:** 11–16
**No. of pupils:** 65
**Fees:** Day £16,401
£ ✎

## Collingwood School
3 Springfield Road, Wallington, Surrey SM6 0BD
**Tel:** 020 8647 4607
**Headmaster:** Mr Leigh Hardie
**Age range:** 3–11
**No. of pupils:** 120
**Fees:** Day £9,360–£9,360
✎

## Croydon High School GDST
Old Farleigh Road, Selsdon, South Croydon, Surrey CR2 8YB
**Tel:** 020 8260 7500
**Headmistress:** Mrs Emma Pattison
**Age range:** G3–18
**No. of pupils:** 565 VIth90
♦ £ ✎ 16+

## Cumnor House Nursery
91 Pampisford Road, South Croydon, Surrey CR2 6DH
**Tel:** +44 (0)20 8660 3445
**Manager:** Mrs Charlotte Figueira BEd(Hons)
**Age range:** 2–4
**No. of pupils:** 200
**Fees:** Day £1,370–£2,945

## CUMNOR HOUSE SCHOOL FOR BOYS
*For further details see p. 81*
168 Pampisford Road, South Croydon, Surrey CR2 6DA
**Tel:** +44 (0)20 8660 3445
**Email:** admissions@cumnorhouse.com
**Website:** www.cumnorhouse.com
**Headmaster:** Mr Daniel Cummings
**Age range:** B2–13
**No. of pupils:** 440
**Fees:** Day £3,375–£4,250

## CUMNOR HOUSE SCHOOL FOR GIRLS
*For further details see p. 82*
1 Woodcote Lane, Purley, Surrey CR8 3HB
**Tel:** +44 (0)20 8660 3445
**Email:** admissions@cumnorhouse.com
**Website:** www.cumnorhouse.com
**Headmistress:** Mrs Amanda McShane
**Age range:** G4–11
**No. of pupils:** 165
**Fees:** Day £3,375–£4,250

## Educare Small School
12 Cowleaze Road, Kingston upon Thames, Surrey KT2 6DZ
**Tel:** 020 8547 0144
**Head Teacher:** Mrs E Steinthal
**Age range:** 3–11
**No. of pupils:** 46
**Fees:** Day £5,040

## Elmhurst School
44-48 South Park Hill Rd, South Croydon, Surrey CR2 7DW
**Tel:** 020 8688 0661
**Headmaster:** Mr M J Apsley BA(Hons), PGCE
**Age range:** B4–11
**No. of pupils:** 207
**Fees:** Day £6,300–£7,545

## Holy Cross Preparatory School
George Road, Kingston upon Thames, Surrey KT2 7NU
**Tel:** 020 8942 0729
**Headteacher:** Mrs S Hair BEd(Hons)
**Age range:** G4–11
**No. of pupils:** 285
**Fees:** Day £12,435

## Homefield Preparatory School
Western Road, Sutton, Surrey SM1 2TE
**Tel:** 0208 642 0965
**Headmaster:** Mr John Towers
**Age range:** B3–13
**No. of pupils:** 350
**Fees:** Day £2,045–£4,380

## Kew College
24-26 Cumberland Road, Kew, Surrey TW9 3HQ
**Tel:** 020 8940 2039
**Head:** Mrs Marianne Austin BSc(Hons) MA(Hons) ACA PGCE
**Age range:** 3–11
**No. of pupils:** 296
**Fees:** Day £7,050–£11,550

## KEW GREEN PREPARATORY SCHOOL
*For further details see p. 83*
Layton House, Ferry Lane, Kew Green, Richmond, Surrey TW9 3AF
**Tel:** 020 8948 5999
**Email:** secretary@kgps.co.uk
**Website:** www.kgps.co.uk
**Headmaster:** Mr J Peck
**Age range:** 4–11
**No. of pupils:** 270
**Fees:** Day £5,626

## King's House School
68 King's Road, Richmond, Surrey TW10 6ES
**Tel:** 020 8940 1878
**Head:** Mr Mark Turner BA, PGCE, NPQH
**Age range:** B3–13 G3–4
**No. of pupils:** 460
**Fees:** Day £2,265–£5,320

## KINGSTON GRAMMAR SCHOOL
*For further details see p. 84*
70 London Rd, Kingston upon Thames, Surrey KT2 6PY
**Tel:** 020 8456 5875
**Email:** enquiries@kgs.org.uk
**Website:** www.kgs.org.uk
**Head:** Mr Stephen Lehec
**Age range:** 11–18
**No. of pupils:** 829
**Fees:** Day £6,225

## Laleham Lea School
29 Peaks Hill, Purley, Surrey CR8 3JJ
**Tel:** 020 8660 3351
**Headteacher:** Mrs J Staunton
**Age range:** 3–11
**Fees:** Day £2,128–£6,405

## Maple House School
23 Parchmore Road, Thornton Heath, Surrey CR7 8LY
**Tel:** 020 8653 1827
**Headteacher:** Mrs Pauline Khoo
**Age range:** 5–10
**No. of pupils:** 97

## MARYMOUNT INTERNATIONAL SCHOOL LONDON
*For further details see p. 87*
George Road, Kingston upon Thames, Surrey KT2 7PE
**Tel:** +44 (0)20 8949 0571
**Email:** admissions@marymountlondon.com
**Website:** www.marymountlondon.com
**Headmistress:** Mrs Margaret Frazier
**Age range:** G11–18
**No. of pupils:** 250
**Fees:** Day £20,015–£22,860 WB £34,365–£37,210 FB £36,030–£38,875

## Oakwood Independent School
Godstone Road, Purley, Surrey CR8 2AN
**Tel:** 020 8668 8080
**Headmaster:** Mr Ciro Candia BA(Hons), PGCE
**Age range:** 3–11
**No. of pupils:** 176
**Fees:** Day £5,280–£7,644

## Old Palace of John Whitgift School
Old Palace Road, Croydon, Surrey CR0 1AX
**Tel:** 020 8686 7347
**Head:** Mrs. C Jewell
**Age range:** B3 months–4 years G3 months–19 years
**No. of pupils:** 740 VIth120
**Fees:** Day £10,086–£13,497

## Old Vicarage School
48 Richmond Hill, Richmond, Surrey TW10 6QX
**Tel:** 020 8940 0922
**Headmistress:** Mrs G D Linthwaite
**Age range:** G4–11
**No. of pupils:** 200
**Fees:** Day £4,380

## Park Hill School
8 Queens Road, Kingston upon Thames, Surrey KT2 7SH
**Tel:** 020 8546 5496
**Principal:** Mrs Marie Christie
**Age range:** 2–7
**No. of pupils:** 100
**Fees:** Day £4,320–£8,130

## Reedham Park School
71A Old Lodge Lane, Purley, Surrey CR8 4DN
**Tel:** 020 8660 6357
**Headteacher:** Mrs Katie Shah
**Age range:** 4–11
**No. of pupils:** 122
**Fees:** Day £3,540–£4,110

## Rokeby School
George Road, Kingston upon Thames, Surrey KT2 7PB
**Tel:** 020 8942 2247
**Head:** Mr J R Peck
**Age range:** B4–13
**No. of pupils:** 370
**Fees:** Day £3,974–£4,948

## Royal Botanic Gardens
School of Horticulture, Kew, Richmond, Surrey TW9 3AB
**Tel:** 020 8332 5545
**Principal:** Emma Fox BEd(Hons), DipHort(Kew)(Hons)
**Fees:** Day £0

## Royal Russell Junior School
Coombe Lane, Croydon, Surrey CR9 5BX
**Tel:** 020 8651 5884
**Junior School Headmaster:** Mr James C Thompson
**Age range:** 3–11
**No. of pupils:** 300
**Fees:** Day £3,660–£10,155

## Royal Russell School
Coombe Lane, Croydon, Surrey CR9 5BX
**Tel:** 020 8657 3669
**Headmaster:** Christopher Hutchinson
**Age range:** 11–18
**No. of pupils:** 590 VIth180
**Fees:** Day £15,285 FB £22,365–£30,240

## Seaton House School
67 Banstead Road South, Sutton, Surrey SM2 5LH
**Tel:** 020 8642 2332
**Headmistress:** Mrs Debbie Morrison Higher Diploma in Education (RSA)
**Age range:** B3–5 G3–11
**No. of pupils:** 164
**Fees:** Day £2,187–£8,955

## Shrewsbury House School
107 Ditton Road, Surbiton, Surrey KT6 6RL
**Tel:** 020 8399 3066
**Headmaster:** Mr K Doble BA, PDM, PGCE
**Age range:** B7–13
**No. of pupils:** 320
**Fees:** Day £13,680

## St David's School
23/25 Woodcote Valley Road, Purley, Surrey CR8 3AL
**Tel:** 020 8660 0723
**Headmistress:** Mrs Lindsay Nash BEd(Hons)
**Age range:** 3–11
**No. of pupils:** 167
**Fees:** Day £2,985–£5,940

## St James Senior Boys School
Church Road, Ashford,
Surrey TW15 3DZ
**Tel:** 01784 266930
**Headmaster:** Mr David Brazier
**Age range:** B11–18
**No. of pupils:** 403 VIth65
**Fees:** Day £18,120

## Staines Preparatory School
3 Gresham Road, Staines upon
Thames, Surrey TW18 2BT
**Tel:** 01784 450909
**Head of School:** Ms Samantha
Sawyer B.Ed (Hons), M.Ed, NPQH
**Age range:** 3–11
**No. of pupils:** 367
**Fees:** Day £9,510–£11,055

## Surbiton High School
13-15 Surbiton Crescent, Kingston
upon Thames, Surrey KT1 2JT
**Tel:** 020 8546 5245
**Principal:** Ann Haydon BSc(Hons)
**Age range:** G4–18
**No. of pupils:** 1210 VIth186
**Fees:** Day £6,390–£10,857

## Sutton High School GDST
55 Cheam Road, Sutton,
Surrey SM1 2AX
**Tel:** 020 8642 0594
**Headmistress:** Mrs Katharine
Crouch
**Age range:** G3–18
**No. of pupils:** 600 VIth60
**Fees:** Day £9,153–£15,450

## The Cedars School
Coombe Road, Lloyd Park,
Croydon, Surrey CR0 5RD
**Tel:** 020 8185 7770
**Headmaster:** Robert Teague Bsc
(Hons)
**Age range:** B11–18

## The Falcons Preparatory School for Boys
41 Few Foot Road, Richmond,
Surrey TW9 2SS
**Tel:** 0844 225 2211
**Headmaster:** Mr Gordon Milne
**Age range:** B7–13
**No. of pupils:** 100
**Fees:** Day £12,660

## The Royal Ballet School
White Lodge, Richmond,
Surrey TW10 5HR
**Tel:** 020 7836 8899
**Director:** Ms Gailene Stock AM
**Age range:** 11–19
**No. of pupils:** VIth80
**Fees:** Day £14,394–£18,946
FB £17,709–£25,588

## The Secretary College
123 South End, Croydon,
Surrey CR0 1BJ
**Tel:** 0208 688 4440
**Principal:** Mr J E K Safo

## The Study School
57 Thetford Road, New
Malden, Surrey KT3 5DP
**Tel:** 020 8942 0754
**Head of School:** Mrs Donna
Brackstone-Drake
**Age range:** 3–11
**No. of pupils:** 134
**Fees:** Day £4,860–£11,388

## TRINITY SCHOOL
*For further details see p. 89*
Shirley Park, Croydon,
Surrey CR9 7AT
**Tel:** 020 8656 9541
**Email:** admissions@trinity.
croydon.sch.uk
**Website:** www.trinity-school.org
**Head:** Alasdair Kennedy MA
(Cantab)
**Age range:** B10–18 G16–18
**No. of pupils:** 1007
**Fees:** Day £16,656

## Unicorn School
238 Kew Road, Richmond,
Surrey TW9 3JX
**Tel:** 020 8948 3926
**Headmaster:** Mr Kit Thompson
**Age range:** 3–11
**Fees:** Day £6,000–£11,010

## Westbury House
80 Westbury Road, New
Malden, Surrey KT3 5AS
**Tel:** 020 8942 5885
**Head of School:** Rosalyn Holiday
**Age range:** 3–11
**Fees:** Day £1,045–£2,507

## Whitgift School
Haling Park, South Croydon,
Surrey CR2 6YT
**Tel:** +44 (0)20 8633 9935
**Headmaster:** Mr Christopher
Ramsey
**Age range:** B10–18
**No. of pupils:** 1464
**Fees:** Day £17,340 WB
£27,924 FB £33,396

# Schools in the South-East

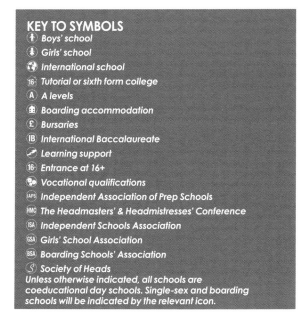

## KEY TO SYMBOLS

- 🧍 Boys' school
- 🧍 Girls' school
- 🌐 International school
- 16 Tutorial or sixth form college
- Ⓐ A levels
- ⚓ Boarding accommodation
- £ Bursaries
- IB International Baccalaureate
- ✎ Learning support
- 16 Entrance at 16+
- 👥 Vocational qualifications
- (IAPS) Independent Association of Prep Schools
- HMC The Headmasters' & Headmistresses' Conference
- (ISA) Independent Schools Association
- (GSA) Girls' School Association
- (BSA) Boarding Schools' Association
- 𝒮 Society of Heads

*Unless otherwise indicated, all schools are coeducational day schools. Single-sex and boarding schools will be indicated by the relevant icon.*

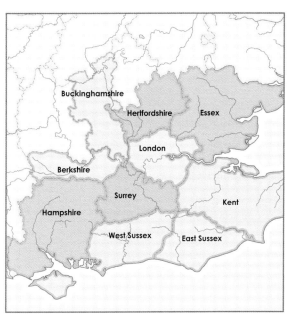

# Berkshire

### ABI College
Reading Campus, 80 London
Street, Reading, Berkshire RG1 4SJ
**Tel:** 0118 956 9111
**Head:** Alan McColm
16+

### Alder Bridge School
Bridge House, Mill Lane, Padworth,
Reading, Berkshire RG7 4JU
**Tel:** 0118 971 4471
**Age range:** 0–14 years
**No. of pupils:** 65
**Fees:** Day £3,354–£8,295

### Bradfield College
Bradfield, Berkshire RG7 6AU
**Tel:** 0118 964 4516
**Headmaster:** Dr Christopher
Stevens
**Age range:** 13–18
**No. of pupils:** 790
**Fees:** Day £29,052 FB £36,315

### Brigidine School Windsor
Queensmead, King's Road,
Windsor, Berkshire SL4 2AX
**Tel:** 01753 863779
**Headmistress:** Mrs Elizabeth
Robinson
**Age range:** B2–7 G3–18
**No. of pupils:** 300
**Fees:** Day £3,945–£11,865

### Caversham School
16 Peppard Road, Caversham,
Reading, Berkshire RG4 8JZ
**Tel:** 01189 478 684
**Head:** Mrs Jacqueline Lawson
**Age range:** 4–11
**No. of pupils:** 60
**Fees:** Day £6,750

### Chiltern College
16 Peppard Road, Caversham,
Reading, Berkshire RG4 8JZ
**Tel:** 0118 947 1847
**Head:** Christine Lawrence
16+

### Claires Court Junior Boys
Maidenhead Thicket,
Maidenhead, Berkshire SL6 3QE
**Tel:** 01628 327700
**Head:** J M E Spanswick
**Age range:** B4–11
**No. of pupils:** 248
**Fees:** Day £7,965–£13,860

### Claires Court Nursery, Girls and Sixth Form
1 College Avenue, Maidenhead,
Berkshire SL6 6AW
**Tel:** 01628 327700
**Head of School:** Mrs M Heywood
**Age range:** B16–18 G3–18
**No. of pupils:** 495 VIth111
**Fees:** Day £5,715–£14,580

### Claires Court Senior Boys
Ray Mill Road East, Maidenhead,
Berkshire SL6 8TE
**Tel:** 01628 327700
**Headmaster:** Mr J M Rayer BSc,
PGCE
**Age range:** B11–16
**No. of pupils:** 335 VIth112
**Fees:** Day £13,860–£14,580

### Crosfields School
Shinfield, Reading,
Berkshire RG2 9BL
**Tel:** 0118 987 1810
**Headmaster:** Mr J P Wansey
**Age range:** 3–13
**No. of pupils:** 510
**Fees:** Day £6,600–£10,710

### Dolphin School
Waltham Road, Hurst, Reading,
Berkshire RG10 0FR
**Tel:** 0118 934 1277
**Head:** Mr Tom Lewis
**Age range:** 3–13
**Fees:** Day £8,340–£11,190

### Eagle House School
Sandhurst, Berkshire GU47 8PH
**Tel:** 01344 772134
**Headmaster:** Mr A P N Barnard
BA(Hons), PGCE
**Age range:** 3–13
**No. of pupils:** 388
**Fees:** Day £11,235–
£17,580 FB £23,610

### Elstree School
Woolhampton, Reading,
Berkshire RG7 5TD
**Tel:** 0118 971 3302
**Headmaster:** Mr S Inglis
**Age range:** B3–13 G3–7
**No. of pupils:** 248
**Fees:** Day £17,775 FB £22,800

### Eton College
Windsor, Berkshire SL4 6DW
**Tel:** 01753 671249
**Head Master:** Simon Henderson MA
**Age range:** B13–18
**No. of pupils:** 1300 VIth520
**Fees:** FB £33,270

### Eton End PNEU School
35 Eton Road, Datchet,
Slough, Berkshire SL3 9AX
**Tel:** 01753 541075
**Headmistress:** Mrs V M Pilgerstorfer
BA(Hons), PGCE
**Age range:** B3–7 G3–11
**No. of pupils:** 245
**Fees:** Day £5,850–£6,900

### Heathfield School
London Road, Ascot,
Berkshire SL5 8BQ
**Tel:** 01344 898342
**Head of School:** Mrs Marina
Gardiner Legge
**Age range:** G11–18
**No. of pupils:** 200

### Hemdean House School
Hemdean Road, Caversham,
Reading, Berkshire RG4 7SD
**Tel:** 0118 947 2590
**Head Teacher:** Mrs H Chalmers BSc
**Age range:** B4–11 G4–11
**Fees:** Day £9,300

### Herries Preparatory School
Dean Lane, Cookham
Dean, Berkshire SL6 9BD
**Tel:** 01628 483350
**Headmistress:** Sophie Green
**Age range:** 3–11
**Fees:** Day £6,645–£8,985

### Highfield Preparatory School
2 West Road, Maidenhead,
Berkshire SL6 1PD
**Tel:** 01628 624918
**Headteacher:** Mrs Joanna Leach
**Age range:** B3–5 G3–11
**Fees:** Day £897–£10,110

### Holme Grange School
Heathlands Road, Wokingham,
Berkshire RG40 3AL
**Tel:** 0118 978 1566
**Headteacher:** Mrs Claire Robinson
**Age range:** 3–16 years
**No. of pupils:** 476
**Fees:** Day £9,885–£14,280

### Impact International College
81 London Street, Reading,
Berkshire RG1 4QA
**Tel:** 0118 956 0610
**Head:** Mr Alan Loveridge
16+

### Kids Inc Day Nursery – Crowthorne
59-61 Dukes Ride, Crowthorne,
Berkshire RG45 6NS
**Tel:** 01344 780670

### Lambrook School
Winkfield Row, Bracknell,
Berkshire RG42 6LU
**Tel:** 01344 882717
**Headmaster:** Mr Jonathan Perry
**Age range:** 3–13
**No. of pupils:** 440
**Fees:** Day £9,078–£15,180 WB
£16,803–£18,009 FB £17,433–£18,639

### Leighton Park School
Shinfield Road, Reading,
Berkshire RG2 7ED
**Tel:** +44 (0) 118 987 9600
**Head:** Nigel Williams BA(Bristol),
MA(London), PGCE
**Age range:** 11–18
**No. of pupils:** 485
**Fees:** Day £21,654 WB
£29,301 FB £34,044

### Long Close School
Upton Court Road, Upton,
Slough, Berkshire SL3 7LU
**Tel:** 01753 520095
**Headteacher:** Melissa McBride
**Age range:** 2–16
**No. of pupils:** 350

### Luckley House School
Luckley Road, Wokingham,
Berkshire RG40 3EU
**Tel:** 0118 978 4175
**Head:** Mrs Jane Tudor
**Age range:** G11–18
**No. of pupils:** 230
**Fees:** Day £15,975 WB
£25,908 FB £27,954

### Ludgrove
Wokingham, Berkshire RG40 3AB
**Tel:** 0118 978 9881
**Head of School:** Mr Simon Barber
**Age range:** B8–13
**No. of pupils:** 190

### Meadowbrook Montessori School
Malt Hill Road, Warfield,
Bracknell, Berkshire RG42 6JQ
**Tel:** 01344 890869
**Director of Education:** Mrs S Gunn
**Age range:** 3–11
**No. of pupils:** 78
**Fees:** Day £10,200

### Newbold School
Popeswood Road, Binfield,
Bracknell, Berkshire RG42 4AH
**Tel:** 01344 421088
**Headteacher:** Mrs P Eastwood
**Age range:** 3–11
**Fees:** Day £3,000–£4,000

**Our Lady's Preparatory School**
The Avenue, Crowthorne,
Wokingham, Berkshire RG45 6PB
**Tel:** 01344 773394
**Headmistress:** Mrs Helene Robinson
**Age range:** 3 months–11 years
**No. of pupils:** 100
**Fees:** Day £5,328–£10,464

**Padworth College**
Padworth, Reading,
Berkshire RG7 4NR
**Tel:** 0118 983 2644
**Principal:** Mr John Aguilar
**Age range:** 13–19
**No. of pupils:** 116 VIth50
**Fees:** Day £14,250 FB £28,392

**PANGBOURNE COLLEGE**
*For further details see p. 94*
Pangbourne, Reading,
Berkshire RG8 8LA
**Tel:** 0118 984 2101
**Email:** registrar@
pangbourne.com
**Website:**
www.pangbourne.com
**Headmaster:** Thomas J C
Garnier
**Age range:** 11–18
**No. of pupils:** 426 VIth133
**Fees:** Day £17,055–£24,036
FB £24,021–£33,996

**Papplewick School**
Windsor Road, Ascot,
Berkshire SL5 7LH
**Tel:** 01344 621488
**Head:** Mr T W Bunbury BA, PGCE
**Age range:** B6–13
**No. of pupils:** 195

**Queen Anne's School**
6 Henley Road, Caversham,
Reading, Berkshire RG4 6DX
**Tel:** 0118 918 7300
**Headmistress:** Mrs Julia Harrington
BA(Hons), PGCE, NPQH
**Age range:** G11–18
**No. of pupils:** 336 VIth100
**Fees:** Day £5,695 WB
£7,545–£7,975 FB £8,395

**Reading Blue Coat School**
Holme Park, Sonning Lane, Sonning,
Reading, Berkshire RG4 6SU
**Tel:** 0118 944 1005
**Headmaster:** Mr Jesse Elzinga
**Age range:** B11–18 G16–18
**No. of pupils:** 710 VIth230
**Fees:** Day £16,119

**Reddam House Berkshire**
Bearwood Road, Sindlesham,
Wokingham, Berkshire RG41 5BG
**Tel:** 0118 974 8300
**Principal:** Mrs Tammy Howard
**Age range:** 3 months–18 years
**No. of pupils:** 480
**Fees:** Day £9,885–£16,800 WB
£26,310–£30,330 FB £27,855–£31,875

**Redroofs School for the Performing Arts (Redroofs Theatre School)**
26 Bath Road, Maidenhead,
Berkshire SL6 4JT
**Tel:** 01628 674092
**Principal:** June Rose
**Age range:** 8–18
**No. of pupils:** 100
**Fees:** Day £4,000

**St Andrew's School**
Buckhold, Pangbourne,
Reading, Berkshire RG8 8QA
**Tel:** 0118 974 4276
**Headmaster:** Mr Jonathan Bartlett
BSc QTS
**Age range:** 3–13
**Fees:** Day £5,250–£17,490 WB £3,240

**St Bernard's Preparatory School**
Hawtrey Close, Slough,
Berkshire SL1 1TB
**Tel:** 01753 521821
**Head Teacher:** Mr N Cheesman
**Age range:** 2–11
**Fees:** Day £2,580–£3,120

**St Edward's School**
64 Tilehurst Road, Reading,
Berkshire RG30 2JH
**Tel:** 0118 957 4342
**Principal:** G W Mottram
**Age range:** B4–13
**No. of pupils:** 170
**Fees:** Day £6,660–£8,550

**St George's Ascot**
Wells Lane, Ascot, Berkshire SL5 7DZ
**Tel:** 01344 629920
**Headmistress:** Mrs Liz Hewer MA
(Hons) (Cantab) PGCE
**Age range:** G11–18
**No. of pupils:** 270 VIth70
**Fees:** Day £21,900 WB
£32,460–£33,570 FB £34,350

**St George's School Windsor Castle**
Windsor, Berkshire SL4 1QF
**Tel:** 01753 865553
**Head Master:** Mr C F McDade
**Age range:** 3–13
**Fees:** Day £8,493–£14,097
WB £18,723 FB £19,203

**St John's Beaumont Preparatory School**
Priest Hill, Old Windsor,
Berkshire SL4 2JN
**Tel:** 01784 432428
**Headmaster:** Mr G E F Delaney
BA(Hons), PGCE, MSc (Oxon)
**Age range:** B3–13
**No. of pupils:** 310
**Fees:** Day £7,140–£13,320
WB £17,520 FB £20,250

**St Joseph's College**
Upper Redlands Road,
Reading, Berkshire RG1 5JT
**Tel:** 0118 966 1000
**Headmaster:** Mr Andrew Colpus
**Age range:** 3–18
**No. of pupils:** VIth64
**Fees:** Day £6,300–£10,770

**St Mary's School Ascot**
St Mary's Road, Ascot,
Berkshire SL5 9JF
**Tel:** 01344 296614
**Headmistress:** Mrs Mary Breen
BSc, MSc
**Age range:** G11–18
**No. of pupils:** 390 VIth120
**Fees:** Day £23,400 FB £32,850

**St Piran's Preparatory School**
Gringer Hill, Maidenhead,
Berkshire SL6 7LZ
**Tel:** 01628 594302
**Headmaster:** Mr J A Carroll
BA(Hons), BPhilEd, PGCE, NPQH
**Age range:** 3–11
**Fees:** Day £9,900–£14,550

**Sunningdale School**
Dry Arch Road, Sunningdale,
Berkshire SL5 9PY
**Tel:** 01344 620159
**Headmaster:** T A C N Dawson MA,
PGCE
**Age range:** B7–13
**No. of pupils:** 90
**Fees:** Day £13,950 FB £17,985

**Teikyo School UK**
Framewood Road, Wexham,
Slough, Berkshire SL2 4QS
**Tel:** 01753 663711
**Headmaster:** A Watanabe BA
**Age range:** 16–18

**The Abbey School**
Kendrick Road, Reading,
Berkshire RG1 5DZ
**Tel:** 0118 987 2256
**Head:** Mrs Rachel S E Dent
**Age range:** G3–18
**No. of pupils:** 1100
**Fees:** Day £16,530

**The Marist Preparatory School**
King's Road, Sunninghill,
Ascot, Berkshire SL5 7PS
**Tel:** 01344 626137
**Headteacher:** J Finlayson
**Age range:** G2–11
**No. of pupils:** 225
**Fees:** Day £8,700–£9,360

**The Marist Schools**
King's Road, Sunninghill,
Ascot, Berkshire SL5 7PS
**Tel:** 01344 624291
**Head of Secondary School:** Mr K
McCloskey
**Age range:** G2–18
**No. of pupils:** 550 VIth60
**Fees:** Day £7,845–£10,695

**The Oratory Preparatory School**
Great Oaks, Goring Heath,
Reading, Berkshire RG8 7SF
**Tel:** 0118 984 4511
**Headmaster:** Mr J J Smith BA, PGCE
**Age range:** 3–13
**No. of pupils:** 400
**Fees:** Day £3,425–£11,475
WB £14,565 FB £15,825

**The Oratory School**
Woodcote, Reading,
Berkshire RG8 0PJ
**Tel:** 01491 683500
**Head Master:** Mr A J Wyles
BSc(Hons), MEd, PGCE, FRGS
**Age range:** B11–18
**No. of pupils:** 380 VIth120
**Fees:** Day £23,250 FB
£21,540–£31,950

**The Vine Christian School**
SORCF Christian Centre,
Basingstoke Road, Three Mile
Cross, Reading, Berkshire RG7 1AT
**Tel:** 0118 988 6464
**Head:** Mrs Joan Muirhead
**Age range:** 5–13
**No. of pupils:** 9

**Upton House School**
115 St Leonard's Road,
Windsor, Berkshire SL4 3DF
**Tel:** 01753 862610
**Headmistress:** Mrs Madeleine
Collins BA(Hons), PGCE(Oxford)
**Age range:** B2–7 G2–11
**No. of pupils:** 280

**Waverley School**
Waverley Way, Finchampstead,
Wokingham, Berkshire RG40 4YD
**Tel:** 0118 973 1121
**Principal:** Mrs Jane Sculpher
**Age range:** 3–11
**Fees:** Day £3,300–£7,362

**Wellington College**
Duke's Ride, Crowthorne,
Berkshire RG45 7PU
**Tel:** +44 (0)1344 444000
**Master:** Mr Julian Thomas
**Age range:** 13–18
**No. of pupils:** 1040
**Fees:** Day £27,930–
£32,085 FB £38,220

# Buckinghamshire

## Akeley Wood School
Akeley Wood, Buckingham,
Buckinghamshire MK18 5AE
**Tel:** 01280 814110
**Headmaster:** Dr Jerry Grundy BA,
PhD
**Age range:** 12 months–18 years
**No. of pupils:** 833 VIth119
**Fees:** Day £7,185–£10,575
£ 16+

## Ashfold School
Dorton House, Dorton, Aylesbury,
Buckinghamshire HP18 9NG
**Tel:** 01844 238237
**Headmaster:** Mr M O M Chitty BSc
**Age range:** 3–13
**No. of pupils:** 280 VIth28
**Fees:** Day £7,320–£12,900
WB £15,084
£

## Broughton Manor Preparatory School
Newport Road, Broughton, Milton
Keynes, Buckinghamshire MK10 9AA
**Tel:** 01908 665234
**Headmaster:** Mr Ross Urquhart
**Age range:** 2 months–11 years
**No. of pupils:** 250
**Fees:** Day £9,600
£

## Caldicott
Crown Lane, Farnham Royal,
Buckinghamshire SL2 3SL
**Tel:** 01753 649301
**Acting Head:** Ms Theroshene
Naidoo MEd
**Age range:** B7–13
**No. of pupils:** 275
**Fees:** Day £16,185–£18,057
FB £26,622
£

## Dair House School
Bishops Blake, Beaconsfield
Road, Farnham Royal,
Buckinghamshire SL2 3BY
**Tel:** 01753 643964
**Headmaster:** Mr Terry Wintle
BEd(Hons)
**Age range:** 3–11
**No. of pupils:** 125
**Fees:** Day £3,060–£4,100
£

**DAVENIES SCHOOL**
*For further details see p. 93*
Station Road, Beaconsfield,
Buckinghamshire HP9 1AA
**Tel:** 01494 685400
**Email:** office@davenies.co.uk
**Website:** www.davenies.co.uk
**Headmaster:** Mr Carl Rycroft
BEd (Hons)
**Age range:** B4–13
**No. of pupils:** 335
**Fees:** Day £11,985–£16,800

## Chesham Preparatory School
Two Dells Lane, Chesham,
Buckinghamshire HP5 3QF
**Tel:** 01494 782619
**Headmaster:** Mr Michael Davies
BA, PGCE
**Age range:** 3–13
**No. of pupils:** 392
**Fees:** Day £8,700–£12,300

## Childfirst Day Nursery Aylesbury
Green End, off Rickford's Hill,
Aylesbury, Buckinghamshire
HP20 2SA
**Tel:** 01296 392516
**Registrar:** Mrs Carole Angood
**Age range:** 2 months–7 years
**No. of pupils:** 80
**Fees:** Day £6,276

## Childfirst Pre School Aylesbury
35 Rickfords Hill, Aylesbury,
Buckinghamshire HP20 2RT
**Tel:** 01296 433224

## Crown House School
19 London Road, High Wycombe,
Buckinghamshire HP11 1BJ
**Tel:** 01494 529927
**Headmaster:** Ben Kenyon
**Age range:** 4–11
**No. of pupils:** 120
**Fees:** Day £5,985–£6,570

## Filgrave School
Filgrave Village, Newport
Pagnell, Milton Keynes,
Buckinghamshire MK16 9ET
**Tel:** 01234 711534
**Headteacher:** Mrs H Schofield
BA(Hons), MA, PGCE
**Age range:** 2–7
**No. of pupils:** 27
**Fees:** Day £5,160
£

## Gateway School
1 High Street, Great Missenden,
Buckinghamshire HP16 9AA
**Tel:** 01494 862407
**Headteacher:** Mrs Sue LaFarge
BA(Hons), PGCE
**Age range:** 2–11
**No. of pupils:** 355
**Fees:** Day £10,002

## Gayhurst School
Bull Lane, Gerrards Cross,
Buckinghamshire SL9 8RJ
**Tel:** 01753 882690
**Headmaster:** A J Sims MA(Cantab)
**Age range:** B3–13 G3–13
**Fees:** Day £9,882–£12,555
£

## Godstowe Preparatory School
Shrubbery Road, High Wycombe,
Buckinghamshire HP13 6PR
**Tel:** 01494 529273
**Headmaster:** Mr David Gainer
**Age range:** B3–7 G3–13
**No. of pupils:** 409
**Fees:** Day £8,505–£13,245
WB £19,455 FB £19,455
£

## Griffin House School
Little Kimble, Aylesbury,
Buckinghamshire HP17 0XP
**Tel:** 01844 346154
**Headmaster:** Mr Tim Walford
**Age range:** 3–11
**No. of pupils:** 100
**Fees:** Day £7,395–£7,695
£

## Heatherton House School
Copperkins Lane,
Chesham Bois, Amersham,
Buckinghamshire HP6 5QB
**Tel:** 01494 726433
**Headteacher:** Mrs Debbie
Isaachsen
**Age range:** B3–4 G3–11
**Fees:** Day £1,068–£12,330
£

## High March School
23 Ledborough Lane, Beaconsfield,
Buckinghamshire HP9 2PZ
**Tel:** 01494 675186
**Headmistress:** Mrs S J Clifford
**Age range:** G3–11
**No. of pupils:** 301
**Fees:** Day £5,475–£14,160
£

## Maltman's Green School
Maltman's Lane, Gerrards Cross,
Buckinghamshire SL9 8RR
**Tel:** 01753 883022
**Headmistress:** Mrs Joanna Pardon
MA, BSc(Hons), PGCE
**Age range:** G2–11
**Fees:** Day £10,200–£13,500
£

## Milton Keynes Preparatory School
Tattenhoe Lane, Milton Keynes,
Buckinghamshire MK3 7EG
**Tel:** 01908 642111
**Heads of School:** Mr C Bates & Mr
S Driver
**Age range:** 3 months–11 years
**No. of pupils:** 500
**Fees:** Day £12,712–£14,700
£

## Pipers Corner School
Pipers Lane, Great
Kingshill, High Wycombe,
Buckinghamshire HP15 6LP
**Tel:** 01494 718 255
**Headmistress:** Mrs H J Ness-Gifford
BA(Hons), PGCE
**Age range:** G4–18
**No. of pupils:** VIth72
**Fees:** Day £7,230–£14,010
WB £18,750–£222,845 FB
£18,990–£23,085
£ 16+

## Sefton Park School
School Lane, Stoke Poges,
Buckinghamshire SL2 4QA
**Tel:** 01753 662167
**Headteacher:** Mr Timothy Thorpe
**Age range:** 11–16
**No. of pupils:** 120

## St Mary's School
94 Packhorse Road, Gerrards
Cross, Buckinghamshire SL9 8JQ
**Tel:** 01753 883370
**Headmistress:** Mrs J A Ross
BA(Hons), NPQH
**Age range:** G3–18
**No. of pupils:** 350 VIth50
**Fees:** Day £5,390–£16,115
£ 16+

## St Teresa's Catholic School & Nursery
Aylesbury Road, Princes
Risborough, Buckinghamshire
HP27 0JW
**Tel:** 01844 345005
**Joint Heads:** Mrs Jane Draper & Mrs
Yasmin Roberts
**Age range:** 3–11
**No. of pupils:** 130
**Fees:** Day £8,985

## Stowe School
Buckingham, Buckinghamshire
MK18 5EH
**Tel:** 01280 818000
**Headmaster:** Dr Anthony
Wallersteiner
**Age range:** 13–18
**No. of pupils:** 769 VIth318
**Fees:** Day £22,500 FB £30,975
£ 16+

## Swanbourne House School
Swanbourne, Milton Keynes,
Buckinghamshire MK17 0HZ
**Tel:** 01296 720264
**Headmaster:** Mr Simon Hitchings
MA (Oxon)
**Age range:** 3–13
**No. of pupils:** 387
**Fees:** Day £1,227–£17,475 FB £22,275
£

### The Beacon School
Chesham Bois, Amersham,
Buckinghamshire HP6 5PF
**Tel:** 01494 433654
**Headmaster:** P Brewster BSc(Hons),
PGCE
**Age range:** B3–13
**No. of pupils:** 470
**Fees:** Day £4,695–£13,200

### The Grove Independent School
Redland Drive, Loughton, Milton
Keynes, Buckinghamshire MK5 8HD
**Tel:** 01908 690590
**Principal:** Mrs Deborah Berkin
**Age range:** 3 months–13 years
**No. of pupils:** 210

### The Webber Independent School
Soskin Drive, Stantonbury
Fields, Milton Keynes,
Buckinghamshire MK14 6DP
**Tel:** 01908 574740
**Principal:** Mrs Hilary Marsden
**Age range:** 3–18
**No. of pupils:** 300 VIth15
**Fees:** Day £3,894–£10,371

### Thornton College
Thornton, Milton Keynes,
Buckinghamshire MK17 0HJ
**Tel:** 01280 812610
**Headmistress:** Miss Agnes T Williams
**Age range:** B2–4+ G2–16
**No. of pupils:** 370
**Fees:** Day £6,300–£10,095 WB
£10,500–£13,305 FB £13,305–£16,545

### Thorpe House School
Oval Way, Gerrards Cross,
Buckinghamshire SL9 8QA
**Tel:** 01753 882474
**Headmaster:** Mr Terence Ayres
**Age range:** B3–16
**Fees:** Day £8,070–£15,570

### Walton Pre-Preparatory School & Nursery
The Old Rectory, Walton
Drive, Milton Keynes,
Buckinghamshire MK7 6BB
**Tel:** 01908 678403
**Headmistress:** Mrs M Ramsbotham
CertEd
**Age range:** 2 months–7 years
**No. of pupils:** 120
**Fees:** Day £8,316

### Wycombe Abbey
High Wycombe,
Buckinghamshire HP11 1PE
**Tel:** +44 (0)1494 897008
**Headmistress:** Mrs Rhiannon J
Wilkinson MA (Oxon) MEd
**Age range:** G11–18
**No. of pupils:** 611
**Fees:** Day £28,350 FB £37,800

# East Sussex

### Ashdown House School
Forest Row, East Sussex RH18 5JY
**Tel:** 01342 822574
**Headmaster:** Haydon Moore
**Age range:** 4–13
**No. of pupils:** 141
**Fees:** Day £2,800 FB £26,700

### Bartholomews Tutorial College
22-23 Prince Albert Street,
Brighton, East Sussex BN1 1HF
**Tel:** 01273 205965/205141
**Governor:** W A Duncombe BSc
**Age range:** 16+
**No. of pupils:** 40 VIth25
**Fees:** Day £23,000 WB
£28,000 FB £30,000

### Battle Abbey School
Battle, East Sussex TN33 0AD
**Tel:** 01424 772385
**Headmaster:** Mr R C Clark
BA(Hons), MA(Ed)
**Age range:** 2–18
**No. of pupils:** 286 VIth48
**Fees:** Day £6,630–£13,390 FB £23,190

### Bede's School
The Dicker, Upper Dicker,
Hailsham, East Sussex BN27 3QH
**Tel:** +44 (0)1323843252
**Head:** Dr Richard Maloney
**Age range:** 12.5–18+
**No. of pupils:** 800 VIth295
**Fees:** Day £15,450 FB £25,725

### Bellerbys College Brighton
1 Billinton Way, Brighton,
East Sussex BN1 4LF
**Tel:** +44 (0)1273 339333
**Principal:** Mr Simon Mower
**Age range:** 13–18

### Bricklehurst Manor Preparatory
Bardown Road, Stonegate,
Wadhurst, East Sussex TN5 7EL
**Tel:** 01580 200448
**Head Teacher:** Mrs K Elliott
**Age range:** 3–11
**No. of pupils:** 117
**Fees:** Day £980–£11,460

### Brighton & Hove High School GDST
Montpelier Road, Brighton,
East Sussex BN1 3AT
**Tel:** 01273 280280
**Head:** Mrs Lorna Duggleby
**Age range:** G3–18
**No. of pupils:** 680 VIth70
**Fees:** Day £5,028–£8,898

### Brighton & Hove Montessori School
67 Stanford Avenue, Brighton,
East Sussex BN1 6FB
**Tel:** 01273 702485
**Headteacher:** Mrs Daisy Cockburn
AMI, MontDip
**Age range:** 2–11
**Fees:** Day £1,400–£5,900

### Brighton College
Eastern Road, Brighton,
East Sussex BN2 0AL
**Tel:** 01273 704200
**Head Master:** Richard Cairns MA
**Age range:** 3–18
**No. of pupils:** 950
**Fees:** Day £9,720–£23,790
WB £32,220–£33,210 FB
£40,230–£42,420

### Brighton Steiner School
John Howard House, Roedean
Road, Brighton, East Sussex BN2 5RA
**Tel:** 01273 386300
**Chair of the College of Teachers:**
Carrie Rawle
**Age range:** 3–16
**Fees:** Day £6,540

### Buckswood School
Broomham Hall, Rye
Road, Guestling, Hastings,
East Sussex TN35 4LT
**Tel:** 01424 813 813
**Headmaster:** Mr Giles Sutton
**Age range:** 10–19
**No. of pupils:** 420

### Buckswood St George's
Westwood House, 7-9
Holmesdale Gardens, Hastings,
East Sussex TN34 1LY
**Tel:** 01424 813696
**College Director:** Ian Godfrey
**Age range:** B16–19 G16–20
**No. of pupils:** VIth50

### Charters Ancaster College
Woodsgate Place, Gunters Lane,
Bexhill-on-Sea, East Sussex TN39 4EB
**Tel:** 01424 216670
**Headmistress:** Mrs Miriam Black
**Age range:** 2–13
**No. of pupils:** 125
**Fees:** Day £5,325–£6,750

### Claremont Preparatory & Nursery School
Ebdens Hill, Baldslow, St Leonards-
on-Sea, East Sussex TN37 7PW
**Tel:** 01424 751555
**Headmistress:** Mrs Diane Durrant
**Age range:** 1–14
**Fees:** Day £5,000–£10,000

### Claremont Senior & Sixth Form School
Bodiam, Nr Robertsbridge,
East Sussex TN32 5UJ
**Tel:** 01580 830396
**Headmaster:** Mr. Giles Perrin

### Darvell School
Darvell Bruderhof, Robertsbridge,
East Sussex TN32 5DR
**Tel:** 01580 883300
**Headteacher:** Mr Arnold Meier
**Age range:** 4–16
**No. of pupils:** 121

### Deepdene School
195 New Church Road, Hove,
East Sussex BN3 4ED
**Tel:** 01273 418984
**Heads:** Mrs Nicola Gane & Miss
Elizabeth Brown
**Age range:** 6 months–11 years
**Fees:** Day £1,800–£6,870

### Dharma School
The White House, Ladies Mile
Road, Patcham, Brighton,
East Sussex BN1 8TB
**Tel:** 01273 502055
**Headmaster:** Kevin Fossey BEd
**Age range:** 3–11
**Fees:** Day £3,000

### Eastbourne College
Old Wish Road, Eastbourne,
East Sussex BN21 4JX
**Tel:** 01323 452323 (Admissions)
**Headmaster:** Mr T Lawson
MA(Oxon)
**Age range:** 13–18
**No. of pupils:** 610 VIth274
**Fees:** Day £22,260–£22,620
FB £33,930–£34,320

### European School of Animal Osteopathy
25 Old Steine, Brighton,
East Sussex BN1 1EL
**Tel:** 01273 673332
**Head:** Jean-Yves Girard
16

### Greenfields Independent Day & Boarding School
Priory Road, Forest Row,
East Sussex RH18 5JD
**Tel:** +44 (0)1342 822189
**Executive Head:** Mr. Jeff Smith
**Age range:** 2–19

### Hove College
48 Cromwell Road, Hove,
East Sussex BN3 3ER
**Tel:** 01273 772577
**Director:** Mr John Veale
16

### Lancing College Preparatory School at Hove
The Droveway, Hove,
East Sussex BN3 6LU
**Tel:** 01273 503452
**Headmistress:** Mrs Kirsty Keep BEd
**Age range:** 3–11
**No. of pupils:** 181
**Fees:** Day £3,765–£15,195

### Lewes New School
Talbot Terrace, Lewes,
East Sussex BN7 1RD
**Tel:** 01273 477074
**Head of School:** Linda Morris
**Age range:** 3–11
**No. of pupils:** 78
**Fees:** Day £7,374

### Lewes Old Grammar School
High Street, Lewes, East
Sussex BN7 1XS
**Tel:** 01273 472634
**Headmaster:** Mr Robert Blewitt
**Age range:** 3–18
**No. of pupils:** 463 VIth50
**Fees:** Day £5,550–£10,815

### Mayfield School
The Old Palace, Mayfield,
East Sussex TN20 6PH
**Tel:** +44 (0)1435 874600
**Head:** Ms Antonia Beary MA, Mphil (Cantab), PGCE
**Age range:** G11–18
**No. of pupils:** 365 VIth100
**Fees:** Day £19,650 FB £31,800

### Michael Hall School
Kidbrooke Park, Priory Road,
Forest Row, East Sussex RH18 5BG
**Tel:** 01342 822275
**Age range:** 3–19
**Fees:** Day £8,858–£12,180
FB £6,876–£7,876

### Moira House Girls School
Upper Carlisle Road, Eastbourne,
East Sussex BN20 7TE
**Tel:** 01323 644144
**Headmaster:** Mr James Sheridan MA, BSc
**Age range:** G0–18
**No. of pupils:** 289

### ROEDEAN SCHOOL
**For further details see p. 97**
Roedean Way, Brighton,
East Sussex BN2 5RQ
**Tel:** 01273 667500
**Email:** info@roedean.co.uk
**Website:** www.roedean.co.uk
**Headmaster:** Mr. Oliver Bond
BA(Essex), PGCE, NPQH
**Age range:** G11–18
**No. of pupils:** 568 VIth171
**Fees:** Day £15,960–£20,865
WB £28,230–£31,470 FB
£30,930–£37,440

### Sacred Heart School
Mayfield Lane, Durgates,
Wadhurst, East Sussex TN5 6DQ
**Tel:** 01892 783414
**Headteacher:** Mrs H Blake BA(Hons), PGCE
**Age range:** 2–11
**No. of pupils:** 121
**Fees:** Day £1,845–£7,956

### Skippers Hill Manor Prep School
Five Ashes, Mayfield, East
Sussex TN20 6HR
**Tel:** 01825 830234
**Headmaster:** Mr M Hammond MA, BA, PGCE
**Age range:** 2–13
**No. of pupils:** 174
**Fees:** Day £7,920–£12,660

### St Andrew's Prep
Meads, Eastbourne, East
Sussex BN20 7RP
**Tel:** 01323 733203
**Headmaster:** Gareth Jones BA(Hons), PGCE
**Age range:** 9 months–13 years
**Fees:** Day £9,735–£16,935
FB £21,435–£24,255

### St Bede's Preparatory School
Duke's Drive, Eastbourne,
East Sussex BN20 7XL
**Tel:** 01323 734222
**Head:** Mr Nicholas Bevington
**Age range:** 3 months–13 years
**No. of pupils:** 395

### St Christopher's School
33 New Church Road, Hove,
East Sussex BN3 4AD
**Tel:** 01273 735404
**Headmaster:** Mr Julian Withers
**Age range:** 4–13
**Fees:** Day £6,570–£8,688

### The Academy of Creative Training
8-10 Rock Place, Brighton,
East Sussex BN2 1PF
**Tel:** 01273 818266
16

### The Drive Prep School
101 The Drive, Hove,
East Sussex BN3 3JE
**Tel:** 01273 738444
**Head Teacher:** Mrs S Parkinson CertEd, CertPerfArts
**Age range:** 7–16
**Fees:** Day £3,885–£7,500

### Torah Academy
31 New Church Road, Hove,
East Sussex BN3 4AD
**Tel:** 01273 328675
**Principal:** P Efune
**Age range:** 4–11

### Vinehall School
Robertsbridge, East Sussex TN32 5JL
**Tel:** 01580 880413
**Headmaster:** Joff Powis
**Age range:** 2–13
**No. of pupils:** 260
**Fees:** Day £8,913–£16,620
FB £19,545–£21,675

### Windlesham School
190 Dyke Road, Brighton,
East Sussex BN1 5AA
**Tel:** 01273 553645
**Headmaster:** Mr John Ingrassia
**Age range:** 3–11
**No. of pupils:** 195
**Fees:** Day £5,835–£8,685

### Windmill Hill Tennis and Golf Academy
Windmill Hill, Hailsham,
East Sussex BN27 4RZ
**Tel:** 08700 339 997
**Managing Director:** Steven P Jones
**Fees:** Day £0
16

# Essex

### Alleyn Court Preparatory School
Wakering Road, Southend-on-Sea, Essex SS3 0PW
**Tel:** 01702 582553
**Headmaster:** Mr Gareth Davies BA(Hons), PGCE
**Age range:** 2–11
**Fees:** Day £2,607–£10,881

### Bliss College
211 Olympic House, 28-42 Clements Road, Ilford, Essex IG1 1BA
**Tel:** 020 8553 7975
**Head:** Mrs Shani Varghese
16

### Brentwood Preparatory School
Middleton Hall Lane,
Brentwood, Essex CM15 8EQ
**Tel:** 01277 243333
**Headmaster:** Mr Jason Whiskerd
**Age range:** 3–11
**No. of pupils:** 415
**Fees:** Day £6,957–£13,914

### Brentwood School
Middleton Hall Lane,
Brentwood, Essex CM15 8EE
**Tel:** 01277 243243
**Headmaster:** Mr Ian Davies
**Age range:** 3–18
**No. of pupils:** 1529
**Fees:** Day £18,216 FB £35,700

## Colchester High School
Wellesley Road, Colchester,
Essex CO3 3HD
**Tel:** 01206 573389
**Principal:** David Young BA(Hons),
PGCE
**Age range:** 2–16
**No. of pupils:** 486
**Fees:** Day £3,300–£10,000
(£) ✏

## Coopersale Hall School
Flux's Lane, off Stewards Green
Road, Epping, Essex CM16 7PE
**Tel:** 01992 577133
**Headmistress:** Miss Kaye Lovejoy
**Age range:** 2–11
**No. of pupils:** 275
**Fees:** Day £3,645–£7,275

## Dame Bradbury's School
Ashdon Road, Saffron
Walden, Essex CB10 2AL
**Tel:** 01799 522348
**Headmistress:** Ms Tracy Handford
**Age range:** 3–11
**No. of pupils:** 254
**Fees:** Day £2,000–£10,950
(£) ✏

## East 15 Acting School
Hatfields, Rectory Lane,
Loughton, Essex IG10 3RY
**Tel:** 020 8508 5983
**Director:** John Baraldi
**Fees:** Day £0
16+

## Elm Green Preparatory School
Parsonage Lane, Little Baddow,
Chelmsford, Essex CM3 4SU
**Tel:** 01245 225230
**Principal:** Ms Ann Milner
**Age range:** 4–11
**No. of pupils:** 220
**Fees:** Day £7,449
✏

## Empire College London
Forest House, 16-20 Clements
Road, Ilford, Essex IG1 1BA
**Tel:** 020 8553 2683
**Head:** Ms Aaiesha Tak
16+

## Felsted Preparatory School
Felsted, Great Dunmow,
Essex CM6 3JL
**Tel:** 01371 822610
**Headmistress:** Mrs Jenny Burrett
BA(Dunelm), MEd(Cantab), PGCE
**Age range:** 4–13
**No. of pupils:** 460
**Fees:** Day £6,390–£13,965 FB £17,850
(♞)(£) ✏

## Felsted School
Felsted, Great Dunmow,
Essex CM6 3LL
**Tel:** +44 (0)1371 822608
**Headmaster:** Mr Chris Townsend
**Age range:** 13–18
**No. of pupils:** 522 VIth426
**Fees:** Day £22,485 WB
£32,235 FB £34,275
(🏠)(♞)(£) (IB) ✏ 16+

## Gosfield School
Cut Hedge Park, Halstead Road,
Gosfield, Halstead, Essex CO9 1PF
**Tel:** 01787 474040
**Headteacher:** Mr Guy Martyn
**Age range:** 4–18
**Fees:** Day £4,740–£13,695 WB
£15,465–£17,310 FB £17,985–£23,130
(🏠)(♞)(£) ✏ 16+

## Great Warley School
Warley Street, Great Warley,
Brentwood, Essex CM13 3LA
**Tel:** 01277 233288
**Head:** Mrs B Harding
**Age range:** 3–11
**Fees:** Day £2,250–£3,500

## Heathcote School
Eves Corner, Danbury,
Chelmsford, Essex CM3 4QB
**Tel:** 01245 223131
**Head Teacher:** Miss H Petersen
**Age range:** 2–11
**Fees:** Day £4,830–£7,245
(£) ✏

## Herington House School
1 Mount Avenue, Hutton,
Brentwood, Essex CM13 2NS
**Tel:** 01277 211595
**Principal:** Mr R. Dudley-Cooke
**Age range:** 3–11
**No. of pupils:** 130
**Fees:** Day £1,955–£3,865
(£) ✏

## Holmwood House Preparatory School
Chitts Hill, Lexden, Colchester,
Essex CO3 9ST
**Tel:** 01206 574305
**Headmaster:** Alexander Mitchell
**Age range:** 4–13
**No. of pupils:** 302
**Fees:** Day £9,450–£16,695
WB £19,968–£21,183
(♞) ✏

## Hutton Manor School
428 Rayleigh Road, Hutton,
Brentwood, Essex CM13 1SD
**Tel:** 01277 245585
**Head:** Mr P Pryke
**Age range:** 3–11
**Fees:** Day £2,975–£3,995

## Kids Inc Day Nursery – Beehive Lane Ilford
229-231 Beehive Lane,
Ilford, Essex IG4 5EB
**Tel:** 020 8550 7400

## Kids Inc Day Nursery – Loughton
29 Old Station Road,
Loughton, Essex IG10 4PE
**Tel:** 020 8502 4488

## Kids Inc Day Nursery – York Road Ilford
81-85 York Road, Ilford,
Essex IG1 3AF
**Tel:** 020 8478 6510

## Littlegarth School
Horkesley Park, Nayland,
Colchester, Essex CO6 4JR
**Tel:** 01206 262332
**Headmaster:** Mr Peter H Jones
**Age range:** 2–11 years
**No. of pupils:** 318
**Fees:** Day £2,700–£3,140
(£) ✏

## London Academy of Management Sciences
9th Floor Wentworth House,
350 Eastern Avenue,
Ilford, Essex IG2 6NN
**Tel:** 020 8554 9169
**Head:** Mr Asif Siddiqui
16+

## London College of Business
6A Monteagle Court, Wakering
Road, Barking, Essex IG11 8PD
**Tel:** 020 8591 2222
**Head:** Mr Zenon Adamek
16+

## London College of Business & Finance
8th Floor, Crown House, Cambridge
Road, Barking, Essex IG11 8NW
**Tel:** 020 8507 8883
**Head:** Mr Sandeep Jethwa
16+

## Maldon Court Preparatory School
Silver Street, Maldon,
Essex CM9 4QE
**Tel:** 01621 853529
**Headteacher:** Mrs L Guest
**Age range:** 3–11
**Fees:** Day £7,305
✏

## New Hall School
The Avenue, Boreham,
Chelmsford, Essex CM3 3HS
**Tel:** 01245 467588
**Principal:** Mrs Katherine Jeffrey MA,
BA, PGCE, MA(Ed Mg), NPQH
**Age range:** Coed 3-11,
Single 11-16, Coed 16–18
**No. of pupils:** 1180 VIth217
**Fees:** Day £9,432–£19,440 WB
£19,038–£27,813 FB £21,033–£29,847
(🏠)(♞)(£) ✏ 16+

## Oxford House School
2-4 Lexden Road, Colchester,
Essex CO3 3NE
**Tel:** 01206 576686
**Head Teacher:** Mrs Sarah Leyshon
**Age range:** 2–11
**No. of pupils:** 158

## Saint Nicholas School
Hillingdon House, Hobbs Cross
Road, Harlow, Essex CM17 0NJ
**Tel:** 01279 429910
**Headmaster:** Mr D Bown
**Age range:** 4–16
**No. of pupils:** 400
**Fees:** Day £9,660–£12,270
(£)

## Saint Pierre School
16 Leigh Road, Leigh-on-Sea,
Southend-on-Sea, Essex SS9 1LE
**Tel:** 01702 474164
**Headmaster:** Mr Chris Perkins
**Age range:** 2–11+
**Fees:** Day £2,062–£6,186
(£)

## St Anne's Preparatory School
New London Road, Chelmsford,
Essex CM2 0AW
**Tel:** 01245 353488
**Head:** Mrs S Robson
**Age range:** 3–11
**No. of pupils:** 160
**Fees:** Day £6,300–£6,600

## St Cedd's School
178a New London Road,
Chelmsford, Essex CM2 0AR
**Tel:** 01245 392810
**Head:** Dr Pamela Edmonds
**Age range:** 3–11
**No. of pupils:** 400
**Fees:** Day £8,550–£10,110
✏

## St John's School
Stock Road, Billericay,
Essex CM12 0AR
**Tel:** 01277 623070
**Head Teacher:** Mrs F Armour
BEd(Hons)
**Age range:** 3–16
**No. of pupils:** 392
**Fees:** Day £4,470–£10,650
✏

## St Margaret's Preparatory School
Gosfield Hall Park, Gosfield,
Halstead, Essex CO9 1SE
**Tel:** 01787 472134
**Headmaster:** Mr. Callum Douglas
**Age range:** 2–11
**Fees:** Day £9,315–£11,280
(£) ✏

## St Mary's School
Lexden Road, Colchester,
Essex CO3 3RB
**Tel:** 01206 572544  Admissions:
01206 216420
**Principal:** Mrs H K Vipond MEd,
BSc(Hons), NPQH
**Age range:** B3–4 G3–16
**No. of pupils:** 430
**Fees:** Day £7,464–£11,340
(♞)(£) ✏

## St Michael's Church Of England Preparatory School
198 Hadleigh Road, Leigh-on-Sea,
Southend-on-Sea, Essex SS9 2LP
**Tel:** 01702 478719
**Head:** Steve Tompkins BSc(Hons),
PGCE, MA, NPQH
**Age range:** 3–11
**No. of pupils:** 271
**Fees:** Day £3,510–£6,990
(£) ✏

## St Philomena's Catholic School
Hadleigh Road, Frinton-on-Sea, Essex CO13 9HQ
**Tel:** 01255 674492
**Headmistress:** Mrs B McKeown DipEd
**Age range:** 4–11
**Fees:** Day £6,000–£7,170
£ ⬦

## Thorpe Hall School
Wakering Road, Southend-on-Sea, Essex SS1 3RD
**Tel:** 01702 582340
**Headmaster:** Mr Andrew Hampton
**Age range:** 2–16 years
**No. of pupils:** 359
**Fees:** Day £7,695–£10,620
£ ⬦

## Trinity School
Brizes Park, Ongar Road, Kelvedon Hatch, Brentwood, Essex CM15 0DG
**Tel:** 01277 374123
**Headmaster:** Reverend M S B Reid BD
**Age range:** 4–18

## Ursuline Preparatory School
Old Great Ropers, Great Ropers Lane, Warley, Brentwood, Essex CM13 3HR
**Tel:** 01277 227152
**Headmistress:** Mrs Pauline Wilson MSc
**Age range:** 3–11
**Fees:** Day £1,835–£3,425
⬦

## Widford Lodge School
Widford Road, Chelmsford, Essex CM2 9AN
**Tel:** 01245 352581
**Headmaster:** Mr Simon Trowell
**Age range:** 2–11
**Fees:** Day £5,400–£7,050
⬦

# Hampshire

## Alton School
Anstey Lane, Alton, Hampshire GU34 2NG
**Tel:** 01420 82070
**Head:** Graham Maher
**No. of pupils:** 502 VIth53
£ 16

## Ballard School
Fernhill Lane, New Milton, Hampshire BH25 5SU
**Tel:** 01425 626900
**Headmaster:** Mr Alastair Reid
**Age range:** 2–16 years
**No. of pupils:** 500
**Fees:** Day £2,370–£4,265
£ ⬦

## Bedales Prep School, Dunhurst
Petersfield, Hampshire GU32 2DP
**Tel:** 01730 300200
**Head of School:** Colin Baty
**Age range:** 8–13
**No. of pupils:** 196
**Fees:** Day £5,500–£6,100
FB £7,223–£8,106
⬔ £ ⬦

## Bedales School
Church Road, Steep, Petersfield, Hampshire GU32 2DG
**Tel:** 01730 711733
**Head:** Keith Budge MA
**Age range:** 13–18
**No. of pupils:** 457
**Fees:** Day £9,272 FB £11,799
⬗ ⬔ £ ⬦ 16

## Boundary Oak School
Roche Court, Fareham, Hampshire PO17 5BL
**Tel:** 01329 280955/820373
**Head:** Mrs Hazel Kellett
**Age range:** 2–13
**No. of pupils:** 120
**Fees:** Day £7,500–£12,510 WB £5,370 FB £7,095–£19,605
⬔ £ ⬦

## Brockwood Park & Inwoods School
Brockwood Park, Bramdean, Hampshire SO24 0LQ
**Tel:** +44 (0)1962 771744
**Co-Principals:** Mr Antonio Autor & Dr Gopal Krishnamurthy
**Age range:** 4–19
**No. of pupils:** 112 VIth39
**Fees:** Day £5,630–£6,400
FB £21,400–£21,400
⬗ ⬔ £ ⬦ 16

## Brookham School
Highfield Lane, Liphook, Hampshire GU30 7LQ
**Tel:** 01428 722005
**Headteacher:** Mrs Sophie Baber
**Age range:** 3–8
**No. of pupils:** 162
**Fees:** Day £10,800–£14,400
⬦

## Churcher's College
Petersfield, Hampshire GU31 4AS
**Tel:** 01730 263033
**Headmaster:** Mr Simon Williams MA, BSc
**Age range:** 3–18 years
**Fees:** Day £9,675–£14,220
£ ⬦ 16

## Clay Hill School
Clay Hill, Lyndhurst, Hampshire SO43 7DE
**Tel:** 023 8028 3633
**Head of School:** Mrs. Helen Sharpe
**Age range:** 5–19

## Daneshill School
Stratfield Turgis, Basingstoke, Hampshire RG27 0AR
**Tel:** 01256 882707
**Headmaster:** S V Spencer CertEd, DipPhysEd
**Age range:** 3–13
**Fees:** Day £3,900–£9,150
⬦

## Ditcham Park School
Ditcham Park, Petersfield, Hampshire GU31 5RN
**Tel:** 01730 825659
**Headmaster:** Mr G Spawforth MA,MEd
**Age range:** 4–16
**No. of pupils:** 371
**Fees:** Day £8,262–£13,851
£ ⬦

## Durlston Court
Becton Lane, Barton-on-Sea, New Milton, Hampshire BH25 7AQ
**Tel:** 01425 610010
**Head of School:** Mr Richard May
**Age range:** 2–13
**No. of pupils:** 296
**Fees:** Day £3,540–£15,390
£ ⬦

## Farleigh School
Red Rice, Andover, Hampshire SP11 7PW
**Tel:** 01264 710766
**Headmaster:** Father Simon Everson
**Age range:** 3–13
**Fees:** Day £3,870–£14,085
FB £16,515–£18,345
⬔ £ ⬦

## Farnborough Hill
Farnborough Road, Farnborough, Hampshire GU14 8AT
**Tel:** 01252 545197
**Headmistress:** Mrs A Neil BA, MEd, PGCE
**Age range:** G11–18
**No. of pupils:** 550 VIth90
**Fees:** Day £14,241
⬕ £ ⬦ 16

## Forres Sandle Manor
Fordingbridge, Hampshire SP6 1NS
**Tel:** 01425 653181
**Headmaster:** Mr M N Hartley BSc(Hons)
**Age range:** 3–13
**No. of pupils:** 264
**Fees:** Day £3,150–£14,205
WB £19,380 FB £19,380
⬔ £ ⬦

## Glenhurst School
16 Beechworth Road, Havant, Hampshire PO9 1AX
**Tel:** 023 9248 4054
**Principal:** Mrs E M Haines
**Age range:** 3 months–8 years
**Fees:** Day £4,500
⬦

## Hampshire Collegiate School
Embley Park, Romsey, Hampshire SO51 6ZE
**Tel:** 01794 512206
**Principal:** Mrs Emma-Kate Henry
**Age range:** 2–18
**No. of pupils:** 683
⬗ ⬔ £ ⬦ 16

## Highfield School
Liphook, Hampshire GU30 7LQ
**Tel:** 01428 728000
**Headmaster:** Mr Philip Evitt MA
**Age range:** 8–13
**No. of pupils:** 292
**Fees:** Day £18,225–£20,850
FB £23,025–£25,275
⬔ £ ⬦

## King Edward VI School
Wilton Road, Southampton, Hampshire SO15 5UQ
**Tel:** 023 8070 4561
**Head Master:** Mr A J Thould MA(Oxon)
**Age range:** 11–18
**No. of pupils:** 970
**Fees:** Day £15,510
£ ⬦ 16

## Kingscourt School
182 Five Heads Road, Catherington, Hampshire PO8 9NJ
**Tel:** 023 9259 3251
**Head of School:** Mr Jamie Lewis
**Age range:** 3–11
**No. of pupils:** 210
**Fees:** Day £2,856

## Lord Wandsworth College
Long Sutton, Hook,
Hampshire RG29 1TB
**Tel:** 01256 862201
**Head of School:** Mr Adam Williams
**Age range:** 11–18 years
**No. of pupils:** 600
**Fees:** Day £19,650–£22,575 WB
£27,225–£30,600 FB £28,140–£32,100

## Mayville High School
35/37 St Simon's Road, Southsea,
Portsmouth, Hampshire PO5 2PE
**Tel:** 023 9273 4847
**Headteacher:** Mrs L Owens B.Ed
**Age range:** 6 months–16 years
**No. of pupils:** 479
**Fees:** Day £5,481–£8,040

## Meoncross School
Burnt House Lane, Stubbington,
Fareham, Hampshire PO14 2EF
**Tel:** 01329 662182
**Headmistress:** Mrs Sarah Ebery BSc
(Hons), MEd
**Age range:** 2–18
**No. of pupils:** 405
**Fees:** Day £7,365–£10,485

## Moyles Court School
Moyles Court, Ringwood,
Hampshire BH24 3NF
**Tel:** 01425 472856
**Headmaster:** Mr Dean
**Age range:** 3–16
**Fees:** Day £3,285–£4,650
FB £6,690–£7,740

## New Forest Small School
1 Southampton Road, Lyndhurst,
Hampshire SO43 7BU
**Tel:** 02380 284 415
**Headteacher:** Mr Nicholas Alp
**Age range:** 3–16

## Portsmouth High School GDST
Kent Road, Southsea, Portsmouth,
Hampshire PO5 3EQ
**Tel:** 023 9282 6714
**Headmistress:** Mrs Jane Prescott
BSc NPQH
**Age range:** G3–18
**No. of pupils:** 500
**Fees:** Day £2,722–£4,550

## Prince's Mead School
Worthy Park House, Kings Worthy,
Winchester, Hampshire SO21 1AN
**Tel:** 01962 888000
**Headmistress:** Miss Penelope Kirk
**Age range:** 4–11
**No. of pupils:** 270
**Fees:** Day £9,600–£14,640

## Ringwood Waldorf School
Folly Farm Lane, Ashley,
Ringwood, Hampshire BH24 2NN
**Tel:** 01425 472664
**Age range:** 3–18
**No. of pupils:** 235
**Fees:** Day £3,622–£7,825

## Rookwood School
Weyhill Road, Andover,
Hampshire SP10 3AL
**Tel:** 01264 325900
**Headmistress:** Mrs L Whetstone MA
**Age range:** 3–16
**Fees:** Day £7,770–£12,780
FB £19,545–£22,875

## Salesian College
Reading Road, Farnborough,
Hampshire GU14 6PA
**Tel:** 01252 893000
**Headmaster:** Mr P A Wilson
BA(Hons), MA, CertEd
**Age range:** B11–18 G16–18
**No. of pupils:** 650 VIth140
**Fees:** Day £9,000

## Sherborne House School
Lakewood Road, Chandlers Ford,
Eastleigh, Hampshire SO53 1EU
**Tel:** 023 8025 2440
**Head Teacher:** Mrs Heather
Hopson-Hill
**Age range:** 3–11
**No. of pupils:** 293
**Fees:** Day £1,044–£8,730

## Sherfield School
Sherfield-on-Loddon, Hook,
Hampshire RG27 0HU
**Tel:** +44 (0)1256 884 800
**Headmaster:** Mr Dick Jaine
**Age range:** 3 months–18 years
**No. of pupils:** 445 VIth16
**Fees:** Day £7,350–£13,890 FB £20,946

## St John's College
Grove Road South, Southsea,
Portsmouth, Hampshire PO5 3QW
**Tel:** 023 9281 5118
**Headmaster:** Mr Timothy Bayley BSc
(Hons), MA, PGCE
**Age range:** 2–18
**No. of pupils:** 560 VIth86
**Fees:** Day £8,910–£11,685
FB £25,200–£27,090

## ST NEOT'S SCHOOL
*For further details see p. 98*
St Neot's Road, Eversley,
Hampshire RG27 0PN
**Tel:** 0118 9739650
**Email:** admissions@
stneotsprep.co.uk
**Website:** www.stneotsprep.co.uk
**Head of School:** Mrs Deborah
Henderson
**Age range:** 2–13 years
**No. of pupils:** 327
**Fees:** Day £4,680–£14,994

## St Nicholas' School
Redfields House, Redfields
Lane, Church Crookham,
Fleet, Hampshire GU52 0RF
**Tel:** 01252 850121
**Headmistress:** Mrs A V Whatmough
BA, CertEd
**Age range:** B3–7 G3–16
**No. of pupils:** 370

## St Swithun's Junior School
Alresford Road, Winchester,
Hampshire SO21 1HA
**Tel:** 01962 835750
**Headmistress:** Mrs R Lyons-Smith
BSc, PGCE, MBA
**Age range:** B3–7 G3–11
**No. of pupils:** 191
**Fees:** Day £1,738–£4,478

## ST SWITHUN'S SCHOOL
*For further details see p. 99*
Alresford Road, Winchester,
Hampshire SO21 1HA
**Tel:** 01962 835700
**Email:** office@stswithuns.com
**Website:** www.stswithuns.com
**Head of School:** Jane Gandee
MA(Cantab)
**Age range:** G11–18
**No. of pupils:** 520

## St Winifred's School
17-19 Winn Road, Southampton,
Hampshire SO17 1EJ
**Tel:** 023 8055 7352
**Head Teacher:** Mr M Brogan
BEd,CertSpNeeds
**Age range:** 3–11
**Fees:** Day £6,330

## St. Mary's Independent School
57 Midanbury Lane, Bitterne Park,
Southampton, Hampshire SO18 4DJ
**Tel:** 023 8067 1267
**Head of School:** Mrs. Owen
**Age range:** 3–16
**No. of pupils:** 470
**Fees:** Day £1,750–£2,350

## Stockton House School
Stockton Avenue, Fleet,
Hampshire GU51 4NS
**Tel:** 01252 616323
**Early Years Manager:** Mrs Jenny
Bounds BA EYPS
**Age range:** 2–5
**Fees:** Day £25.50–£70

## The Gregg School
Townhill Park House, Cutbush Lane,
Southampton, Hampshire SO18 2GF
**Tel:** 023 8047 2133
**Headteacher:** Mrs S Sellers PGDip,
MSc, BSc(Hons), NPQH, PGCE
**Age range:** 11–16
**No. of pupils:** 300
**Fees:** Day £11,970

## The Grey House School
Mount Pleasant, Hartley Wintney,
Hampshire RG27 8PW
**Tel:** 01252 842353
**Head:** Mrs C E Allen BEd(Cantab)
**Age range:** 4–11+
**Fees:** Day £7,365–£8,994

## The King's School
Lakesmere House, Allington Lane,
Fair Oak, Eastleigh, Southampton,
Hampshire SO50 7DB
**Tel:** 023 8060 0986
**Head of School:** Mrs H Bowden BA
(Hons), PGCE
**Age range:** 3–16
**No. of pupils:** 256
**Fees:** Day £3,900–£6,840

## The Pilgrims' School
3 The Close, Winchester,
Hampshire SO23 9LT
**Tel:** 01962 854189
**Headmaster:** Mr Tom Burden
**Age range:** B4–13
**No. of pupils:** 250
**Fees:** Day £18,150–£18,690
FB £23,580

## The Portsmouth Grammar School
High Street, Portsmouth,
Hampshire PO1 2LN
**Tel:** +44 (0)23 9236 0036
**Headmaster:** Mr J E Priory MA
**Age range:** 2–18
**No. of pupils:** 1556 VIth336
**Fees:** Day £9,510–£14,817

## The Stroud School
Highwood House, Highwood Lane,
Romsey, Hampshire SO51 9ZH
**Tel:** 01794 513231
**Headmaster:** Mr Joel Worrall
**Age range:** 3–13

## Twyford School
Twyford, Winchester,
Hampshire SO21 1NW
**Tel:** 01962 712269
**Headmaster:** Dr S J Bailey BEd,
PhD, FRSA
**Age range:** 3–13
**Fees:** Day £6,726–£18,570 WB £4,800

## Walhampton
Walhampton, Lymington,
Hampshire SO41 5ZG
**Tel:** 01590 613 300
**Headmaster:** Mr Titus Mills
**Age range:** 2–13
**No. of pupils:** 353
**Fees:** Day £8,025–£15,555
FB £20,790

**Wessex Tutors**
44 Shirley Road, Southampton,
Hampshire SO15 3EU
**Tel:** 023 8033 4719
**Principal:** Mrs J E White BA(London)
**Age range:** 14–21
**Fees:** Day £800–£10,000
16↑

**West Hill Park
Preparatory School**
Titchfield, Fareham,
Hampshire PO14 4BS
**Tel:** 01329 842356
**Headmaster:** A P Ramsay
BEd(Hons), MSc
**Age range:** 2–13
**No. of pupils:** 288
**Fees:** Day £8,985–£14,985
FB £13,785–£19,785
👤 £ ✎

**Winchester College**
College Street, Winchester,
Hampshire SO23 9NA
**Tel:** 01962 621247
**Headmaster:** Dr. T R Hands
**Age range:** B13–18
**No. of pupils:** 690 VIth280
**Fees:** FB £36,678
👤 👥 👤 £ ✎ 16↑

**Woodhill School, Botley**
Brook Lane, Botley, Southampton,
Hampshire SO30 2ER
**Tel:** 01489 781112
**Head Teacher:** Mrs M Dacombe
**Age range:** 3–11
**No. of pupils:** 100
**Fees:** Day £2,199–£4,965

**Yateley Manor School**
51 Reading Road, Yateley,
Hampshire GU46 7UQ
**Tel:** 01252 405500
**Headmaster:** Mr R J Williams
MA(Hons)Edinburgh, PGCE Bedford
**Age range:** 3–13
**No. of pupils:** 453
**Fees:** Day £4,500–£12,150
£ ✎

# Hertfordshire

**Abbot's Hill School**
Bunkers Lane, Hemel Hempstead,
Hertfordshire HP3 8RP
**Tel:** 01442 240333
**Headmistress:** Mrs E Thomas BA
(Hons), PGCE, NPQH
**No. of pupils:** 510
👤 £ ✎

**Aldenham School**
Elstree, Hertfordshire WD6 3AJ
**Tel:** 01923 858122
**Headmaster:** Mr James C Fowler
MA
**Age range:** 3–18
**No. of pupils:** 700
**Fees:** Day £15,291–£21,414
FB £21,099–£31,384
👥 👤 £ ✎ 16↑

**Aldwickbury School**
Wheathampstead Road,
Harpenden, Hertfordshire AL5 1AD
**Tel:** 01582 713022
**Headmaster:** Mr V W Hales
**Age range:** B4–13
**No. of pupils:** 330
**Fees:** Day £2,002–£3,012
WB £3,800–£3,884
👤 👤 £ ✎ ✎

**Beechwood Park School**
Markyate, St Albans,
Hertfordshire AL3 8AW
**Tel:** 01582 840333
**Headmaster:** Mr E Balfour BA
(Hons), PGCE
**Age range:** 3–13
**No. of pupils:** 532
**Fees:** Day £10,560–£15,825
WB £19,575
👤 £ ✎

**BERKHAMSTED SCHOOL**
*For further details see p. 92*
Overton House, 131 High
Street, Berkhamsted,
Hertfordshire HP4 2DJ
**Tel:** 01442 358001
**Email:** admissions@
berkhamstedschool.org
**Website:**
www.berkhamstedschool.org
**Principal:** Mr Richard Backhouse
MA(Cantab)
**Age range:** 3–18
**No. of pupils:** 1772 VIth402
**Fees:** Day £10,365–£20,250
WB £27,115 FB £32,255
👥 👤 £ ✎ 16↑

**Bhaktivedanta
Manor School**
Hilfield Lane, Aldenham, Watford,
Hertfordshire WD25 8EZ
**Tel:** 01923 851000 Ext:241
**Headteacher:** Mrs. Wendy Harrison
**Age range:** 4–12
**No. of pupils:** 45
**Fees:** Day £1,680

**Bishop's Stortford College**
10 Maze Green Road, Bishop's
Stortford, Hertfordshire CM23 2PJ
**Tel:** 01279 838575
**Headmaster:** Mr Jeremy Gladwin
**Age range:** 13–18
**No. of pupils:** VIth249
**Fees:** Day £18,915–£19,086
WB £28,665–£28,839 FB
£28,950–£30,273
👥 👤 £ 16↑

**Bishop's Stortford
College Prep School**
Maze Green Road, Bishop's
Stortford, Hertfordshire CM23 2PH
**Tel:** 01279 838607
**Head of the Prep School:** Mr Bill
Toleman
**Age range:** 4–13
**No. of pupils:** 590
**Fees:** Day £8,745–£15,132 WB
£20,010–£21,726 FB £20,226–£22,857
👥 👤 £

**Champneys International
College of Health & Beauty**
Chesham Road, Wigginton,
Tring, Hertfordshire HP23 6HY
**Tel:** 01442 291333
**College Principal:** Ms Pam Clegg
**Age range:** 16+
**No. of pupils:** 61
**Fees:** Day £3,000–£9,050
16↑ £ 16↑

**Charlotte House
Preparatory School**
88 The Drive, Rickmansworth,
Hertfordshire WD3 4DU
**Tel:** 01923 772101
**Head:** Miss P Woodcock
**Age range:** G3–11
**No. of pupils:** 140
**Fees:** Day £6,900–£11,100
👤 👤 ✎

**Duncombe School**
4 Warren Park Road, Bengeo,
Hertford, Hertfordshire SG14 3JA
**Tel:** 01992 414100
**Headmaster:** Mr Jeremy Phelan
M.A. (Ed)
**Age range:** 2–11
**No. of pupils:** 325
**Fees:** Day £9,075–£12,585
£ ✎

**Edge Grove School**
Aldenham Village,
Hertfordshire WD25 8NL
**Tel:** 01923 855724
**Headmaster:** Mr Ben Evans BA
(Hons), PGCE
**Age range:** 3–13
**No. of pupils:** 494
**Fees:** Day £6,675–£16,305 WB £5,970
👤 £ ✎

**Egerton Rothesay School**
Durrants Lane, Berkhamsted,
Hertfordshire HP4 3UJ
**Tel:** 01442 865275
**Headteacher:** Mr Colin Parker
BSc(Hons), Dip.Ed (Oxon), PGCE,
C.Math MIMA
**Age range:** 6–19
**No. of pupils:** 179
**Fees:** Day £15,555–£22,140
✎

**Haberdashers'
Aske's School**
Butterfly Lane, Elstree,
Borehamwood,
Hertfordshire WD6 3AF
**Tel:** 020 8266 1700
**Headmaster:** Mr P B Hamilton MA
**Age range:** B5–18
**No. of pupils:** 1402 VIth310
**Fees:** Day £10,641–£14,103
👤 £ 16↑

**Haberdashers' Aske's
School for Girls**
Aldenham Road,
Elstree, Borehamwood,
Hertfordshire WD6 3BT
**Tel:** 020 8266 2300
**Headmistress:** Miss Biddie A
O'Connor MA (Oxon)
**Age range:** G4–18
**No. of pupils:** 1190
**Fees:** Day £15,192–£17,433
👤 £ 16↑

**Haileybury**
Haileybury, Hertford,
Hertfordshire SG13 7NU
**Tel:** +44 (0)1992 706200
**The Master:** Mr Martin Collier MA
BA PGCE
**Age range:** 11–18
**No. of pupils:** 804 VIth323
**Fees:** Day £16,455–£24,753
FB £20,796–£32,784
👥 👤 £ IB ✎ 16↑

**Haresfoot School**
Chesham Road, Berkhamsted,
Hertfordshire HP4 2SZ
**Tel:** 01442 872742
**Principal:** Mrs Carole Hawkins BA,
PGCE
**Age range:** 0–11
**Fees:** Day £1,845–£7,770

**Heath Mount School**
Woodhall Park, Watton-at-Stone,
Hertford, Hertfordshire SG14 3NG
**Tel:** 01920 830230
**Headmaster:** Mr C Gillam
BEd(Hons)
**Age range:** 3–13
**Fees:** Day £6,480–£16,695
WB £17,690–£21,945

**High Elms Manor School**
High Elms Lane, Watford,
Hertfordshire WD25 0JX
**Tel:** 01923 681 103
**Headmistress:** Ms Liadain O'Neill BA
(Hons), AMI 0-3, AMI 3-6, Early Years
FdA Dist.+
**Age range:** 2–11
**No. of pupils:** 100
**Fees:** Day £11,850

**Howe Green House School**
Great Hallingbury, Bishop's
Stortford, Hertfordshire CM22 7UF
**Tel:** 01279 657706
**Head of School:** Mrs Deborah Mills
**Age range:** 2–11
**Fees:** Day £5,946–£9,444

**Immanuel College**
87/91 Elstree Road, Bushey,
Hertfordshire WD23 4EB
**Tel:** 020 8950 0604
**Headmaster:** Mr Philip Skelker MA
**Age range:** 11–18
**No. of pupils:** 520 VIth127
**Fees:** Day £10,995

**Kingshott**
St Ippolyts, Hitchin,
Hertfordshire SG4 7JX
**Tel:** 01462 432009
**Headmaster:** Mr Iain Gilmour
**Age range:** 3–13
**No. of pupils:** 372
**Fees:** Day £4,770–£10,350

**Little Acorns Montessori School**
Lincolnsfield Centre,
Bushey Hall Drive, Bushey,
Hertfordshire WD23 2ER
**Tel:** 01923 230705
**Head of School:** Lola Davies BPA,
AMIDip
**Age range:** 2–6
**No. of pupils:** 28
**Fees:** Day £2,120

**Lochinver House School**
Heath Road, Little Heath, Potters
Bar, Hertfordshire EN6 1LW
**Tel:** 01707 653064
**Headmaster:** Ben Walker BA(Hons),
PGCE, CELTA
**Age range:** B4–13
**No. of pupils:** 349
**Fees:** Day £9,000–£11,826

**Lockers Park**
Lockers Park Lane, Hemel
Hempstead, Hertfordshire HP1 1TL
**Tel:** 01442 251712
**Headmaster:** Mr C R Wilson
**Age range:** B4–13 G4–7
**No. of pupils:** 170
**Fees:** Day £10,050–
£16,530 FB £23,160

**Longwood School**
Bushey Hall Drive, Bushey,
Hertfordshire WD23 2QG
**Tel:** 01923 253715
**Head Teacher:** Mrs Muriel Garman
**Age range:** 3–11
**Fees:** Day £4,590–£5,790

**Manor Lodge School**
Rectory Lane, Ridge Hill, Shenley,
Hertfordshire WD7 9BG
**Tel:** 01707 642424
**Headmaster:** Mr G Dunn CertEd
**Age range:** 3–11
**No. of pupils:** 430
**Fees:** Day £10,650–£11,910

**Merchant Taylors' Prep**
Moor Farm, Sandy Lodge
Road, Rickmansworth,
Hertfordshire WD3 1LW
**Tel:** 01923 825648
**Headmaster:** Dr T D Lee BEd(Hons)
**Age range:** B4–13
**No. of pupils:** 300
**Fees:** Day £2,613–£9,414

**Princess Helena College**
Preston, Hitchin,
Hertfordshire SG4 7RT
**Tel:** 01462 443888
**Headmistress:** Mrs Sue Wallace-
Woodroffe
**Age range:** G11–18
**No. of pupils:** 194 VIth35
**Fees:** Day £15,585–£18,975
FB £22,185–£27,585

**Queenswood**
Shepherd's Way, Brookmans Park,
Hatfield, Hertfordshire AL9 6NS
**Tel:** 01707 602500
**Principal:** Mrs P C Edgar BA(Hons)
London, PGCE
**Age range:** G11–18
**No. of pupils:** 400 VIth120
**Fees:** Day £19,485–£21,825
FB £26,295–£28,665

**Radlett Preparatory School**
Kendal Hall, Watling Street,
Radlett, Hertfordshire WD7 7LY
**Tel:** 01923 856812
**Principal:** Mr G White BEd (Hons)
**Age range:** 4–11
**Fees:** Day £9,180

**Rudolf Steiner School**
Langley Hill, Kings Langley,
Hertfordshire WD4 9HG
**Tel:** 01923 262505
**No. of pupils:** 405
**Fees:** Day £2,985–£7,800

**Sherrardswood School**
Lockleys, Welwyn,
Hertfordshire AL6 0BJ
**Tel:** 01438 714282
**Headmistress:** Mrs L Corry
**Age range:** 2–18
**No. of pupils:** 357
**Fees:** Day £6,720–£12,750

**St Albans High School for Girls**
Townsend Avenue, St Albans,
Hertfordshire AL1 3SJ
**Tel:** 01727 853800
**Headmistress:** Mrs Jenny Brown
MA (Oxon)
**Age range:** G4–18
**No. of pupils:** 940 VIth170
**Fees:** Day £4,650–£5,910

**St Albans School**
Abbey Gateway, St Albans,
Hertfordshire AL3 4HB
**Tel:** 01727 855521
**Headmaster:** Mr JWJ Gillespie
MA(Cantab), FRSA
**Age range:** B11–18 G16–18
**No. of pupils:** 870
**Fees:** Day £17,238

**St Albans Tutors**
69 London Road, St Albans,
Hertfordshire AL1 1LN
**Tel:** 01727 842348
**Principals:** Mr. A N Jemal & Mr Elvis
Cotena
**Age range:** 15+
**Fees:** Day £3,400

**St Christopher School**
Barrington Road, Letchworth,
Hertfordshire SG6 3JZ
**Tel:** 01462 650 850
**Head:** Richard Palmer
**Age range:** 3–18
**No. of pupils:** 511 VIth78
**Fees:** Day £3,375–£14,505
FB £15,600–£25,470

**St Columba's College**
King Harry Lane, St Albans,
Hertfordshire AL3 4AW
**Tel:** 01727 855185
**Headmaster:** David R Buxton
**Age range:** B4–18
**No. of pupils:** 860 VIth150
**Fees:** Day £8,235–£10,416

**St Columba's College Prep School**
King Harry Lane, St Albans,
Hertfordshire AL3 4AW
**Tel:** 01727 862616
**Head of Prep:** Mrs Ruth Loveman
**Age range:** B4–11
**No. of pupils:** 250
**Fees:** Day £9,702–£12,087

**St Edmund's College & Prep School**
Old Hall Green, Nr Ware,
Hertfordshire SG11 1DS
**Tel:** 01920 824247
**Head:** Paulo Durán BA MA
**Age range:** 3–18
**No. of pupils:** 799 VIth135
**Fees:** Day £9,465–£14,955 WB
£19,830–£22,575 FB £21,855–£24,990

**St Edmund's Prep**
Old Hall Green, Ware,
Hertfordshire SG11 1DS
**Tel:** 01920 824239
**Head:** Mr Steven Cartwright BSc
(Surrey)
**Age range:** 3–11
**No. of pupils:** 185
**Fees:** Day £8,484–£12,252

**St Francis' College**
Broadway, Letchworth Garden
City, Hertfordshire SG6 3PJ
**Tel:** 01462 670511
**Headmistress:** Mrs B Goulding
**Age range:** G3–18
**No. of pupils:** 460 VIth75
**Fees:** Day £8,670–£13,830 WB
£19,425–£22,875 FB £24,195–£27,645

**St Hilda's**
High Street, Bushey,
Hertfordshire WD23 3DA
**Tel:** 020 8950 1751
**Headmistress:** Miss Sarah-Jane
Styles MA
**Age range:** B2–4 G2–11
**Fees:** Day £4,635–£8,685

**St Hilda's School**
28 Douglas Road, Harpenden,
Hertfordshire AL5 2ES
**Tel:** 01582 712307
**Headmaster:** Mr Dan Sayers
**Age range:** G3–11 years
**No. of pupils:** 144
**Fees:** Day £5,715–£9,975

### St John's Preparatory School
The Ridgeway, Potters Bar, Hertfordshire EN6 5QT
**Tel:** 01707 657294
**Headmistress:** Mrs C Tardios BA(Hons)
**Age range:** 4–11
**No. of pupils:** 184
**Fees:** Day £8,190–£8,730

### St Joseph's In The Park
St Mary's Lane, Hertingfordbury, Hertford, Hertfordshire SG14 2LX
**Tel:** 01992 513810
**Head of School:** Mr Douglas Brown
**Age range:** 3–11
**No. of pupils:** 150
**Fees:** Day £5,430–£16,011

### St Margaret's School, Bushey
Merry Hill Road, Bushey, Hertfordshire WD23 1DT
**Tel:** 020 8416 4400
**Head:** Mrs Rose Hardy MA(Oxon), MEd, FRSA
**Age range:** G4–18 years
**No. of pupils:** 450 VIth100
**Fees:** Day £14,730 WB £20,220–£23,670 FB £27,600

### Stanborough School
Stanborough Park, Garston, Watford, Hertfordshire WD25 9JT
**Tel:** 01923 673268
**Head Teacher:** Ms Lorraine Dixon
**Age range:** 3–19
**No. of pupils:** 300 VIth20
**Fees:** Day £3,660–£5,500 WB £12,834–£15,846

### Stormont
The Causeway, Potters Bar, Hertfordshire EN6 5HA
**Tel:** 01707 654037
**Head of School:** Mrs Sharon Martin
**Age range:** G4–11
**Fees:** Day £10,215–£10,680

### The Christian School (Takeley)
Dunmow Road, Brewers End, Takeley, Bishop's Stortford, Hertfordshire CM22 6QH
**Tel:** 01279 871182
**Headmaster:** M E Humphries
**Age range:** 5–16
**Fees:** Day £3,720

### The King's School
Elmfield, Ambrose Lane, Harpenden, Hertfordshire AL5 4DU
**Tel:** 01582 767566
**Principal:** Mr Clive John Case BA, HDE
**Age range:** 5–16
**Fees:** Day £6,960

### The Purcell School, London
Aldenham Road, Bushey, Hertfordshire WD23 2TS
**Tel:** 01923 331100
**Headteacher:** Mr. Stephen Yeo
**Age range:** 10–18
**No. of pupils:** 180

### Tring Park School for the Performing Arts
Tring Park, Tring, Hertfordshire HP23 5LX
**Tel:** 01442 824255
**Principal:** Mr Stefan Anderson MA, ARCM, ARCT
**Age range:** 8–19
**No. of pupils:** 350 VIth263
**Fees:** Day £14,430–£22,965 FB £24,540–£34,710

### Westbrook Hay Prep School
London Road, Hemel Hempstead, Hertfordshire HP1 2RF
**Tel:** 01442 256143
**Headmaster:** Keith D Young BEd(Hons)
**Age range:** 3–13
**No. of pupils:** 300
**Fees:** Day £10,125–£14,580

### York House School
Redheath, Sarratt Road, Croxley Green, Rickmansworth, Hertfordshire WD3 4LW
**Tel:** 01923 772395
**Headmaster:** Jon Gray BA(Ed)
**Age range:** 3–13
**No. of pupils:** 240
**Fees:** Day £10,845

# Kent

### Ashford School
East Hill, Ashford, Kent TN24 8PB
**Tel:** 01233 739030
**Head:** Mr M R Buchanan BSc(Hons), CertEd, NPQH, CPhys
**Age range:** 3 months–18 years
**No. of pupils:** 835 VIth170
**Fees:** Day £8,400–£16,200 WB £28,500 FB £32,400

### Beech Grove School
Beech Grove Bruderhof, Sandwich Road, Nonington, Dover, Kent CT15 4HH
**Tel:** 01304 842980
**Head:** Mr Benjamin Shirky
**Age range:** 4–14
**No. of pupils:** 63

### Beechwood Sacred Heart
12 Pembury Road, Tunbridge Wells, Kent TN2 3QD
**Tel:** 01892 532747
**Headmaster:** Mr Aaron Lennon BA(Hons)
**Age range:** 3–18
**No. of pupils:** 400 VIth70
**Fees:** Day £9,060–£15,936 WB £23,460 FB £26,460

### Benenden School
Cranbrook, Kent TN17 4AA
**Tel:** 01580 240592
**Headmistress:** Mrs S Price
**Age range:** G11–18
**No. of pupils:** 550
**Fees:** FB £35,700

### Bethany School
Curtisden Green, Goudhurst, Cranbrook, Kent TN17 1LB
**Tel:** 01580 211273
**Headmaster:** Mr Francie Healy BSc, HDipEd, NPQH
**Age range:** 11–18 years
**No. of pupils:** 313 VIth98
**Fees:** Day £16,245–£17,925 WB £25,185–£27,825 FB £27,165–£30,585

### Bronte School
Mayfield, 7 Pelham Road, Gravesend, Kent DA11 0HN
**Tel:** 01474 533805
**Headmistress:** Ms Emma Wood
**Age range:** 4–11
**No. of pupils:** 120
**Fees:** Day £7,950

### Bryony School
Marshall Road, Rainham, Gillingham, Kent ME8 0AJ
**Tel:** 01634 231511
**Joint Head:** Mr D Edmunds
**Age range:** 2–11
**No. of pupils:** 168
**Fees:** Day £5,862–£6,352

### Canterbury Steiner School
Garlinge Green, Chartham, Canterbury, Kent CT4 5RU
**Tel:** 01227 738285
**Age range:** 3–18
**Fees:** Day £3,246–£4,405.50

### CATS Canterbury
68 New Dover Road, Canterbury, Kent CT1 3LQ
**Tel:** +44 (0)1227866540
**Principal:** Mr. James Slocombe BSc(Hons), PGCE, QTS, MA, FRSA
**Age range:** 14–18
**No. of pupils:** 400

### Chartfield School
45 Minster Road, Westgate on Sea, Kent CT8 8DA
**Tel:** 01843 831716
**Head & Proprietor:** Miss L P Shipley
**Age range:** 4–11
**No. of pupils:** 50
**Fees:** Day £2,580–£3,000

### Cobham Hall School
Cobham, Kent DA12 3BL
**Tel:** 01474 823371
**Headmistress:** Dr Sandra Coates-Smith BSc, PhD
**Age range:** G11–18
**No. of pupils:** 180

### Derwent Lodge School for Girls
Somerhill, Tonbridge, Kent TN11 0NJ
**Tel:** 01732 352124
**Head of School:** Mrs Helen Hoffmann
**Age range:** G7–11
**No. of pupils:** 134
**Fees:** Day £12,675

### Dover College
Effingham Crescent, Dover, Kent CT17 9RH
**Tel:** 01304 205969
**Headmaster:** Mr Gareth Doodes MA (Hons)
**Age range:** 3–18
**No. of pupils:** 301
**Fees:** Day £7,500–£15,600 WB £20,250–£24,000 FB £24,000–£30,000

## Dulwich Preparatory School
Coursehorn, Cranbrook,
Kent TN17 3NP
**Tel:** 01580 712179
**Headmaster:** Mr Paul David
BEd(Hons)
**Age range:** 3–13
**No. of pupils:** 535
**Fees:** Day £4,890–£14,400

## Elliott Park School
18-20 Marina Drive, Minster,
Sheerness, Kent ME12 2DP
**Tel:** 01795 873372
**Head:** Ms Colleen Hiller
**Age range:** 3–11
**No. of pupils:** 65
**Fees:** Day £5,025

## European School of Osteopathy
Boxley House, The Street, Boxley,
Maidstone, Kent ME14 3DZ
**Tel:** 01622 671 558
**Principal:** Mr Renzo Molinari DO

## Fosse Bank School
Mountains, Noble Tree
Road, Hildenborough,
Tonbridge, Kent TN11 8ND
**Tel:** 01732 834212
**Headmistress:** Mrs Lovatt-Young
**Age range:** 3–11
**No. of pupils:** 124
**Fees:** Day £1,560–£10,671

## Gad's Hill School
Higham, Rochester,
Medway, Kent ME3 7PA
**Tel:** 01474 822366
**Headmaster:** Mr D G Craggs BSc,
MA, NPQH, FCollP, FRSA
**Age range:** 3–16
**No. of pupils:** 370
**Fees:** Day £6,000–£7,600

## Haddon Dene School
57 Gladstone Road,
Broadstairs, Kent CT10 2HY
**Tel:** 01843 861176
**Head:** Mrs E Rowe
**Age range:** 3–11
**No. of pupils:** 200
**Fees:** Day £4,950–£6,135

## Hilden Grange School
62 Dry Hill Park Road,
Tonbridge, Kent TN10 3BX
**Tel:** 01732 352706
**Headmaster:** Mr J Withers BA(Hons)
**Age range:** 3–13
**No. of pupils:** 311

## Hilden Oaks School & Nursery
38 Dry Hill Park Road,
Tonbridge, Kent TN10 3BU
**Tel:** 01732 353941
**Head of School:** Mrs. K J M Joiner
**Fees:** Day £8,985–£11,988

## Holmewood House School
Langton Green, Tunbridge
Wells, Kent TN3 0EB
**Tel:** 01892 860000
**Headmaster:** Mr J D B Marjoribanks
BEd
**Age range:** 3–13
**No. of pupils:** 439
**Fees:** Day £2,160–£17,460
WB £20,640

## Kent College
Whitstable Road, Canterbury,
Kent CT2 9DT
**Tel:** 01227 763231
**Executive Head Master:** Dr David
Lamper
**Age range:** 3–18
**No. of pupils:** 704
**Fees:** Day £16,221–£17,995
FB £24,741–£33,981

## Kent College Junior School
Harbledown, Canterbury,
Kent CT2 9AQ
**Tel:** 01227 762436
**Headmaster:** Mr Andrew Carter
**Age range:** 0–11
**No. of pupils:** 190
**Fees:** Day £8,220–£15,621 FB £24,375

## Kent College Pembury
Old Church Road, Pembury,
Tunbridge Wells, Kent TN2 4AX
**Tel:** +44 (0)1892 822006
**Headmistress:** Mrs Sally-Anne
Huang MA(Oxon), MSc, PGCE
**Age range:** G3–18
**No. of pupils:** 650 VIth102
**Fees:** Day £7,887–£17,322
FB £21,471–£27,924

## Kids Inc Day Nursery – Bluewater
West Village, Bluewater,
Greenhithe, Kent DA9 9SE
**Tel:** 01322 386624

## King's Preparatory School, Rochester
King Edward Road, Rochester,
Medway, Kent ME1 1UB
**Tel:** 01634 888577
**Headmaster:** Mr R Overend
**Age range:** 8–13
**No. of pupils:** 220
**Fees:** Day £12,765–
£14,490 FB £21,150

## King's Rochester
Satis House, Boley Hill,
Rochester, Kent ME1 1TE
**Tel:** 01634 888555
**Principal:** Mr J Walker
**Age range:** 3–18
**No. of pupils:** 263
**Fees:** Day £18,705 FB £30,390

## Linton Park School
3 Eccleston Road, Tovil,
Maidstone, Kent ME17 4HT
**Tel:** 01622 740820
**Headteacher:** Mr C Allen
**Age range:** 7–18
**No. of pupils:** 134

## Lorenden Preparatory School
Painter's Forstal, Faversham,
Kent ME13 0EN
**Tel:** 01795 590030
**Headmistress:** Mrs K Uttley
**Age range:** 3–11
**No. of pupils:** 120
**Fees:** Day £8,340–£12,105

## Marlborough House School
High Street, Hawkhurst,
Kent TN18 4PY
**Tel:** 01580 753555
**Headmaster:** Mr Martyn Ward BEd
(Hons)
**Age range:** 2 3/4–13
**No. of pupils:** 334
**Fees:** Day £8,475–£17,535

## Meredale Independent Primary School
Solomon Road, Rainham,
Gillingham, Kent ME8 8EB
**Tel:** 01634 231405
**Headteacher:** Miss Michelle
Ingledew
**Age range:** 3–11
**No. of pupils:** 53
**Fees:** Day £5,100

## Northbourne Park School
Betteshanger, Deal, Kent CT14 0NW
**Tel:** 01304 611215/218
**Headmaster:** Mr Sebastian Rees
BA(Hons), PGCE, NPQH
**Age range:** 3–13
**No. of pupils:** 149
**Fees:** Day £7,632–£16,326
WB £20,376 FB £23,673

## Radnor House, Sevenoaks
Combe Bank Drive,
Sevenoaks, Kent TN14 6AE
**Tel:** 01959 563720
**Head:** Mr David Paton BComm
(Hons) PGCE MA
**Age range:** 2.5–18
**No. of pupils:** 250

## Rochester Independent College
Star Hill, Rochester,
Medway, Kent ME1 1XF
**Tel:** 01634 828115
**Principals:** Alistair Brownlow, Brian
Pain, Pauline Bailey
**Age range:** 11–19
**No. of pupils:** 306 VIth233
**Fees:** Day £12,000–£16,500 WB
£25,650–£27,300 FB £27,450–£29,100

## Rose Hill School
Coniston Avenue, Tunbridge
Wells, Kent TN4 9SY
**Tel:** 01892 525591
**Headmaster:** Mr D Westcombe
BA, PGCE
**Age range:** 3–13
**Fees:** Day £3,040–£4,130

## Russell House School
Station Road, Otford,
Sevenoaks, Kent TN14 5QU
**Tel:** 01959 522352
**Headmaster:** Mr Craig McCarthy
**Age range:** 2–11
**No. of pupils:** 189

## Sackville School
Tonbridge Rd, Hildenborough,
Tonbridge, Kent TN11 9HN
**Tel:** 01732 838888
**Headmaster:** Mr Justin Foster-
Gandey BSc (hons)
**Age range:** 11–18
**No. of pupils:** 160 VIth29
**Fees:** Day £14,850

## Saint Ronan's School
Water Lane, Hawkhurst,
Kent TN18 5DJ
**Tel:** 01580 752271
**Headmaster:** William Trelawny-
Vernon BSc(Hons)
**Age range:** 3–13
**No. of pupils:** 300
**Fees:** Day £6,951–£11,892

## Sevenoaks Preparatory School
Godden Green, Sevenoaks,
Kent TN15 0JU
**Tel:** 01732 762336
**Headmaster:** Mr Luke Harrison
**Age range:** 2–13
**No. of pupils:** 388
**Fees:** Day £3,552–£11,910

## Sevenoaks School
High Street, Sevenoaks,
Kent TN13 1HU
**Tel:** +44 (0)1732 455133
**Head:** Dr Katy Ricks MA, DPhil
**Age range:** 11–18
**No. of pupils:** 1080
**Fees:** Day £22,455–£25,497
FB £35,865–£38,907

## Shernold School
Hill Place, Queens Avenue, Maidstone, Kent ME16 0ER
**Tel:** 01622 752868
**Head Teacher:** Ms. Sandra Dinsmore
**Age range:** 3–11
**No. of pupils:** 142
**Fees:** Day £3,525–£4,200
£

## Solefield School
Solefield Road, Sevenoaks, Kent TN13 1PH
**Tel:** 01732 452142
**Headmaster:** Mr D A Philps BSc(Hons)
**Age range:** B4–13
**No. of pupils:** 180
**Fees:** Day £9,990–£12,060
⚥

## Somerhill Pre-Prep
Somerhill, Five Oak Green Road, Tonbridge, Kent TN11 0NJ
**Tel:** 01732 352124
**Headmistress:** Mrs J Ruth Sorensen BEd(Hons), CertEd
**Age range:** 3–7
**No. of pupils:** 245

## Spring Grove School
Harville Road, Wye, Ashford, Kent TN25 5EZ
**Tel:** 01233 812337
**Headmaster:** Mr Bill Jones
**Age range:** 2–11
**No. of pupils:** 194
**Fees:** Day £2,050–£3,125
£

## St Andrew's School
24-28 Watts Avenue, Rochester, Medway, Kent ME1 1SA
**Tel:** 01634 843479
**Principal:** Mrs E Steinmann-Gilbert
**Age range:** 2–11
**No. of pupils:** 367
**Fees:** Day £6,672–£7,059

## St Christopher's School
New Dover Road, Canterbury, Kent CT1 3DT
**Tel:** 01227 462960
**The Master:** Mr D Evans
**Age range:** 3–11
**Fees:** Day £7,600
£

## St Edmund's Junior School
St Thomas Hill, Canterbury, Kent CT2 8HU
**Tel:** 01227 475600
**Master:** R G Bacon BA(Hons) (Durham)
**Age range:** 3–13
**No. of pupils:** 230
**Fees:** Day £6,969–£14,211 WB £18,969 FB £20,817

## St Edmund's School
St Thomas' Hill, Canterbury, Kent CT2 8HU
**Tel:** 01227 475601
**Head:** Louise Moelwyn-Hughes
**Age range:** 3–18
**No. of pupils:** 535
**Fees:** Day £18,651 FB £29,781
⚥ 16

## St Faith's at Ash School
5 The Street, Ash, Canterbury, Kent CT3 2HH
**Tel:** 01304 813409
**Headmaster:** Mr Lawrence Groves
**Age range:** 2–11
**No. of pupils:** 225
**Fees:** Day £6,435–£8,100
£

## St Joseph's Convent Prep School
46 Old Road East, Gravesend, Kent DA12 1NR
**Tel:** 01474 533012
**Head Teacher:** Mrs Carola Timney
**Age range:** 3–11
**No. of pupils:** 146
**Fees:** Day £6,655

## St Lawrence College
Ramsgate, Kent CT11 7AE
**Tel:** 01843 572931
**Principal:** Mr Antony Spencer
**Age range:** 3–18
**No. of pupils:** 640 VIth115
**Fees:** Day £7,470–£18,495 FB £26,055–£34,635
£ 16

## St Michael's Preparatory School
Otford Court, Otford, Sevenoaks, Kent TN14 5SA
**Tel:** 01959 522137
**Headteacher:** Mrs Jill Aisher
**Age range:** 2–13
**No. of pupils:** 472
**Fees:** Day £2,064–£12,555
£

## Steephill School
Off Castle Hill, Fawkham, Longfield, Kent DA3 7BG
**Tel:** 01474 702107
**Head:** Mrs C Birtwell BSc, MBA, PGCE
**Age range:** 3–11
**No. of pupils:** 131
**Fees:** Day £6,860
£

## Sutton Valence Preparatory School
Chart Sutton, Maidstone, Kent ME17 3RF
**Tel:** 01622 842117
**Head:** Miss C Corkran
**Age range:** 3–11
**No. of pupils:** 320
**Fees:** Day £8,700–£13,365

## Sutton Valence School
North Street, Sutton Valence, Kent ME17 3HL
**Tel:** 01622 845200
**Headmaster:** Bruce Grindlay MA Cantab, MusB, FRCO, CHM
**Age range:** 11–18
**No. of pupils:** 570
£ 16

## The Granville School
2 Bradbourne Park Road, Sevenoaks, Kent TN13 3LJ
**Tel:** 01732 453039
**Headmistress:** Mrs J Scott BEd(Cantab)
**Age range:** B3–4 G3–11
**No. of pupils:** 195
**Fees:** Day £5,445–£14,040
£

## The Junior King's School, Canterbury
Milner Court, Sturry, Canterbury, Kent CT2 0AY
**Tel:** 01227 714000
**Headmaster:** Mr Peter Wells BEd(Hons)
**Age range:** 3–13
**Fees:** Day £8,610–£14,610 FB £19,830

## The King's School, Canterbury
The Precincts, Canterbury, Kent CT1 2ES
**Tel:** 01227 595501
**Head:** Mr P Roberts
**Age range:** 13–18
**No. of pupils:** 858 VIth385
**Fees:** Day £26,700 FB £35,295
£ 16

## The Mead School
16 Frant Road, Tunbridge Wells, Kent TN2 5SN
**Tel:** 01892 525837
**Headmistress:** Mrs A Culley CertEd(Oxon)
**Age range:** 3–11
**No. of pupils:** 188
**Fees:** Day £3,900–£9,945

## The New Beacon School
Brittains Lane, Sevenoaks, Kent TN13 2PB
**Tel:** 01732 452131
**Headmaster:** Mr M Piercy BA(Hons)
**Age range:** B4–13
**No. of pupils:** 400
**Fees:** Day £11,025–£15,270 WB £180–£180
£

## Tonbridge School
Tonbridge, Kent TN9 1JP
**Tel:** 01732 365555
**Headmaster:** T H P Haynes
**Age range:** B13–18
**No. of pupils:** 787
**Fees:** Day £29,229 FB £38,964
£ 16

## Walthamstow Hall Pre-Prep and Junior School
Sevenoaks, Kent TN13 3LD
**Tel:** 01732 451334
**Headmistress:** Mrs Jill Milner MA(Oxford)
**Age range:** G2–11
**No. of pupils:** 218
**Fees:** Day £1,230–£9,990

## Walthamstow Hall School
Sevenoaks, Kent TN13 3UL
**Tel:** 01732 451334
**Headmistress:** Mrs J Milner MA(Oxford)
**Age range:** G2–18
**No. of pupils:** 500 VIth80
**Fees:** Day £8,070–£13,710
£ 16

## Wellesley House
114 Ramsgate Road, Broadstairs, Kent CT10 2DG
**Tel:** 01843 862991
**Headmaster:** Mr S T P O'Malley MA(Hons), PGCE
**Age range:** 7–13
**No. of pupils:** 133
**Fees:** Day £14,985–£17,850 FB £22,575
£

## Yardley Court
Somerhill, Five Oak Green Road, Tonbridge, Kent TN11 0NJ
**Tel:** 01732 352124
**Headmaster:** J T Coakley MA, BA(Hons), PGCE
**Age range:** B7–13
**No. of pupils:** 260
**Fees:** Day £13,150
£

# Surrey

### Aberdour School
Brighton Road, Burgh Heath,
Tadworth, Surrey KT20 6AJ
**Tel:** 01737 354119
**Headmaster:** Mr S. D. Collins
**Age range:** 2–13 years
**No. of pupils:** 357
**Fees:** Day £1,350–£4,650

### ACS Cobham International School
Heywood, Portsmouth Road,
Cobham, Surrey KT11 1BL
**Tel:** +44 (0) 1932 867251
**Head of School:** Mr A Eysele
**Age range:** 2–18
**No. of pupils:** 1460
**Fees:** Day £10,690–£25,050
FB £36,810–£39,310

### ACS Egham International School
Woodlee, London Road,
Egham, Surrey TW20 0HS
**Tel:** +44 (0) 1784 430 800
**Head of School:** Jeremy Lewis
**Age range:** 3–18
**Fees:** Day £7,080–£24,020

### Aldro School
Shackleford, Godalming,
Surrey GU8 6AS
**Tel:** 01483 810266
**Headmaster:** Mr D W N Aston
BA(Hons), PGCE
**Age range:** B7–13
**No. of pupils:** 220
**Fees:** Day £14,610 FB £18,795

### Amesbury
Hazel Grove, Hindhead,
Surrey GU26 6BL
**Tel:** 01428 604322
**Headmaster:** Mr Nigel Taylor MA
**Age range:** 2–13
**No. of pupils:** 360

### Banstead Preparatory School
Sutton Lane, Banstead,
Surrey SM7 3RA
**Tel:** 01737 363601
**Head:** Ms Vicky Ellis

### Barfield School
Guildford Road, Runfold,
Farnham, Surrey GU10 1PB
**Tel:** 01252 782271
**Head of School:** James Reid
**Age range:** 2–13 years
**No. of pupils:** 170
**Fees:** Day £3,168–£13,620

### Barrow Hills School
Roke Lane, Witley, Godalming,
Surrey GU8 5NY
**Tel:** +44 (0)1428 683639
**Headmaster:** Mr Sean Skehan
**Age range:** 2–13
**No. of pupils:** 235
**Fees:** Day £14,985

### Belmont Preparatory School
Feldemore, Holmbury St Mary,
Dorking, Surrey RH5 6LQ
**Tel:** 01306 730852
**Headmistress:** Mrs Helen Skrine BA,
PGCE, NPQH, FRSA
**Age range:** 2–13
**No. of pupils:** 227
**Fees:** Day £6,120–£10,428
WB £15,345

### Bishopsgate School
Bishopsgate Road, Englefield
Green, Egham, Surrey TW20 0YJ
**Tel:** 01784 432109
**Headmaster:** Mr Andrew Cowell
BEd, CPSE
**Age range:** 3–13
**Fees:** Day £4,500–£12,726

### Box Hill School
Old London Road, Mickleham,
Dorking, Surrey RH5 6EA
**Tel:** 01372 373382
**Headmaster:** Mr Corydon Lowde
**Age range:** 11–18
**No. of pupils:** 425 VIth96
**Fees:** Day £16,140–£17,170
WB £24,600–£25,800 FB
£29,970–£35,850

### Bramley School
Chequers Lane, Walton-on-the-
Hill, Tadworth, Surrey KT20 7ST
**Tel:** 01737 812004
**Head of School:** Ms Paula Burgess
**Age range:** G3–11
**No. of pupils:** 78
**Fees:** Day £5,355–£12,285

### Cambridge Management College
4-8 Castle Street, Oakington,
Kingston upon Thames,
Surrey KT11SS
**Tel:** 08003166282
**Principal:** Dr Peter Holmes

### Caterham School
Harestone Valley, Caterham,
Surrey CR3 6YA
**Tel:** 01883 343028
**Head:** Mr C. W. Jones MA(Cantab)
**Age range:** 11–18
**No. of pupils:** VIth321

### Charterhouse
Godalming, Surrey GU7 2DX
**Tel:** +44 (0)1483 291501
**Headmaster:** Dr Alex Peterken
**Age range:** B13–18 G16–18
**No. of pupils:** 820

### Chinthurst School
Tadworth Street, Tadworth,
Surrey KT20 5QZ
**Tel:** 01737 812011
**Head:** Miss Catherine Trundle
**Age range:** B3–11
**No. of pupils:** 170
**Fees:** Day £10,650–£14,340

### City of London Freemen's School
Ashtead Park, Ashtead,
Surrey KT21 1ET
**Tel:** 01372 277933
**Headmaster:** Mr R Martin
**Age range:** 7–18
**No. of pupils:** 877 VIth213
**Fees:** Day £10,872–
£14,598 FB £23,238

### Claremont Fan Court School
Claremont Drive, Esher,
Surrey KT10 9LY
**Tel:** 01372 467841
**Head of Senior School:** Mr
Jonathan Insall-Reid
**Age range:** 2–18
**No. of pupils:** 780
**Fees:** Day £2,205–£17,085

### Coworth Flexlands School
Chertsey Road, Chobham,
Woking, Surrey GU24 8TE
**Tel:** 01276 855707
**Headmistress:** Mrs Anne Sweeney
**Age range:** B2.5–7 G2.5–11
**No. of pupils:** 150
**Fees:** Day £8,250–£12,825

### Cranleigh Preparatory School
Horseshoe Lane, Cranleigh,
Surrey GU6 8QH
**Tel:** 01483 274199
**Headmaster:** Mr M T Wilson BSc
**Age range:** 7–13
**No. of pupils:** 290
**Fees:** Day £11,385 FB £14,025

### Cranleigh School
Horseshoe Lane, Cranleigh,
Surrey GU6 8QQ
**Tel:** +44 (0) 1483 273666
**Headmaster:** Mr Martin Reader MA,
MPhil, MBA
**Age range:** 7–18 (including
Prep School)
**No. of pupils:** 626 VIth250
**Fees:** Day £29,985 FB £36,615

### Cranmore School
Epsom Road, West Horsley,
Surrey KT24 6AT
**Tel:** 01483 280340
**Headmaster:** Mr Michael Connolly
BSc, BA, MA, MEd
**Age range:** 2.5–13
**No. of pupils:** 479
**Fees:** Day £11,850

### Danes Hill School
Leatherhead Road, Oxshott,
Surrey KT22 0JG
**Tel:** 01372 842509
**Headmaster:** Mr W Murdock BA
**Age range:** 3–13
**No. of pupils:** 872
**Fees:** Day £6,405–£17,745

### Danesfield Manor School
Rydens Avenue, Walton-on-
Thames, Surrey KT12 3JB
**Tel:** 01932 220930
**Principal:** Mrs Helen Chalmers
**Age range:** 2–11
**No. of pupils:** 170
**Fees:** Day £8,400

### Downsend School
1 Leatherhead Road,
Leatherhead, Surrey KT22 8TJ
**Tel:** 01372 372197
**Headmaster:** Mr Ian Thorpe
**Age range:** 2–13
**No. of pupils:** 740
**Fees:** Day £13,455

### Downsend School
Ashtead Lodge, 22 Oakfield
Road, Ashtead, Surrey KT21 2RE
**Tel:** 01372 385439
**Head Teacher:** Mrs K Barrett
**Age range:** 2–6
**No. of pupils:** 66
**Fees:** Day £2,190–£8,250

### Downsend School
Epsom Lodge, 6 Norman Avenue,
Epsom, Surrey KT17 3AB
**Tel:** 01372 385438
**Head Teacher:** Miss J Birchall
**Age range:** 2–6
**No. of pupils:** 110
**Fees:** Day £2,325–£11,640

### Downsend School
Leatherhead Lodge, Epsom Road,
Leatherhead, Surrey KT22 8ST
**Tel:** 01372 372123
**Headteacher:** Mrs Gill Brooks
**Age range:** 2–6
**Fees:** Day £6,780–£8,250

**Drayton House School**
35 Austen Road, Guildford,
Surrey GU1 3NP
**Tel:** 01483 504707
**Headmistress:** Mrs J Tyson-Jones
Froebel Cert.Ed. London University
**Age range:** 3 months–7 years
**Fees:** Day £4,420–£12,500

**Duke of Kent School**
Peaslake Road, Ewhurst,
Surrey GU6 7NS
**Tel:** 01483 277313
**Head:** Mrs Judith Fremont-Barnes
**Age range:** 3–16
**No. of pupils:** 234
**Fees:** Day £4,860–£14,130 WB
£13,350–£16,770 FB £15,735–£18,855

**Dunottar School**
High Trees Road, Reigate,
Surrey RH2 7EL
**Tel:** 01737 761945
**Head of School:** Mr Mark Tottman
**Age range:** 11–18
**No. of pupils:** 319
**Fees:** Day £15,492

**Edgeborough**
Frensham, Farnham,
Surrey GU10 3AH
**Tel:** 01252 792495
**Headmaster:** Mr C J Davies BA
**Age range:** 2–13
**No. of pupils:** 285
**Fees:** Day £9,105–£14,850
WB £16,752–£18,282

**Emberhurst School**
94 Ember Lane, Esher,
Surrey KT10 8EN
**Tel:** 020 8398 2933
**Headmistress:** Mrs P Chadwick BEd
**Age range:** 2 +–7+
**No. of pupils:** 70
**Fees:** Day £2,265–£6,495

**Epsom College**
Epsom, Surrey KT17 4JQ
**Tel:** 01372 821000
**Headmaster:** Mr Jay A Piggot MA
**Age range:** 13–18
**No. of pupils:** 730
**Fees:** Day £21,255 FB £31,098

**Essendene Lodge School**
Essendene Road, Caterham,
Surrey CR3 5PB
**Tel:** 01883 348349
**Head Teacher:** Mrs J Wermig
**Age range:** 2–11
**No. of pupils:** 153
**Fees:** Day £2,775–£5,550

**Ewell Castle School**
Church Street, Ewell, Epsom,
Surrey KT17 2AW
**Tel:** 020 8393 1413
**Principal:** Mr Peter Harris
**Age range:** 3–18
**No. of pupils:** 557
**Fees:** Day £4,740–£15,975

**Feltonfleet School**
Cobham, Surrey KT11 1DR
**Tel:** 01932 862264
**Headmaster:** P C Ward
**Age range:** 3–13
**No. of pupils:** 356
**Fees:** Day £7,680–£11,250
WB £15,750

**Focus School – Hindhead Campus**
Tilford Road, Hindhead,
Surrey GU26 6SJ
**Tel:** 01428 601800
**Head:** Mr S Hardy
**Age range:** 8–18
**No. of pupils:** 90

**Frensham Heights**
Rowledge, Farnham,
Surrey GU10 4EA
**Tel:** 01252 792561
**Headmaster:** Mr Andrew Fisher BA,
MEd, FRSA
**Age range:** 3–18
**No. of pupils:** 497 VIth105
**Fees:** Day £5,205–£15,300
FB £19,485–£22,680

**Glenesk School**
Ockham Road North, East
Horsley, Surrey KT24 6NS
**Tel:** 01483 282329
**Headmistress:** Mrs S Christie-Hall
**Age range:** 2–7
**Fees:** Day £1,350–£8,112

**Greenfield**
Brooklyn Road, Woking,
Surrey GU22 7TP
**Tel:** 01483 772525
**Headmistress:** Mrs Tania Botting BEd
**Age range:** 3–11
**No. of pupils:** 179
**Fees:** Day £4,284–£9,450

**Guildford High School**
London Road, Guildford,
Surrey GU1 1SJ
**Tel:** 01483 561440
**Headmistress:** Mrs F J Boulton BSc,
MA
**Age range:** G4–18
**No. of pupils:** 980 VIth160
**Fees:** Day £10,176–£16,512

**Guildford Secretarial & Business College**
17 Chapel Street, Guildford,
Surrey GU1 3UL
**Tel:** 01483 564885
**Corporate Training Manager:** Mrs V
Alexander
**Fees:** Day £0

**Hall Grove School**
London Road, Bagshot,
Surrey GU19 5HZ
**Tel:** 01276 473059
**Headmaster:** Mr Alastair Graham
**Age range:** 3–13
**No. of pupils:** 452
**Fees:** Day £10,455–£13,650

**Halstead Preparatory School**
Woodham Rise, Woking,
Surrey GU21 4EE
**Tel:** 01483 772682
**Headmistress:** Mrs P Austin
**Age range:** G3–11
**No. of pupils:** 220
**Fees:** Day £2,673–£12,162

**Hampton Court House**
Hampton Court Road, East
Molesey, Surrey KT8 9BS
**Tel:** 020 8943 0889
**Headmaster:** Mr Guy Holloway
**Age range:** 3–16
**No. of pupils:** VIth20
**Fees:** Day £7,842–£10,017

**HawleyHurst School**
Fernhill Road, Blackwater,
Camberley, Surrey GU17 9HU
**Tel:** 01276 587190
**Principal:** Miss V S Smit
**Age range:** 2–19

**Hazelwood School**
Wolf's Hill, Limpsfield,
Oxted, Surrey RH8 0QU
**Tel:** 01883 712194
**Head:** Mrs Maxine Shaw
**Age range:** 2–13
**No. of pupils:** 399
**Fees:** Day £3,585–£11,100

**Hoe Bridge School**
Hoe Place, Old Woking Road,
Woking, Surrey GU22 8JE
**Tel:** 01483 760018 &
01483 772194
**Head:** Mr N Arkell BSc
**Age range:** 2–14
**Fees:** Day £5,355–£14,080

**Hurtwood House**
Holmbury St Mary, Dorking,
Surrey RH5 6NU
**Tel:** 01483 279000
**Principal:** Mr Cosmo Jackson
**Age range:** 16–18
**No. of pupils:** 300
**Fees:** FB £30,600–£35,100

**International School of London (ISL) Surrey**
Old Woking Road, Woking,
Surrey GU22 8HY
**Tel:** +44 (0)1483 750409
**Campus Principal & Head of
Secondary:** Richard Parker
**Age range:** 2–18 years
**No. of pupils:** 252
**Fees:** Day £17,700–£21,900

**Kids Inc Day Nursery – Guildford**
Railton Road, Queen Elizabeth
Park, Guildford, Surrey GU2 9LX
**Tel:** 01483 237999

**King Edward's Witley**
Godalming, Surrey GU8 5SG
**Tel:** +44 (0)1428 686700
**Headmaster:** Mr John Attwater MA
**Age range:** 11–18
**No. of pupils:** 410 VIth185
**Fees:** Day £19,950 FB £30,780

**Kingswood House School**
56 West Hill, Epsom, Surrey KT19 8LG
**Tel:** 01372 723590
**Headmaster:** Mr Duncan Murphy
BA (Hons), MEd, FRSA, Member of
IAPS & SoH
**Age range:** B3–16
**No. of pupils:** 210

**Lanesborough**
Maori Road, Guildford,
Surrey GU1 2EL
**Tel:** 01483 880489
**Head:** Mrs Clare Turnbull BA(Hons)
MEd
**Age range:** B3–13
**No. of pupils:** 350
**Fees:** Day £10,479–£14,688

**Lingfield College**
Racecourse Road, Lingfield,
Surrey RH7 6PH
**Tel:** 01342 833176
**Headmaster:** Mr R Bool
**Age range:** 2–18
**No. of pupils:** 935
**Fees:** Day £11,250–£14,600

**Longacre School**
Hullbrook Lane, Shamley Green,
Guildford, Surrey GU5 0NQ
**Tel:** 01483 893225
**Head of School:** Mr Matthew Bryan
**Age range:** 2–11
**No. of pupils:** 260

**Lyndhurst School**
36 The Avenue, Camberley,
Surrey GU15 3NE
**Tel:** 01276 22895
**Head:** Mr A Rudkin BEd(Hons)
**Age range:** 2–11
**Fees:** Day £9,690–£11,655

**Manor House School**
Manor House Lane, Little Bookham,
Leatherhead, Surrey KT23 4EN
**Tel:** 01372 458538
**Headmistress:** Tracey Fantham
**Age range:** G2–16
**No. of pupils:** 360
**Fees:** Day £750–£4,070

**Micklefield School**
10/12 Somers Road, Reigate,
Surrey RH2 9DU
**Tel:** 01737 242615
**Headmistress:** Mrs L Rose BEd(Hons),
CertEd, Dip PC
**Age range:** 3–11
**No. of pupils:** 272
**Fees:** Day £2,565–£9,030

**Milbourne Lodge School**
Arbrook Lane, Esher,
Surrey KT10 9EG
**Tel:** 01372 462737
**Head:** Mrs Judy Waite
**Age range:** 4–13
**No. of pupils:** 276
**Fees:** Day £11,760–£14,664

**New Life Christian
Primary School**
Cairo New Road, Croydon,
Surrey CR0 1XP
**Tel:** 020 8680 7671 Ext:327

**Notre Dame School**
Cobham, Surrey KT11 1HA
**Tel:** 01932 869990
**Head of Seniors:** Mrs Anna King
MEd, MA (Cantab), PGCE
**Age range:** 2–18
**No. of pupils:** 600

**Oakhyrst Grange School**
160 Stanstead Road,
Caterham, Surrey CR3 6AF
**Tel:** 01883 343344
**Headmaster:** Mr A Gear
**Age range:** 4–11
**No. of pupils:** 142
**Fees:** Day £1,107–£2,450

**Parkside School**
The Manor, Stoke d'Abernon,
Cobham, Surrey KT11 3PX
**Tel:** 01932 862749
**Headmaster:** Mr David Aylward
BEd(Hons), MA
**Age range:** B2–13 G2–4
**No. of pupils:** 382
**Fees:** Day £1,089–£13,350

**Prior's Field**
Priorsfield Road, Godalming,
Surrey GU7 2RH
**Tel:** 01483 810551
**Head of School:** Mrs T Kirnig
**Age range:** G11–18
**No. of pupils:** 450
**Fees:** Day £15,855 FB £25,575

**Reed's School**
Sandy Lane, Cobham,
Surrey KT11 2ES
**Tel:** 01932 869001
**Headmaster:** Mr Mark Hoskins BA
MA MSc
**Age range:** B11–18 G16–18
**No. of pupils:** 650 VIth230
**Fees:** Day £16,938–£21,184
FB £22,582–£28,023

**Reigate Grammar School**
Reigate Road, Reigate,
Surrey RH2 0QS
**Tel:** 01737 222231
**Headmaster:** Mr Shaun Fenton MA
(Oxon) MEd (Oxon)
**Age range:** 11–18
**No. of pupils:** 969 VIth262
**Fees:** Day £17,460

**Reigate St Mary's Prep
& Choir School**
Chart Lane, Reigate,
Surrey RH2 7RN
**Tel:** 01737 244880
**Headmaster:** Mr Marcus Culverwell
MA
**Age range:** 3–11
**No. of pupils:** 350

**Ripley Court School**
Rose Lane, Ripley, Surrey GU23 6NE
**Tel:** 01483 225217
**Headmaster:** Mr A J Gough
**Age range:** 3–13
**No. of pupils:** 281
**Fees:** Day £8,985–£13,680

**Rowan Preparatory School**
6 Fitzalan Road, Claygate,
Surrey KT10 0LX
**Tel:** 01372 462627
**Headmistress:** Mrs Susan Clarke
BEd, NPQH
**Age range:** G2–11
**No. of pupils:** 317
**Fees:** Day £10,866–£14,418

**Royal Grammar
School, Guildford**
High Street, Guildford,
Surrey GU1 3BB
**Tel:** 01483 880600
**Headmaster:** Dr J M Cox BSc, PhD
**Age range:** B11–18
**No. of pupils:** 940
**Fees:** Day £17,595

**Royal School of
Needlework**
Apartment 12A, Hampton
Court Palace, East Molesey,
Surrey KT8 9AU
**Tel:** 020 8943 1432
**Principal:** Mrs E Elvin
**Age range:** 17–30
**No. of pupils:** 24
**Fees:** Day £0

**Rydes Hill Preparatory
School**
Rydes Hill House, Aldershot Road,
Guildford, Surrey GU2 8BP
**Tel:** 01483 563160
**Headmistress:** Mrs Stephanie Bell
MA(Oxon)
**Age range:** B3–7 G3–11
**No. of pupils:** 180

**Shrewsbury Lodge School**
22 Milbourne Lane, Esher,
Surrey KT10 9EA
**Tel:** 01372 462781
**Head:** Mr James Tilly BA (Hons), QTS
**Age range:** 3–7
**Fees:** Day £2,655–£4,232

**Sir William Perkins's School**
Guildford Road, Chertsey,
Surrey KT16 9BN
**Tel:** 01932 574900
**Head:** Mr C Muller
**Age range:** G11–18 years
**No. of pupils:** 605 VIth140
**Fees:** Day £14,163

**St Catherine's School**
Bramley, Guildford, Surrey GU5 0DF
**Tel:** 01483 893363
**Headmistress:** Mrs A M Phillips
MA(Cantab)
**Age range:** G4–18
**No. of pupils:** 900
**Fees:** Day £7,695–£15,660 FB £25,770

**St Christopher's School**
6 Downs Road, Epsom,
Surrey KT18 5HE
**Tel:** 01372 721807
**Headteacher:** Mrs A C Thackray
MA, BA(Hons)
**Age range:** 3–7
**No. of pupils:** 137
**Fees:** Day £1,250–£2,450

**St Edmund's School**
Portsmouth Road, Hindhead,
Surrey GU26 6BH
**Tel:** 01428 604808
**Headmaster:** Mr A J Walliker
MA(Cantab), MBA, PGCE
**Age range:** 2–16
**No. of pupils:** 410
**Fees:** Day £3,195–£5,315

**St George's College**
Weybridge Road, Addlestone,
Weybridge, Surrey KT15 2QS
**Tel:** 01932 839300
**Headmaster:** Mr Joe Peake
**Age range:** 11–18
**No. of pupils:** 909 VIth250
**Fees:** Day £15,120–£17,235

**St George's Junior School**
Thames Street, Weybridge,
Surrey KT13 8NL
**Tel:** 01932 839400
**Head Master:** Mr Antony Hudson
MA (CANTAB), PGCE, NPQH
**Age range:** 3–11 years
**No. of pupils:** 644
**Fees:** Day £4,980–£12,915

**St Hilary's School**
Holloway Hill, Godalming,
Surrey GU7 1RZ
**Tel:** 01483 416551
**Headmistress:** Mrs Jane
Whittingham BEdCert,
ProfPracSpLD
**Age range:** B2–7 G2–11
**No. of pupils:** 250
**Fees:** Day £10,092–£14,850

**St Ives School**
Three Gates Lane, Haslemere,
Surrey GU27 2ES
**Tel:** 01428 643734
**Headteacher:** Mrs S E Cattaneo
CertEd
**Age range:** B3–4 G3–11
**No. of pupils:** 149
**Fees:** Day £6,600–£9,225

**St John's School**
Epsom Road, Leatherhead,
Surrey KT22 8SP
**Tel:** 01372 373000
**Head of School:** Mrs Rowena Cole
**Age range:** 11–18
**No. of pupils:** 761
**Fees:** Day £23,580 WB £29,790

**St Teresa's Effingham
(Preparatory School)**
Effingham, Surrey RH5 6ST
**Tel:** 01372 453456
**Headmaster:** Mr. Mike Farmer
**Age range:** B2–4 G2–11
**No. of pupils:** 100
**Fees:** Day £735–£11,235
WB £19,845 FB £21,780

**St Teresa's Effingham
(Senior School)**
Beech Avenue, Effingham,
Surrey RH5 6ST
**Tel:** 01372 452037
**Head:** Mr Michael Farmer
**Age range:** G3–18
**No. of pupils:** 640 VIth90
**Fees:** Day £16,980–£17,595 WB
£27,489–£27,795 FB £29,340–£29,955

### St. Andrew's School
Church Hill House, Horsell,
Woking, Surrey GU21 4QW
**Tel:** 01483 760943
**Headmaster:** Mr A Perks
**Age range:** 3–13
**No. of pupils:** 313
**Fees:** Day £3,690–£14,520

### Surbiton Preparatory School
3 Avenue Elmers, Surbiton,
Surrey KT6 4SP
**Tel:** 020 8390 6640
**Head of Surbiton High, Junior Girls' & Bo:** Ms C Bufton BA(Hons)
**Age range:** B4–11
**No. of pupils:** 135
**Fees:** Day £6,783–£9,246

### Tante Marie Culinary Academy
Woodham House, Carlton Road,
Woking, Surrey GU21 4HF
**Tel:** 01483 726957
**Principal:** Mr Andrew Maxwell
**Age range:** 16–60
**No. of pupils:** 72
**Fees:** Day £20,750

### TASIS The American School in England
Coldharbour Lane, Thorpe,
Surrey TW20 8TE
**Tel:** +44 (0)1932 582316
**Head of School:** Mr Bryan Nixon
**Age range:** 3–18
**No. of pupils:** 700
**Fees:** Day £10,900–£23,190 FB £41,870

### The Hawthorns School
Pendell Court, Bletchingley,
Redhill, Surrey RH1 4QJ
**Tel:** 01883 743048
**Headmaster:** Mr A E Floyd BSc(Hons), PGCE
**Age range:** 2–13
**No. of pupils:** 535
**Fees:** Day £1,920–£12,600

### The Royal Senior School, Haslemere
Farnham Lane, Haslemere,
Surrey GU27 1HQ
**Tel:** 01428 603052
**Principal:** Mrs Anne Lynch BA, PGCE, FRSA
**Age range:** 11–18 years
**No. of pupils:** 243
**Fees:** Day £17,400–£17,700 WB £26,100–£26,400 FB £29,700–£30,000

### Tormead School
27 Cranley Road, Guildford,
Surrey GU1 2JD
**Tel:** 01483 575101
**Headmistress:** Mrs Christina Foord
**Age range:** G4–18
**No. of pupils:** 760 VIth120
**Fees:** Day £5,520–£11,565

### Warlingham Park School
Chelsham Common,
Warlingham, Surrey CR6 9PB
**Tel:** 01883 626844
**Headmaster:** Mr M R Donald BSc
**Age range:** 3–11
**No. of pupils:** 96
**Fees:** Day £4,110–£8,310

### Weston Green School
Weston Green Road, Thames
Ditton, Surrey KT7 0JN
**Tel:** 020 8398 2778
**Head:** Mrs Lucia Harvey CertEd
**Age range:** 4–8
**Fees:** Day £4,574–£7,800

### Westward Preparatory School
47 Hersham Road, Walton-on-Thames, Surrey KT12 1LE
**Tel:** 01932 220911
**Headmistress:** Mrs P Robertson CertEd
**Age range:** 3–12
**No. of pupils:** 140
**Fees:** Day £4,560–£5,655

### Woldingham School
Marden Park, Woldingham,
Surrey CR3 7YA
**Tel:** 01883 349431
**Headmistress:** Mrs Jayne Triffitt MA(Oxon)
**Age range:** G11–18
**No. of pupils:** 530 VIth150
**Fees:** Day £23,700 FB £28,410

### Woodcote House School
Snows Ride, Windlesham,
Surrey GU20 6PF
**Tel:** 01276 472115
**Headmaster:** Mr Henry Knight
**Age range:** B7–13
**No. of pupils:** 100
**Fees:** Day £14,025 FB £18,900

### World Federation of Hairdressing & Beauty Schools
PO Box 367, Coulsdon,
Surrey CR5 2TP
**Tel:** 01737 551355

### Yehudi Menuhin School
Stoke Road, Stoke d'Abernon,
Cobham, Surrey KT11 3QQ
**Tel:** 01932 864739
**Headmaster:** Dr. Richard J Hillier MA(Cantab), PhD
**Age range:** 7–19
**No. of pupils:** 80 VIth36
**Fees:** FB £41,928

# West Berkshire

### Brockhurst & Marlston House Schools
Hermitage, Newbury, West
Berkshire RG18 9UL
**Tel:** 01635 200293
**Joint Heads:** Mr David Fleming & Mrs Caroline Riley
**Age range:** G3–13
**No. of pupils:** 275
**Fees:** Day £7,410–£12,450 WB £16,530 FB £16,530

### Cheam School
Headley, Newbury, West
Berkshire RG19 8LD
**Tel:** +44 (0)1635 268242
**Headmaster:** Mr Martin Harris
**Age range:** 3–13
**No. of pupils:** 407
**Fees:** Day £3,805–£6,655 FB £8,995

### Downe House School
Hermitage Road, Cold Ash,
Thatcham, West Berkshire RG18 9JJ
**Tel:** 01635 200286
**Headmistress:** Mrs E McKendrick BA(Liverpool)
**Age range:** G11–18
**No. of pupils:** VIth174
**Fees:** Day £25,440 FB £35,160

### Horris Hill
Newtown, Newbury, West
Berkshire RG20 9DJ
**Tel:** 01635 40594
**Headmaster:** Mr G F Tollit B.A.(Hons)
**Age range:** B7–13
**No. of pupils:** 120
**Fees:** Day £5,600 FB £8,900

### Marlston House Preparatory School
Hermitage, Newbury, West
Berkshire RG18 9UL
**Tel:** 01635 200293
**Headmistress:** Mrs Caroline Riley MA, BEd
**Age range:** G3–13
**No. of pupils:** 110
**Fees:** Day £7,410–£12,450 WB £16,530

### Newbury Hall
Enborne Road, (corner of
Rockingham Road), Newbury,
West Berkshire RG14 6AD
**Tel:** +44 (0)1635 36879

### St Gabriel's
Sandleford Priory, Newbury,
West Berkshire RG20 9BD
**Tel:** 01635 555680
**Principal:** Mr Richard Smith MA (Hons), MEd, PGCE
**Age range:** B6 months–11 G6 months–18
**No. of pupils:** 469 VIth40
**Fees:** Day £10,308–£16,830

### St Michael's School
Harts Lane, Burghclere, Newbury,
West Berkshire RG20 9JW
**Tel:** 01635 278137
**Headmaster:** Rev. Fr. Patrick Summers
**Age range:** 5–18
**No. of pupils:** VIth5

### The Cedars School
Church Road, Aldermaston,
West Berkshire RG7 4LR
**Tel:** 0118 971 4251
**Headteacher:** Mrs Jane O'Halloran
**Age range:** 4–11
**No. of pupils:** 50
**Fees:** Day £8,250

### The Royal Berkshire Academy of Performing Arts
42 Pembroke, Bracknell,
West Berkshire RG12 7RD
**Tel:** 020 7193 9485
**Age range:** 8–19

### Thorngrove School
The Mount, Highclere, Newbury,
West Berkshire RG20 9PS
**Tel:** 01635 253172
**Headmaster:** Mr Adam King
**Age range:** 2–13
**Fees:** Day £11,070–£13,860

# West Sussex

## Ardingly College
College Road, Ardingly, Haywards Heath, West Sussex RH17 6SQ
**Tel:** +44 (0)1444 893320
**Headmaster:** Mr Ben Figgis
**Age range:** 13–18
**No. of pupils:** 559
**Fees:** Day £22,380–£23,610 FB £30,480–£32,130

## Ardingly College Preparatory School
Haywards Heath, West Sussex RH17 6SQ
**Tel:** 01444 893200
**Headmaster:** Mr Chris Calvey BEd
**Age range:** 2–13
**Fees:** Day £5,925–£13,950

## Ashton Park School
Brinsbury Campus East, Stane Street, North Heath, Pulborough, West Sussex RH20 1DJ
**Tel:** 01798 875836
**Head:** Mr G Holding
**Age range:** 11–16
**No. of pupils:** 66

## Brambletye
Brambletye, East Grinstead, West Sussex RH19 3PD
**Tel:** 01342 321004
**Headmaster:** Will Brooks
**Age range:** 2–13
**No. of pupils:** 280
**Fees:** Day £7,260–£19,635 FB £23,400–£23,940

## Burgess Hill Girls
Keymer Road, Burgess Hill, West Sussex RH15 0EG
**Tel:** 01444 241050
**Head of School:** Liz Laybourn
**Age range:** B2.5–4 G2.5–18
**No. of pupils:** 550 VIth87
**Fees:** Day £7,350–£16,950 FB £27,300–£30,450

## Chichester High Schools Sixth Form
Kingsham Road, Chichester, West Sussex PO19 8AE
**Tel:** +44 1243 832 546

## Christ's Hospital
Horsham, West Sussex RH13 0LJ
**Tel:** 01403 211293
**Headmaster:** Mr Simon Reid
**Age range:** 11–18
**No. of pupils:** 900
**Fees:** Day £16,950–£21,330 FB £32,790

## Conifers School
Egmont Road, Midhurst, West Sussex GU29 9BG
**Tel:** 01730 813243
**Headmistress:** Mrs Emma Smyth
**Age range:** 2–13
**No. of pupils:** 104
**Fees:** Day £6,030–£8,400

## Copthorne Prep School
Effingham Lane, Copthorne, West Sussex RH10 3HR
**Tel:** 01342 712311
**Headmaster:** Mr Chris Jones
**Age range:** 2–13
**No. of pupils:** 340
**Fees:** Day £2,860–£4,980 WB £5,650

## Cottesmore School
Buchan Hill, Pease Pottage, West Sussex RH11 9AU
**Tel:** 01293 520648
**Head:** T F Rogerson
**Age range:** 4–13
**No. of pupils:** 150
**Fees:** Day £4,800–£12,600 WB £16,875 FB £18,750

## Cumnor House Sussex
London Road, Danehill, Haywards Heath, West Sussex RH17 7HT
**Tel:** 01825 792 006
**Headmaster:** Christian Heinrich
**Age range:** 2–13
**No. of pupils:** 385
**Fees:** Day £8,025–£18,795 FB £22,365

## Dorset House School
The Manor, Church Lane, Bury, Pulborough, West Sussex RH20 1PB
**Tel:** 01798 831456
**Headmaster:** R C M Brown MA, PGCE
**Age range:** 3–13
**No. of pupils:** 135
**Fees:** Day £7,290–£14,595 WB £15,810–£17,685

## Farlington School
Strood Park, Horsham, West Sussex RH12 3PN
**Tel:** 01403 282573
**Headmistress:** Ms Louise Higson BSc, PGCE
**Age range:** G3–18
**No. of pupils:** 300
**Fees:** Day £5,660 WB £9,170 FB £9,600

## Great Ballard School
Eartham, Chichester, West Sussex PO18 0LR
**Tel:** 01243 814236
**Head:** Mr Richard Evans
**Age range:** 2–13
**No. of pupils:** 136
**Fees:** Day £8,250–£15,300 WB £16,350 FB £23,700

## Great Walstead School
East Mascalls Lane, Lindfield, Haywards Heath, West Sussex RH16 2QL
**Tel:** 01444 483528
**Headmaster:** Mr C Baty NPQH, BEd(Waikato NZ)
**Age range:** 2.5–13
**No. of pupils:** 465
**Fees:** Day £7,695–£14,835

## Handcross Park School
Handcross, Haywards Heath, West Sussex RH17 6HF
**Tel:** 01444 400526
**Headmaster:** Mr Richard Brown
**Age range:** 2–13
**No. of pupils:** 339
**Fees:** Day £3,060–£6,040 FB £5,090–£7,720

## Hurstpierpoint College
College Lane, Hurstpierpoint, West Sussex BN6 9JS
**Tel:** 01273 833636
**Headmaster:** Mr. T J Manly BA, MSc
**Age range:** 4–18
**No. of pupils:** 1156
**Fees:** Day £8,790–£22,860 WB £28,800

## Hurstpierpoint College Prep School
Hurstpierpoint, West Sussex BN6 9JS
**Tel:** 01273 834975
**Head:** Mr I D Pattison BSc
**Age range:** 4–13
**No. of pupils:** 360

## Lancing College
Lancing, West Sussex BN15 0RW
**Tel:** 01273 465805
**Head Master:** Mr Dominic T Oliver MPhil
**Age range:** 13–18
**No. of pupils:** 550 VIth255
**Fees:** Day £7,710 FB £10,970

## Lancing College Preparatory School at Worthing
Broadwater Road, Worthing, West Sussex BN14 8HU
**Tel:** 01903 201123
**Head:** Mrs Heather Beeby
**Age range:** 2–13
**No. of pupils:** 165
**Fees:** Day £765–£10,380

## Oakwood Preparatory School
Chichester, West Sussex PO18 9AN
**Tel:** 01243 575209
**Headteacher:** Mrs Clare Bradbury
**Age range:** 2.5–11
**No. of pupils:** 260
**Fees:** Day £1,600–£4,565

## Our Lady of Sion School
Gratwicke Road, Worthing, West Sussex BN11 4BL
**Tel:** 01903 204063
**Headmaster:** Mr M Scullion MA, BEd
**Age range:** 2–18
**No. of pupils:** 528 VIth55
**Fees:** Day £5,715–£9,150

## Pennthorpe School
Church Street, Horsham, West Sussex RH12 3HJ
**Tel:** 01403 822391
**Headmaster:** Mr Matthew King BA(Hons)
**Age range:** 2–13
**No. of pupils:** 362
**Fees:** Day £1,392–£12,690

## Rikkyo School in England
Guildford Road, Rudgwick, Horsham, West Sussex RH12 3BE
**Tel:** 01403 822107
**Headmaster:** Mr Roger Munechika
**Age range:** 10–18
**No. of pupils:** 116
**Fees:** FB £15,000–£21,600

## Seaford College
Lavington Park, Petworth, West Sussex GU28 0NB
**Tel:** 01798 867392
**Headmaster:** J P Green MA BA
**Age range:** 7–18
**No. of pupils:** 732 VIth194
**Fees:** Day £10,020–£20,775 WB £20,880–£28,140 FB £32,130

## Shoreham College
St Julians Lane, Shoreham-by-Sea, West Sussex BN43 6YW
**Tel:** 01273 592681
**Headmaster:** Mr R Taylor-West
**Age range:** 3–16 years
**No. of pupils:** 375
**Fees:** Day £8,550–£13,350

## Slindon College
Slindon House, Slindon, Arundel,
West Sussex BN18 0RH
**Tel:** 01243 814320
**Headmaster:** Mr D Quick
**Age range:** B8–18
**No. of pupils:** 80 VIth17
**Fees:** Day £7,053 WB
£10,445 FB £10,445

## Sompting Abbotts Preparatory School for Boys and Girls
Church Lane, Sompting,
West Sussex BN15 0AZ
**Tel:** 01903 235960
**Principal:** Mrs P M Sinclair
**Age range:** 2–13
**No. of pupils:** 185
**Fees:** Day £7,860–£10,095

## The Prebendal School
52-55 West Street, Chichester,
West Sussex PO19 1RT
**Tel:** 01243 772220
**Headteacher:** Mrs L Salmond Smith
**Age range:** 3–13
**No. of pupils:** 181
**Fees:** Day £7,695–£14,610
WB £18,930 FB £20,100

## The Towers Convent School
Convent of the Blessed Sacrement,
Henfield Road, Upper Beeding,
Steyning, West Sussex BN44 3TF
**Tel:** 01903 812185
**Headmistress:** Mrs Clare Trelfa
**Age range:** B2–8 G2–16
**No. of pupils:** 320
**Fees:** Day £7,320–£10,200

## Westbourne House School
Shopwyke, Chichester,
West Sussex PO20 2BH
**Tel:** 01243 782739
**Headmaster:** Mr Martin Barker
**Age range:** 2.5–13 years
**No. of pupils:** 420
**Fees:** Day £9,960–£17,160 FB £20,940

## Windlesham House School
Washington, Pulborough,
West Sussex RH20 4AY
**Tel:** 01903 874700
**Headmaster:** Mr Richard Foster
BEd(Hons)
**Age range:** 4–13
**No. of pupils:** 350

## Worth School
Paddockhurst Road, Turners Hill,
Crawley, West Sussex RH10 4SD
**Tel:** +44 (0)1342 710200
**Head Master:** Gino Carminati MA,
FRSA
**Age range:** 11–18
**No. of pupils:** 580 VIth222
**Fees:** Day £20,235 FB £27,849

# International Schools in London and the South-East

# London

## Central London

### CATS London
43-45 Bloomsbury Square,
London WC1A 2RA
**Tel:** 02078 411580
**Principal:** Mario Di Clemente
**Age range:** 15–24
🌍 🏫 £ 16+

### ÉCOLE JEANNINE MANUEL – LONDON
*For further details see p. 50*
43-45 Bedford Square,
London WC1B 3DN
**Tel:** 020 3829 5970
**Email:** contact@jmanuel.uk.net
**Website:** www.ecole
jeanninemanuel.org.uk
**Head of School:** Pauline Prévot
**Age range:** 3–18 years
**No. of pupils:** 350
**Fees:** Day £17,460
🌍 £ IB

## North London

### Dwight School London
6 Friern Barnet Lane,
London N11 3LX
**Tel:** +44 (0)20 8920 0637
**Head:** Mrs Alison Cobbin BA, Dip
Ed, MBA
**Age range:** 3–18
🌍 £ IB 🏊 16+

## North-West London

### College Francais Bilingue De Londres
87 Holmes Road, Kentish
Town, London NW5 3AX
**Tel:** +44 (0) 20 7993 7400
**Principal:** Mr François-Xavier Gabet
**Age range:** 5–15
**No. of pupils:** 210
🌍

### International Community School
4 York Terrace East, Regents
Park, London NW1 4PT
**Tel:** +44 20 7935 1206
**Head of School:** Ms Rose Threlfall
**Age range:** 3–18
**No. of pupils:** 260
**Fees:** Day £16,650–£22,100
🌍 IB 🏊 16+

### Mill Hill School
The Ridgeway, Mill Hill
Village, London NW7 1QS
**Tel:** 020 8959 1176
**Head:** Dr Dominic Luckett
**Age range:** 13–18
**No. of pupils:** 689 VIth259
**Fees:** Day £13,860 FB £21,900
🌍 🏫 £ 🏊 16+

## Southbank International School – Hampstead
16 Netherhall Gardens,
London NW3 5TH
**Tel:** 020 7243 3803
**Principal:** Shirley Harwood
**Age range:** 3–11
🌍 IB 🏊

### The American School in London
One Waverley Place,
London NW8 0NP
**Tel:** 020 7449 1221
**Head:** Mrs Coreen Hester
**Age range:** 4–18
**No. of pupils:** 1350
**Fees:** Day £21,950–£25,650
🌍 16+

### The Mount, Mill Hill International
Milespit Hill, London NW7 2RX
**Tel:** +44 (0)20 3826 33
**Head of School:** Ms Sarah Bellotti
**Age range:** 13–17
**No. of pupils:** 68
**Fees:** Day £23,799 WB
£33,618 FB £39,549
🌍 🏫

## South-East London

### Bellerbys College London
Bounty House, Greenwich,
London SE8 3DE
**Tel:** +44 (0)208 694 7000
**Principal:** Ms Alison Baines
**Age range:** 15–19
🌍 16+ 🏫

### Dulwich College
London SE21 7LD
**Tel:** 020 8693 3601
**Master:** Dr J A F Spence
**Age range:** B7–18
**No. of pupils:** 1589 VIth470
**Fees:** Day £18,231 WB
£35,679 FB £38,052
👦 🌍 🏫 £ 🏊 16+

### St Dunstan's College
Stanstead Road, London SE6 4TY
**Tel:** 020 8516 7200
**Headmistress:** Mrs J D Davies BSc
**Age range:** 3–18
**No. of pupils:** 870
🌍 £ 16+

## South-West London

### Centre Academy London
92 St John's Hill, Battersea,
London SW11 1SH
**Tel:** 020 7738 2344
**Principal:** Dr. Duncan Rollo BA,
MA, PhD
**Age range:** 9–19
**Fees:** Day £27,600–£40,100
🌍 £ 16+

## Eaton Square School
79 Eccleston Square,
London SW1V 1PP
**Tel:** 020 7931 9469
**Headmaster:** Mr Sebastian Hepher
BEd(Hons)
**Age range:** 2–13
**No. of pupils:** 529
**Fees:** Day £4,080–£19,785
🌍 £ 🏊 🏫

### Ecole Charles De Gaulle – Wix
Clapham Common North
Side, London SW4 0AJ
**Tel:** +44 20 7738 0287
**Headteacher:** Mr Blanchard
**Age range:** 5–11
**No. of pupils:** 100
🌍

### Ecole Marie D'Orliac
60 Clancarty Road, London SW6 3AA
**Tel:** +44 7736 020 58 63
**Principal:** Mr Olivier Rauch
**Age range:** 4–11
**No. of pupils:** 50
🌍

### HILL HOUSE INTERNATIONAL JUNIOR SCHOOL
*For further details see p. 54*
17 Hans Place, Chelsea,
London SW1X 0EP
**Tel:** 020 7584 1331
**Email:** info@hillhouseschool.co.uk
**Website:**
www.hillhouseschool.co.uk
**Principals:** Richard, Janet,
William & Edmund Townend
**Age range:** 4–13
**No. of pupils:** 740 VIth70
£ 🏊

### King's College School
Southside, Wimbledon
Common, London SW19 4TT
**Tel:** 020 8255 5300
**Head Master:** A D Halls MA
**Age range:** B11–18 G16–18
**No. of pupils:** 967
**Fees:** Day £18,975–£20,985
👦 🌍 £ IB 16+

### Lycée Français Charles de Gaulle
35 Cromwell Road, London SW7 2DG
**Tel:** 020 7584 6322
**Head of School:** Mr Olivier Rauch
**Age range:** 5–19
**No. of pupils:** 4000
🌍 £ 🏊 16+

### St Paul's School
Lonsdale Road, Barnes,
London SW13 9JT
**Tel:** 020 8748 9162
**High Master:** Prof Mark Bailey
**Age range:** B13–18
**No. of pupils:** 897
**Fees:** Day £19,674 FB £29,466
👦 🌍 🏫 £ 🏊 16+

## Wandsworth Preparatory School
The Old Library, 2 Allfarthing
Lane, London SW18 2PQ
**Tel:** 0208 870 4133
**Head of School:** Miss Bridget Saul
**No. of pupils:** 90
**Fees:** Day £4,458
🌍 £

### Westminster School
Little Dean's Yard, Westminster,
London SW1P 3PF
**Tel:** 020 7963 1003
**Headmaster:** Mr Patrick Derham
**Age range:** B13–18 G16–18
**No. of pupils:** 744
**Fees:** Day £26,130–
£28,566 FB £37,740
👦 🌍 🏫 £ 🏊 16+

## West London

### Bales College
742 Harrow Road, Kensal
Town, London W10 4AA
**Tel:** 020 8960 5899
**Principal:** William Moore
**Age range:** 11–19
**No. of pupils:** 90
**Fees:** Day £7,950–£8,550 FB £16,050
🌍 16+ 🏫 £

### DLD COLLEGE LONDON
*For further details see p. 48*
199 Westminster Bridge
Road, London SE1 7FX
**Tel:** +44 (0)20 7935 8411
**Email:** dld@dld.org
**Website:** www.dldcollege.co.uk
**Principal:** Irfan H Latif BSc (Hons)
PGCE FRSA FRSC
**No. of pupils:** 440
**Fees:** Day £19,000–£23,000
FB £16,500–£24,000
🌍 16+ 🏫 £ 🏊

### Ecole Francaise Jacques Prevert
59 Brook Green, London W6 7BE
**Tel:** 020 7602 6871
**Principal:** P Possenti
**Age range:** 4–11
🌍

### Fulham Prep School
200 Greyhound Road,
London W14 9SD
**Tel:** 020 7386 2444
**Head of School:** Mr Neil Brooks
**Age range:** 4–18
**No. of pupils:** 647
**Fees:** Day £16,335–£19,200
🌍 🏊

### Halcyon London International School
33 Seymour Place, London W1H 5AU
**Tel:** +44 (0)20 7258 1169
**Director:** Mr Barry Mansfield
**Age range:** 11–18
**No. of pupils:** 160

### Instituto Español Vicente Cañada Blanch
317 Portobello Road,
London W10 5SZ
**Tel:** +44 (0) 20 8969 2664
**Principal:** Mr A Vitria
**Age range:** 4–19
**No. of pupils:** 405

### International School of London (ISL) London
139 Gunnersbury Avenue,
Ealing, London W3 8LG
**Tel:** +44 (0)20 8992 5823
**Middle & Lower School Principal:** Andrew Mitchell
**Age range:** 3–18 years
**No. of pupils:** 480
**Fees:** Day £18,000–£24,600

### King Fahad Academy
Bromyard Avenue, Acton,
London W3 7HD
**Tel:** 020 8743 0131
**Director General:** Dr Abdulghani Alharbi
**Age range:** 3–19
**No. of pupils:** 550
**Fees:** Day £3,300–£4,300

### Southbank International School – Fitzrovia
17 Conway Street, London W1T 6BN
**Tel:** +44 2076 312600

### Southbank International School – Kensington
36-38 Kensington Park Road, London W11 3BU
**Tel:** +44 (0)20 7243 3803
**Interim Principal:** Jonathan Coward
**Age range:** 3–18

### Southbank International School – Westminster
63-65 Portland Place,
London W1B 1QR
**Tel:** 020 7243 3803
**Interim Principal:** Siobhan McGrath
**Age range:** 11–18/19

### The Godolphin and Latymer School
Iffley Road, Hammersmith,
London W6 0PG
**Tel:** +44 (0)20 8741 1936
**Head Mistress:** Dr Frances Ramsey
**Age range:** G11–18
**No. of pupils:** 800

# Berkshire

### Bradfield College
Bradfield, Berkshire RG7 6AU
**Tel:** 0118 964 4516
**Headmaster:** Dr Christopher Stevens
**Age range:** 13–18
**No. of pupils:** 790
**Fees:** Day £29,052 FB £36,315

### Eton College
Windsor, Berkshire SL4 6DW
**Tel:** 01753 671249
**Head Master:** Simon Henderson MA
**Age range:** B13–18
**No. of pupils:** 1300 VIth520
**Fees:** FB £33,270

### Heathfield School
London Road, Ascot,
Berkshire SL5 8BQ
**Tel:** 01344 898342
**Head of School:** Mrs Marina Gardiner Legge
**Age range:** G11–18
**No. of pupils:** 200

### Leighton Park School
Shinfield Road, Reading,
Berkshire RG2 7ED
**Tel:** +44 (0) 118 987 9600
**Head:** Nigel Williams BA(Bristol), MA(London), PGCE
**Age range:** 11–18
**No. of pupils:** 485
**Fees:** Day £21,654 WB £29,301 FB £34,044

### Luckley House School
Luckley Road, Wokingham,
Berkshire RG40 3EU
**Tel:** 0118 978 4175
**Head:** Mrs Jane Tudor
**Age range:** G11–18
**No. of pupils:** 230
**Fees:** Day £15,975 WB £25,908 FB £27,954

### LVS ASCOT
*For further details see p. 96*
London Road, Ascot,
Berkshire SL5 8DR
**Tel:** 01344 882770
**Email:** enquiries@lvs.
ascot.sch.uk
**Website:** www.lvs.ascot.sch.uk
**Headmistress:** Mrs Christine Cunniffe BA (Hons), MMus, MBA
**Age range:** 4–18
**No. of pupils:** 830
**Fees:** Day £9,708–£18,609 FB £24,846–£32,694

### Padworth College
Padworth, Reading,
Berkshire RG7 4NR
**Tel:** 0118 983 2644
**Principal:** Mr John Aguilar
**Age range:** 13–19
**No. of pupils:** 116 VIth50
**Fees:** Day £14,250 FB £28,392

### PANGBOURNE COLLEGE
*For further details see p. 94*
Pangbourne, Reading,
Berkshire RG8 8LA
**Tel:** 0118 984 2101
**Email:** registrar@
pangbourne.com
**Website:** www.pangbourne.com
**Headmaster:** Thomas J C Garnier
**Age range:** 11–18
**No. of pupils:** 426 VIth133
**Fees:** Day £17,055–£24,036 FB £24,021–£33,996

### Queen Anne's School
6 Henley Road, Caversham,
Reading, Berkshire RG4 6DX
**Tel:** 0118 918 7300
**Headmistress:** Mrs Julia Harrington BA(Hons), PGCE, NPQH
**Age range:** G11–18
**No. of pupils:** 336 VIth100
**Fees:** Day £5,695 WB £7,545–£7,975 FB £8,395

### Reddam House Berkshire
Bearwood Road, Sindlesham,
Wokingham, Berkshire RG41 5BG
**Tel:** 0118 974 8300
**Principal:** Mrs Tammy Howard
**Age range:** 3 months–18 years
**No. of pupils:** 480
**Fees:** Day £9,885–£16,800 WB £26,310–£30,330 FB £27,855–£31,875

### St George's Ascot
Wells Lane, Ascot, Berkshire SL5 7DZ
**Tel:** 01344 629920
**Headmistress:** Mrs Liz Hewer MA (Hons) (Cantab) PGCE
**Age range:** G11–18
**No. of pupils:** 270 VIth70
**Fees:** Day £21,900 WB £32,460–£33,570 FB £34,350

### St Mary's School Ascot
St Mary's Road, Ascot,
Berkshire SL5 9JF
**Tel:** 01344 296614
**Headmistress:** Mrs Mary Breen BSc, MSc
**Age range:** G11–18
**No. of pupils:** 390 VIth120
**Fees:** Day £23,400 FB £32,850

### The Abbey School
Kendrick Road, Reading,
Berkshire RG1 5DZ
**Tel:** 0118 987 2256
**Head:** Mrs Rachel S E Dent
**Age range:** G3–18
**No. of pupils:** 1100
**Fees:** Day £16,530

### The Oratory School
Woodcote, Reading,
Berkshire RG8 0PJ
**Tel:** 01491 683500
**Head Master:** Mr A J Wyles BSc(Hons), MEd, PGCE, FRGS
**Age range:** B11–18
**No. of pupils:** 380 VIth120
**Fees:** Day £23,250 FB £21,540–£31,950

### Wellington College
Duke's Ride, Crowthorne,
Berkshire RG45 7PU
**Tel:** +44 (0)1344 444000
**Master:** Mr Julian Thomas
**Age range:** 13–18
**No. of pupils:** 1040
**Fees:** Day £27,930–£32,085 FB £38,220

# Buckinghamshire

### Thornton College
Thornton, Milton Keynes,
Buckinghamshire MK17 0HJ
**Tel:** 01280 812610
**Headmistress:** Miss Agnes T Williams
**Age range:** B2–4+ G2–16
**No. of pupils:** 370
**Fees:** Day £6,300–£10,095 WB
£10,500–£13,305 FB £13,305–£16,545

### Wycombe Abbey
High Wycombe,
Buckinghamshire HP11 1PE
**Tel:** +44 (0)1494 897008
**Headmistress:** Mrs Rhiannon J
Wilkinson MA (Oxon) MEd
**Age range:** G11–18
**No. of pupils:** 611
**Fees:** Day £28,350 FB £37,800

# East Sussex

### Battle Abbey School
Battle, East Sussex TN33 0AD
**Tel:** 01424 772385
**Headmaster:** Mr R C Clark
BA(Hons), MA(Ed)
**Age range:** 2–18
**No. of pupils:** 286 VIth48
**Fees:** Day £6,630–£13,390 FB £23,190

### Bede's School
The Dicker, Upper Dicker,
Hailsham, East Sussex BN27 3QH
**Tel:** +44 (0)1323843252
**Head:** Dr Richard Maloney
**Age range:** 12.5–18+
**No. of pupils:** 800 VIth295
**Fees:** Day £15,450 FB £25,725

### Bellerbys College Brighton
1 Billinton Way, Brighton,
East Sussex BN1 4LF
**Tel:** +44 (0)1273 339333
**Principal:** Mr Simon Mower
**Age range:** 13–18

### Brighton College
Eastern Road, Brighton,
East Sussex BN2 0AL
**Tel:** 01273 704200
**Head Master:** Richard Cairns MA
**Age range:** 3–18
**No. of pupils:** 950
**Fees:** Day £9,720–£23,790
WB £32,220–£33,210 FB
£40,230–£42,420

### Buckswood School
Broomham Hall, Rye
Road, Guestling, Hastings,
East Sussex TN35 4LT
**Tel:** 01424 813 813
**Headmaster:** Mr Giles Sutton
**Age range:** 10–19
**No. of pupils:** 420

### Eastbourne College
Old Wish Road, Eastbourne,
East Sussex BN21 4JX
**Tel:** 01323 452323 (Admissions)
**Headmaster:** Mr T Lawson
MA(Oxon)
**Age range:** 13–18
**No. of pupils:** 610 VIth274
**Fees:** Day £22,260–£22,620
FB £33,930–£34,320

### Greenfields Independent Day & Boarding School
Priory Road, Forest Row,
East Sussex RH18 5JD
**Tel:** +44 (0)1342 822189
**Executive Head:** Mr. Jeff Smith
**Age range:** 2–19

### Mayfield School
The Old Palace, Mayfield,
East Sussex TN20 6PH
**Tel:** +44 (0)1435 874600
**Head:** Ms Antonia Beary MA, Mphil
(Cantab), PGCE
**Age range:** G11–18
**No. of pupils:** 365 VIth100
**Fees:** Day £19,650 FB £31,800

### Michael Hall School
Kidbrooke Park, Priory Road,
Forest Row, East Sussex RH18 5BG
**Tel:** 01342 822275
**Age range:** 3–19
**Fees:** Day £8,858–£12,180
FB £6,876–£7,876

### Moira House Girls School
Upper Carlisle Road, Eastbourne,
East Sussex BN20 7TE
**Tel:** 01323 644144
**Headmaster:** Mr James Sheridan
MA, BSc
**Age range:** G0–18
**No. of pupils:** 289

### ROEDEAN SCHOOL
**For further details see p. 97**
Roedean Way, Brighton,
East Sussex BN2 5RQ
**Tel:** 01273 667500
**Email:** info@roedean.co.uk
**Website:** www.roedean.co.uk
**Headmaster:** Mr. Oliver Bond
BA(Essex), PGCE, NPQH
**Age range:** G11–18
**No. of pupils:** 568 VIth171
**Fees:** Day £15,960–£20,865
WB £28,230–£31,470 FB
£30,930–£37,440

# Essex

### Brentwood School
Middleton Hall Lane,
Brentwood, Essex CM15 8EE
**Tel:** 01277 243243
**Headmaster:** Mr Ian Davies
**Age range:** 3–18
**No. of pupils:** 1529
**Fees:** Day £18,216 FB £35,700

### Chigwell School
High Road, Chigwell, Essex IG7 6QF
**Tel:** 020 8501 5700
**Headmaster:** Mr M E Punt MA, MSc
**Age range:** 4–18
**No. of pupils:** 915 VIth185
**Fees:** Day £10,200–£16,020
FB £26,730–£26,730

### Felsted School
Felsted, Great Dunmow,
Essex CM6 3LL
**Tel:** +44 (0)1371 822608
**Headmaster:** Mr Chris Townsend
**Age range:** 13–18
**No. of pupils:** 522 VIth426
**Fees:** Day £22,485 WB
£32,235 FB £34,275

### Gosfield School
Cut Hedge Park, Halstead Road,
Gosfield, Halstead, Essex CO9 1PF
**Tel:** 01787 474040
**Headteacher:** Mr Guy Martyn
**Age range:** 4–18
**No. of pupils:** VIth21
**Fees:** Day £4,740–£13,695 WB
£15,465–£17,310 FB £17,985–£23,130

### New Hall School
The Avenue, Boreham,
Chelmsford, Essex CM3 3HS
**Tel:** 01245 467588
**Principal:** Mrs Katherine Jeffrey MA,
BA, PGCE, MA(Ed Mg), NPQH
**Age range:** Coed 3-11,
Single 11-16, Coed 16–18
**No. of pupils:** 1180 VIth217
**Fees:** Day £9,432–£19,440 WB
£19,038–£27,813 FB £21,033–£29,847

# Hampshire

### Bedales School
Church Road, Steep, Petersfield,
Hampshire GU32 2DG
**Tel:** 01730 711733
**Head:** Keith Budge MA
**Age range:** 13–18
**No. of pupils:** 457
**Fees:** Day £9,272 FB £11,799

### Brockwood Park & Inwoods School
Brockwood Park, Bramdean,
Hampshire SO24 0LQ
**Tel:** +44 (0)1962 771744
**Co-Principals:** Mr Antonio Autor &
Dr Gopal Krishnamurthy
**Age range:** 4–19
**No. of pupils:** 112 VIth39
**Fees:** Day £5,630–£6,400
FB £21,400–£21,400

### Hampshire Collegiate School
Embley Park, Romsey,
Hampshire SO51 6ZE
**Tel:** 01794 512206
**Principal:** Mrs Emma-Kate Henry
**Age range:** 2–18
**No. of pupils:** 683

### Lord Wandsworth College
Long Sutton, Hook,
Hampshire RG29 1TB
**Tel:** 01256 862201
**Head of School:** Mr Adam Williams
**Age range:** 11–18 years
**No. of pupils:** 600
**Fees:** Day £19,650–£22,575 WB
£27,225–£30,600 FB £28,140–£32,100

### Moyles Court School
Moyles Court, Ringwood,
Hampshire BH24 3NF
**Tel:** 01425 472856
**Headmaster:** Mr Dean
**Age range:** 3–16
**Fees:** Day £3,285–£4,650
FB £6,690–£7,740

### Rookwood School
Weyhill Road, Andover,
Hampshire SP10 3AL
**Tel:** 01264 325900
**Headmistress:** Mrs L Whetstone MA
**Age range:** 3–16
**Fees:** Day £7,770–£12,780
FB £19,545–£22,875

### Sherfield School
Sherfield-on-Loddon, Hook,
Hampshire RG27 0HU
**Tel:** +44 (0)1256 884 800
**Headmaster:** Mr Dick Jaine
**Age range:** 3 months–18 years
**No. of pupils:** 445 VIth16
**Fees:** Day £7,350–£13,890 FB £20,946

### St John's College
Grove Road South, Southsea,
Portsmouth, Hampshire PO5 3QW
**Tel:** 023 9281 5118
**Headmaster:** Mr Timothy Bayley BSc
(Hons), MA, PGCE
**Age range:** 2–18
**No. of pupils:** 560 VIth86
**Fees:** Day £8,910–£11,685
FB £25,200–£27,090

### ST SWITHUN'S SCHOOL
*For further details see p. 99*
Alresford Road, Winchester,
Hampshire SO21 1HA
**Tel:** 01962 835700
**Email:** office@stswithuns.com
**Website:** www.stswithuns.com
**Head of School:** Jane Gandee
MA(Cantab)
**Age range:** G11–18
**No. of pupils:** 520

### The Portsmouth Grammar School
High Street, Portsmouth,
Hampshire PO1 2LN
**Tel:** +44 (0)23 9236 0036
**Headmaster:** Mr J E Priory MA
**Age range:** 2–18
**No. of pupils:** 1556 VIth336
**Fees:** Day £9,510–£14,817

### Winchester College
College Street, Winchester,
Hampshire SO23 9NA
**Tel:** 01962 621247
**Headmaster:** Dr. T R Hands
**Age range:** B13–18
**No. of pupils:** 690 VIth280
**Fees:** FB £36,678

# Hertfordshire

### Aldenham School
Elstree, Hertfordshire WD6 3AJ
**Tel:** 01923 858122
**Headmaster:** Mr James C Fowler
MA
**Age range:** 3–18
**No. of pupils:** 700
**Fees:** Day £15,291–£21,414
FB £21,099–£31,384

### BERKHAMSTED SCHOOL
*For further details see p. 92*
Overton House, 131 High
Street, Berkhamsted,
Hertfordshire HP4 2DJ
**Tel:** 01442 358001
**Email:** admissions@
berkhamstedschool.org
**Website:**
www.berkhamstedschool.org
**Principal:** Mr Richard Backhouse
MA(Cantab)
**Age range:** 3–18
**No. of pupils:** 1772 VIth402
**Fees:** Day £10,365–£20,250
WB £27,115 FB £32,255

### Bishop's Stortford College
10 Maze Green Road, Bishop's
Stortford, Hertfordshire CM23 2PJ
**Tel:** 01279 838575
**Headmaster:** Mr Jeremy Gladwin
**Age range:** 13–18
**No. of pupils:** VIth249
**Fees:** Day £18,915–£19,086
WB £28,665–£28,839 FB
£28,950–£30,273

### Bishop's Stortford College Prep School
Maze Green Road, Bishop's
Stortford, Hertfordshire CM23 2PH
**Tel:** 01279 838607
**Head of the Prep School:** Mr Bill
Toleman
**Age range:** 4–13
**No. of pupils:** 590
**Fees:** Day £8,745–£15,132 WB
£20,010–£21,726 FB £20,226–£22,857

### Haileybury
Haileybury, Hertford,
Hertfordshire SG13 7NU
**Tel:** +44 (0)1992 706200
**The Master:** Mr Martin Collier MA
BA PGCE
**Age range:** 11–18
**No. of pupils:** 804 VIth323
**Fees:** Day £16,455–£24,753
FB £20,796–£32,784

### Princess Helena College
Preston, Hitchin,
Hertfordshire SG4 7RT
**Tel:** 01462 443888
**Headmistress:** Mrs Sue Wallace-
Woodroffe
**Age range:** G11–18
**No. of pupils:** 194 VIth35
**Fees:** Day £15,585–£18,975
FB £22,185–£27,585

### St Christopher School
Barrington Road, Letchworth,
Hertfordshire SG6 3JZ
**Tel:** 01462 650 850
**Head:** Richard Palmer
**Age range:** 3–18
**No. of pupils:** 511 VIth78
**Fees:** Day £3,375–£14,505
FB £15,600–£25,470

### St Edmund's College & Prep School
Old Hall Green, Nr Ware,
Hertfordshire SG11 1DS
**Tel:** 01920 824247
**Head:** Paulo Durán BA MA
**Age range:** 3–18
**No. of pupils:** 799 VIth135
**Fees:** Day £9,465–£14,955 WB
£19,830–£22,575 FB £21,855–£24,990

### St Francis' College
Broadway, Letchworth Garden
City, Hertfordshire SG6 3PJ
**Tel:** 01462 670511
**Headmistress:** Mrs B Goulding
**Age range:** G3–18
**No. of pupils:** 460 VIth75
**Fees:** Day £8,670–£13,830 WB
£19,425–£22,875 FB £24,195–£27,645

### St Margaret's School, Bushey
Merry Hill Road, Bushey,
Hertfordshire WD23 1DT
**Tel:** 020 8416 4400
**Head:** Mrs Rose Hardy MA(Oxon),
MEd, FRSA
**Age range:** G4–18 years
**No. of pupils:** 450 VIth100
**Fees:** Day £14,730 WB
£20,220–£23,670 FB £27,600

**Stanborough School**
Stanborough Park, Garston,
Watford, Hertfordshire WD25 9JT
**Tel:** 01923 673268
**Head Teacher:** Ms Lorraine Dixon
**Age range:** 3–19
**No. of pupils:** 300 VIth20
**Fees:** Day £3,660–£5,500
WB £12,834–£15,846

**The Purcell School, London**
Aldenham Road, Bushey,
Hertfordshire WD23 2TS
**Tel:** 01923 331100
**Headteacher:** Mr. Stephen Yeo
**Age range:** 10–18
**No. of pupils:** 180

**The Royal Masonic
School for Girls**
Rickmansworth Park,
Rickmansworth,
Hertfordshire WD3 4HF
**Tel:** 01923 773168
**Headmaster:** Mr Kevin Carson
M.Phil (Cambridge)
**Age range:** G4–18
**No. of pupils:** 930 VIth165
**Fees:** Day £10,455–£15,915 WB
£18,345–£25,935 FB £19,350–£28,140

**Tring Park School for
the Performing Arts**
Tring Park, Tring,
Hertfordshire HP23 5LX
**Tel:** 01442 824255
**Principal:** Mr Stefan Anderson MA,
ARCM, ARCT
**Age range:** 8–19
**No. of pupils:** 350 VIth263
**Fees:** Day £14,430–£22,965
FB £24,540–£34,710

# Kent

**Ashford School**
East Hill, Ashford, Kent TN24 8PB
**Tel:** 01233 739030
**Head:** Mr M R Buchanan BSc(Hons),
CertEd, NPQH, CPhys
**Age range:** 3 months–18 years
**No. of pupils:** 835 VIth170
**Fees:** Day £8,400–£16,200
WB £28,500 FB £32,400

**Ashgrove School**
116 Widmore Road,
Bromley, Kent BR1 3BE
**Tel:** 020 8460 4143
**Principal:** Patricia Ash CertEd,
BSc(Hons), PhD, CMath, FIMA
**Age range:** 4–11
**No. of pupils:** 106
**Fees:** Day £8,730

**Benenden School**
Cranbrook, Kent TN17 4AA
**Tel:** 01580 240592
**Headmistress:** Mrs S Price
**Age range:** G11–18
**No. of pupils:** 550
**Fees:** FB £35,700

**Bethany School**
Curtisden Green, Goudhurst,
Cranbrook, Kent TN17 1LB
**Tel:** 01580 211273
**Headmaster:** Mr Francie Healy BSc,
HDipEd, NPQH
**Age range:** 11–18 years
**No. of pupils:** 313 VIth98
**Fees:** Day £16,245–£17,925 WB
£25,185–£27,825 FB £27,165–£30,585

**CATS Canterbury**
68 New Dover Road,
Canterbury, Kent CT1 3LQ
**Tel:** +44 (0)1227866540
**Principal:** Mr. James Slocombe
BSc(Hons), PGCE, QTS, MA, FRSA
**Age range:** 14–18
**No. of pupils:** 400

**Cobham Hall School**
Cobham, Kent DA12 3BL
**Tel:** 01474 823371
**Headmistress:** Dr Sandra Coates-
Smith BSc, PhD
**Age range:** G11–18
**No. of pupils:** 180

**Dover College**
Effingham Crescent,
Dover, Kent CT17 9RH
**Tel:** 01304 205969
**Headmaster:** Mr Gareth Doodes
MA (Hons)
**Age range:** 3–18
**No. of pupils:** 301
**Fees:** Day £7,500–£15,600
WB £20,250–£24,000 FB
£24,000–£30,000

**Farringtons School**
Perry Street, Chislehurst,
Kent BR7 6LR
**Tel:** 020 8467 0256
**Head:** Mrs Dorothy Nancekievill
**Age range:** 3–18
**No. of pupils:** 681 VIth94
**Fees:** Day £14,610 WB
£28,830 FB £30,600

**Kent College**
Whitstable Road, Canterbury,
Kent CT2 9DT
**Tel:** 01227 763231
**Executive Head Master:** Dr David
Lamper
**Age range:** 3–18
**No. of pupils:** 704
**Fees:** Day £16,221–£17,995
FB £24,741–£33,981

**Kent College Pembury**
Old Church Road, Pembury,
Tunbridge Wells, Kent TN2 4AX
**Tel:** +44 (0)1892 822006
**Headmistress:** Mrs Sally-Anne
Huang MA(Oxon), MSc, PGCE
**Age range:** G3–18
**No. of pupils:** 650 VIth102
**Fees:** Day £7,887–£17,322
FB £21,471–£27,924

**King's Rochester**
Satis House, Boley Hill,
Rochester, Kent ME1 1TE
**Tel:** 01634 888555
**Principal:** Mr J Walker
**Age range:** 13–18
**No. of pupils:** 263
**Fees:** Day £18,705 FB £30,390

**Rochester Independent
College**
Star Hill, Rochester,
Medway, Kent ME1 1XF
**Tel:** 01634 828115
**Principals:** Alistair Brownlow, Brian
Pain, Pauline Bailey
**Age range:** 11–19
**No. of pupils:** 306 VIth233
**Fees:** Day £12,000–£16,500 WB
£25,650–£27,300 FB £27,450–£29,100

**Sevenoaks School**
High Street, Sevenoaks,
Kent TN13 1HU
**Tel:** +44 (0)1732 455133
**Head:** Dr Katy Ricks MA, DPhil
**Age range:** 11–18
**No. of pupils:** 1080
**Fees:** Day £22,455–£25,497
FB £35,865–£38,907

**St Edmund's School**
St Thomas' Hill, Canterbury,
Kent CT2 8HU
**Tel:** 01227 475601
**Head:** Louise Moelwyn-Hughes
**Age range:** 3–18
**No. of pupils:** 535
**Fees:** Day £18,651 FB £29,781

**St Lawrence College**
Ramsgate, Kent CT11 7AE
**Tel:** 01843 572931
**Principal:** Mr Antony Spencer
**Age range:** 3–18
**No. of pupils:** 640 VIth115
**Fees:** Day £7,470–£18,495
FB £26,055–£34,635

**Sutton Valence School**
North Street, Sutton
Valence, Kent ME17 3HL
**Tel:** 01622 845200
**Headmaster:** Bruce Grindlay MA
Cantab, MusB, FRCO, CHM
**Age range:** 11–18
**No. of pupils:** 570

**The King's School,
Canterbury**
The Precincts, Canterbury,
Kent CT1 2ES
**Tel:** 01227 595501
**Head:** Mr P Roberts
**Age range:** 13–18
**No. of pupils:** 858 VIth385
**Fees:** Day £26,700 FB £35,295

**Tonbridge School**
Tonbridge, Kent TN9 1JP
**Tel:** 01732 365555
**Headmaster:** T H P Haynes
**Age range:** B13–18
**No. of pupils:** 787
**Fees:** Day £29,229 FB £38,964

# Middlesex

### ACS Hillingdon International School
Hillingdon Court, 108 Vine Lane, Hillingdon, Uxbridge, Middlesex UB10 0BE
**Tel:** +44 (0) 1895 259 771
**Head of School:** Linda LaPine
**Age range:** 4–18
**No. of pupils:** 520
**Fees:** Day £17,260–£23,110

### North London Collegiate School
Canons, Canons Drive, Edgware, Middlesex HA8 7RJ
**Tel:** +44 (0)20 8952 0912
**Headmistress:** Mrs Sarah Clark
**Age range:** G4–18
**No. of pupils:** 1080
**Fees:** Day £5,530–£6,545

### Radnor House
Pope's Villa, Cross Deep, Twickenham, Middlesex TW1 4QG
**Tel:** 020 8891 6264
**Head of School:** Mr. David Paton MA

### St Helen's School
Eastbury Road, Northwood, Middlesex HA6 3AS
**Tel:** +44 (0)1923 843210
**Headmistress:** Dr Mary Short BA, PhD
**Age range:** G3–18
**No. of pupils:** VIth165

# Surrey

### ACS Cobham International School
Heywood, Portsmouth Road, Cobham, Surrey KT11 1BL
**Tel:** +44 (0) 1932 867251
**Head of School:** Mr A Eysele
**Age range:** 2–18
**No. of pupils:** 1460
**Fees:** Day £10,690–£25,050 FB £36,810–£39,310

### ACS Egham International School
Woodlee, London Road, Egham, Surrey TW20 0HS
**Tel:** +44 (0) 1784 430 800
**Head of School:** Jeremy Lewis
**Age range:** 3–18
**Fees:** Day £7,080–£24,020

### Box Hill School
Old London Road, Mickleham, Dorking, Surrey RH5 6EA
**Tel:** 01372 373382
**Headmaster:** Mr Corydon Lowde
**Age range:** 11–18
**No. of pupils:** 425 VIth96
**Fees:** Day £16,140–£17,170 WB £24,600–£25,800 FB £29,970–£35,850

### Caterham School
Harestone Valley, Caterham, Surrey CR3 6YA
**Tel:** 01883 343028
**Head:** Mr C. W. Jones MA(Cantab)
**Age range:** 11–18
**No. of pupils:** VIth321

### Charterhouse
Godalming, Surrey GU7 2DX
**Tel:** +44 (0)1483 291501
**Headmaster:** Dr Alex Peterken
**Age range:** B13–18 G16–18
**No. of pupils:** 820

### City of London Freemen's School
Ashtead Park, Ashtead, Surrey KT21 1ET
**Tel:** 01372 277933
**Headmaster:** Mr R Martin
**Age range:** 7–18
**No. of pupils:** 877 VIth213
**Fees:** Day £10,872–£14,598 FB £23,238

### Cranleigh School
Horseshoe Lane, Cranleigh, Surrey GU6 8QQ
**Tel:** +44 (0) 1483 273666
**Headmaster:** Mr Martin Reader MA, MPhil, MBA
**Age range:** 7–18 (including Prep School)
**No. of pupils:** 626 VIth250
**Fees:** Day £29,985 FB £36,615

### Duke of Kent School
Peaslake Road, Ewhurst, Surrey GU6 7NS
**Tel:** 01483 277313
**Head:** Mrs Judith Fremont-Barnes
**Age range:** 3–16
**No. of pupils:** 234
**Fees:** Day £4,860–£14,130 WB £13,350–£16,770 FB £15,735–£18,855

### Epsom College
Epsom, Surrey KT17 4JQ
**Tel:** 01372 821000
**Headmaster:** Mr Jay A Piggot MA
**Age range:** 13–18
**No. of pupils:** 730
**Fees:** Day £21,255 FB £31,098

### Frensham Heights
Rowledge, Farnham, Surrey GU10 4EA
**Tel:** 01252 792561
**Headmaster:** Mr Andrew Fisher BA, MEd, FRSA
**Age range:** 3–18
**No. of pupils:** 497 VIth105
**Fees:** Day £5,205–£15,300 FB £19,485–£22,680

### International School of London (ISL) Surrey
Old Woking Road, Woking, Surrey GU22 8HY
**Tel:** +44 (0)1483 750409
**Campus Principal & Head of Secondary:** Richard Parker
**Age range:** 2–18 years
**No. of pupils:** 252
**Fees:** Day £17,700–£21,900

### King Edward's Witley
Godalming, Surrey GU8 5SG
**Tel:** +44 (0)1428 686700
**Headmaster:** Mr John Attwater MA
**Age range:** 11–18
**No. of pupils:** 410 VIth185
**Fees:** Day £19,950 FB £30,780

### MARYMOUNT INTERNATIONAL SCHOOL LONDON
**For further details see p. 87**
George Road, Kingston upon Thames, Surrey KT2 7PE
**Tel:** +44 (0)20 8949 0571
**Email:** admissions@marymountlondon.com
**Website:** www.marymountlondon.com
**Headmistress:** Mrs Margaret Frazier
**Age range:** G11–18
**No. of pupils:** 250
**Fees:** Day £20,015–£22,860 WB £34,365–£37,210 FB £36,030–£38,875

### Prior's Field
Priorsfield Road, Godalming, Surrey GU7 2RH
**Tel:** 01483 810551
**Head of School:** Mrs T Kirnig
**Age range:** G11–18
**No. of pupils:** 450
**Fees:** Day £15,855 FB £25,575

### Reed's School
Sandy Lane, Cobham, Surrey KT11 2ES
**Tel:** 01932 869001
**Headmaster:** Mr Mark Hoskins BA MA MSc
**Age range:** B11–18 G16–18
**No. of pupils:** 650 VIth230
**Fees:** Day £16,938–£21,184 FB £22,582–£28,023

### Royal Russell School
Coombe Lane, Croydon, Surrey CR9 5BX
**Tel:** 020 8657 3669
**Headmaster:** Christopher Hutchinson
**Age range:** 11–18
**No. of pupils:** 590 VIth180
**Fees:** Day £15,285 FB £22,365–£30,240

### St Catherine's School
Bramley, Guildford, Surrey GU5 0DF
**Tel:** 01483 893363
**Headmistress:** Mrs A M Phillips MA(Cantab)
**Age range:** G4–18
**No. of pupils:** 900
**Fees:** Day £7,695–£15,660 FB £25,770

### St James Senior Boys School
Church Road, Ashford, Surrey TW15 3DZ
**Tel:** 01784 266930
**Headmaster:** Mr David Brazier
**Age range:** B11–18
**No. of pupils:** 403 VIth65
**Fees:** Day £18,120

### St John's School
Epsom Road, Leatherhead, Surrey KT22 8SP
**Tel:** 01372 373000
**Head of School:** Mrs Rowena Cole
**Age range:** 11–18
**No. of pupils:** 761
**Fees:** Day £23,580 WB £29,790

**St Teresa's Effingham (Senior School)**
Beech Avenue, Effingham,
Surrey RH5 6ST
**Tel:** 01372 452037
**Head:** Mr Michael Farmer
**Age range:** G3–18
**No. of pupils:** 640 VIth90
**Fees:** Day £16,980–£17,595 WB
£27,489–£27,795 FB £29,340–£29,955
(symbols)

**TASIS The American School in England**
Coldharbour Lane, Thorpe,
Surrey TW20 8TE
**Tel:** +44 (0)1932 582316
**Head of School:** Mr Bryan Nixon
**Age range:** 3–18
**No. of pupils:** 700
**Fees:** Day £10,900–
£23,190 FB £41,870
(symbols)

**The Royal Senior School, Haslemere**
Farnham Lane, Haslemere,
Surrey GU27 1HQ
**Tel:** 01428 603052
**Principal:** Mrs Anne Lynch BA,
PGCE, FRSA
**Age range:** 11–18 years
**No. of pupils:** 243
**Fees:** Day £17,400–£17,700
WB £26,100–£26,400 FB
£29,700–£30,000
(symbols)

**Whitgift School**
Haling Park, South Croydon,
Surrey CR2 6YT
**Tel:** +44 (0)20 8633 9935
**Headmaster:** Mr Christopher
Ramsey
**Age range:** B10–18
**No. of pupils:** 1464
**Fees:** Day £17,340 WB
£27,924 FB £33,396
(symbols)

**Woldingham School**
Marden Park, Woldingham,
Surrey CR3 7YA
**Tel:** 01883 349431
**Headmistress:** Mrs Jayne Triffitt
MA(Oxon)
**Age range:** G11–18
**No. of pupils:** 530 VIth150
**Fees:** Day £23,700 FB £28,410
(symbols)

**Yehudi Menuhin School**
Stoke Road, Stoke d'Abernon,
Cobham, Surrey KT11 3QQ
**Tel:** 01932 864739
**Headmaster:** Dr. Richard J Hillier
MA(Cantab), PhD
**Age range:** 7–19
**No. of pupils:** 80 VIth36
**Fees:** FB £41,928
(symbols)

# West Berkshire

**Downe House School**
Hermitage Road, Cold Ash,
Thatcham, West Berkshire RG18 9JJ
**Tel:** 01635 200286
**Headmistress:** Mrs E McKendrick
BA(Liverpool)
**Age range:** G11–18
**No. of pupils:** VIth174
**Fees:** Day £25,440 FB £35,160
(symbols)

# West Sussex

**Ardingly College**
College Road, Ardingly, Haywards
Heath, West Sussex RH17 6SQ
**Tel:** +44 (0)1444 893320
**Headmaster:** Mr Ben Figgis
**Age range:** 13–18
**No. of pupils:** 559
**Fees:** Day £22,380–£23,610
FB £30,480–£32,130
(symbols)

**Burgess Hill Girls**
Keymer Road, Burgess Hill,
West Sussex RH15 0EG
**Tel:** 01444 241050
**Head of School:** Liz Laybourn
**Age range:** B2.5–4 G2.5–18
**No. of pupils:** 550 VIth87
**Fees:** Day £7,350–£16,950
FB £27,300–£30,450
(symbols)

**Christ's Hospital**
Horsham, West Sussex RH13 0LJ
**Tel:** 01403 211293
**Headmaster:** Mr Simon Reid
**Age range:** 11–18
**No. of pupils:** 900
**Fees:** Day £16,950–
£21,330 FB £32,790
(symbols)

**Farlington School**
Strood Park, Horsham,
West Sussex RH12 3PN
**Tel:** 01403 282573
**Headmistress:** Ms Louise Higson
BSc, PGCE
**Age range:** G3–18
**No. of pupils:** 300
**Fees:** Day £5,660 WB
£9,170 FB £9,600
(symbols)

**Hurstpierpoint College**
College Lane, Hurstpierpoint,
West Sussex BN6 9JS
**Tel:** 01273 833636
**Headmaster:** Mr. T J Manly BA, MSc
**Age range:** 4–18
**No. of pupils:** 1156
**Fees:** Day £8,790–£22,860
WB £28,800
(symbols)

**Lancing College**
Lancing, West Sussex BN15 0RW
**Tel:** 01273 465805
**Head Master:** Mr Dominic T Oliver
MPhil
**Age range:** 13–18
**No. of pupils:** 550 VIth255
**Fees:** Day £7,710 FB £10,970
(symbols)

**Rikkyo School in England**
Guildford Road, Rudgwick,
Horsham, West Sussex RH12 3BE
**Tel:** 01403 822107
**Headmaster:** Mr Roger Munechika
**Age range:** 10–18
**No. of pupils:** 116
**Fees:** FB £15,000–£21,600
(symbols)

**Seaford College**
Lavington Park, Petworth,
West Sussex GU28 0NB
**Tel:** 01798 867392
**Headmaster:** J P Green MA BA
**Age range:** 7–18
**No. of pupils:** 732 VIth194
**Fees:** Day £10,020–£20,775 WB
£20,880–£28,140 FB £32,130
(symbols)

**Slindon College**
Slindon House, Slindon, Arundel,
West Sussex BN18 0RH
**Tel:** 01243 814320
**Headmaster:** Mr D Quick
**Age range:** B8–18
**No. of pupils:** 80 VIth17
**Fees:** Day £7,053 WB
£10,445 FB £10,445
(symbols)

**The Towers Convent School**
Convent of the Blessed Sacrement,
Henfield Road, Upper Beeding,
Steyning, West Sussex BN44 3TF
**Tel:** 01903 812185
**Headmistress:** Mrs Clare Trelfa
**Age range:** B2–8 G2–16
**No. of pupils:** 320
**Fees:** Day £7,320–£10,200
(symbols)

**Worth School**
Paddockhurst Road, Turners Hill,
Crawley, West Sussex RH10 4SD
**Tel:** +44 (0)1342 710200
**Head Master:** Gino Carminati MA,
FRSA
**Age range:** 11–18
**No. of pupils:** 580 VIth222
**Fees:** Day £20,235 FB £27,849
(symbols)

# Specialist schools and sixth form colleges

# London

## Central London

### CATS London
43-45 Bloomsbury Square,
London WC1A 2RA
**Tel:** 02078 411580
**Principal:** Mario Di Clemente
**Age range:** 15–24

### City of London School
Queen Victoria Street,
London EC4V 3AL
**Tel:** 020 3680 6300
**Head:** Mr A R Bird MSc
**Age range:** B10–18
**No. of pupils:** 930 VIth250
**Fees:** Day £16,731

### City of London School for Girls
St Giles' Terrace, Barbican,
London EC2Y 8BB
**Tel:** 020 7847 5500
**Headmistress:** Mrs E Harrop
**Age range:** G7–18
**No. of pupils:** 725

### Italia Conti Academy of Theatre Arts
Italia Conti House, 23 Goswell
Road, London EC1M 7AJ
**Tel:** 020 7608 0047
**Principal:** Anne Sheward
**Age range:** 10–21

### The College of Central London
Tower Bridge Business Centre, 46-48
East Smithfield, London E1W 1AW
**Tel:** +44 (0) 20 3667 7607
**Principal:** Nicolas Kailides
**Fees:** Day £3,300

## East London

### Al-Mizan School
46 Whitechapel Road,
London E1 1JX
**Tel:** 020 7650 3070
**Head:** Mr Ziaurr Ahman
**Age range:** B7–18
**No. of pupils:** 200 VIth13
**Fees:** Day £2,400

### Forest School
College Place, Snaresbrook,
London E17 3PY
**Tel:** 020 8520 1744
**Warden:** Mr Anthony Faccinello
**Age range:** 4–18
**No. of pupils:** 1355 VIth260
**Fees:** Day £11,049–£16,335

## North London

### Channing School
The Bank, Highgate, London N6 5HF
**Tel:** 020 8340 2328
**Head:** Mrs B M Elliott
**Age range:** G4–18
**No. of pupils:** 746 VIth108
**Fees:** Day £14,085–£15,255

### Dwight School London
6 Friern Barnet Lane,
London N11 3LX
**Tel:** +44 (0)20 8920 0637
**Head:** Mrs Alison Cobbin BA, Dip
Ed, MBA
**Age range:** 3–18

### Greek Secondary School of London
Avenue Lodge, Bounds Green
Road, London N22 7EU
**Tel:** 020 8881 9320
**Headteacher:** Antonia Valavani
**Age range:** 13–18
**No. of pupils:** 200

### Highgate
North Road, Highgate,
London N6 4AY
**Tel:** 020 8340 1524
**Head Master:** Mr A S Pettitt MA
**Age range:** 3–18
**No. of pupils:** 1541 VIth312
**Fees:** Day £15,135–£17,475

## North-West London

### Fine Arts College, Hampstead
24 Lambolle Place, Belsize
Park, London NW3 4PG
**Tel:** 020 7586 0312
**Co Principals:** Candida Cave &
Nicholas Cochrane
**Age range:** 13–19
**No. of pupils:** 115
**Fees:** Day £6,000–£15,600

### Francis Holland School, Regent's Park, NW1
Clarence Gate, Ivor Place,
Regent's Park, London NW1 6XR
**Tel:** 020 7723 0176
**Head:** Mr C B Fillingham MA (King's
College London)
**Age range:** G11–18
**No. of pupils:** 495 VIth120
**Fees:** Day £19,260

## International Community School
4 York Terrace East, Regents
Park, London NW1 4PT
**Tel:** +44 20 7935 1206
**Head of School:** Ms Rose Threlfall
**Age range:** 3–18
**No. of pupils:** 260
**Fees:** Day £16,650–£22,100

### Lakefield Catering & Educational Centre
Maresfield Gardens,
Hampstead, London NW3 5RY
**Tel:** 020 7794 5669
**Course Director:** Mrs Maria Brown
**Age range:** G16–24
**No. of pupils:** 16
**Fees:** FB £1,160

### London Academy of Dressmaking and Design
18 Dobree Avenue, Willesden,
London NW10 2AE
**Tel:** 020 8451 7174
**Principal:** Mrs P A Parkinson MA
**Age range:** 13+
**Fees:** Day £2,650

### Mill Hill School
The Ridgeway, Mill Hill
Village, London NW7 1QS
**Tel:** 020 8959 1176
**Head:** Dr Dominic Luckett
**Age range:** 13–18
**No. of pupils:** 689 VIth259
**Fees:** Day £13,860 FB £21,900

### NW5 Theatre School
14 Fortess Road, London NW5 2EU
**Tel:** 020 7482 3236
**Founder:** George O'Gorman
**Age range:** 16–30
**Fees:** Day £3,600

### South Hampstead High School GDST
3 Maresfield Gardens,
London NW3 5SS
**Tel:** 020 7435 2899
**Headmistress:** Mrs J E Stephen BSc
**Age range:** G4–18
**No. of pupils:** 852 VIth162
**Fees:** Day £9,342–£12,006

### Swaminarayan School
260 Brentfield Road, Neasden,
London NW10 8HE
**Tel:** 020 8965 8381
**Headteacher:** Nilesh Manani
**Age range:** 2–18
**No. of pupils:** 452 VIth36
**Fees:** Day £7,818–£10,707

## The American School in London
One Waverley Place,
London NW8 0NP
**Tel:** 020 7449 1221
**Head:** Mrs Coreen Hester
**Age range:** 4–18
**No. of pupils:** 1350
**Fees:** Day £21,950–£25,650

### The King Alfred School
Manor Wood, North End
Road, London NW11 7HY
**Tel:** 020 8457 5200
**Head:** Robert Lobatto MA (Oxon)
**Age range:** 4–18
**No. of pupils:** 650 VIth100
**Fees:** Day £14,862–£17,916

### University College School
Frognal, Hampstead,
London NW3 6XH
**Tel:** 020 7435 2215
**Headmaster:** Mr M J Beard MA
**Age range:** B11–18
**No. of pupils:** 850 VIth300
**Fees:** Day £16,005

### Wentworth Tutorial College
6-10 Brentmead Place,
London NW11 9LH
**Tel:** 020 8458 8524/5
**Principal:** Alan Davies BSc, MSc
**Age range:** 14–19
**No. of pupils:** 115

## South-East London

### Alleyn's School
Townley Road, Dulwich,
London SE22 8SU
**Tel:** 020 8557 1500
**Headmaster:** Dr G Savage MA,
PhD, FRSA
**Age range:** 4–18
**No. of pupils:** 1252 VIth302
**Fees:** Day £16,395–£18,852

### Blackheath High School GDST
Vanbrugh Park, Blackheath,
London SE3 7AG
**Tel:** 020 8853 2929
**Head:** Mrs Carol Chandler-
Thompson BA (Hons) Exeter, PGCE
Exeter
**Age range:** G3–18
**No. of pupils:** 780

## Colfe's School
Horn Park Lane, Lee,
London SE12 8AW
**Tel:** 020 8852 2283
**Head:** Mr R F Russell MA(Cantab)
**Age range:** 3–18
**No. of pupils:** 1120
**Fees:** Day £11,934–£16,110

## Dulwich College
London SE21 7LD
**Tel:** 020 8693 3601
**Master:** Dr J A F Spence
**Age range:** B7–18
**No. of pupils:** 1589 VIth470
**Fees:** Day £18,231 WB
£35,679 FB £38,052

## Eltham College
Grove Park Road, Mottingham,
London SE9 4QF
**Tel:** 0208 857 1455
**Headmaster:** Guy Sanderson
**Age range:** B7–18 G16–18
**No. of pupils:** 830 VIth220
**Fees:** Day £17,058

## James Allen's Girls' School
144 East Dulwich Grove,
Dulwich, London SE22 8TE
**Tel:** 020 8693 1181
**Head of School:** Mrs Sally-Anne
Huang MA, MSc
**Age range:** G4–18
**No. of pupils:** 1075

## Riverston School
63-69 Eltham Road, Lee
Green, London SE12 8UF
**Tel:** 020 8318 4327
**Headmistress:** Mrs S E Salathiel
**Age range:** 9 months–19 years
**No. of pupils:** 215

## St Dunstan's College
Stanstead Road, London SE6 4TY
**Tel:** 020 8516 7200
**Headmistress:** Mrs J D Davies BSc
**Age range:** 3–18
**No. of pupils:** 870

## Sydenham High
## School GDST
19 Westwood Hill, London SE26 6BL
**Tel:** 020 8557 7000
**Headmistress:** Mrs Katharine
Woodcock
**Age range:** G4–18
**No. of pupils:** 600 VIth70
**Fees:** Day £12,780–£16,251

# South-West London

## Abbey College – London
22 Grosvenor Gardens,
Belgravia, London SW1W 0DH
**Tel:** 020 7824 7300
**Principal:** Mr Mark Love BEd
**Age range:** 14–19
**No. of pupils:** 150 VIth150
**Fees:** Day £5,950–£16,400
FB £30,200

## Centre Academy London
92 St John's Hill, Battersea,
London SW11 1SH
**Tel:** 020 7738 2344
**Principal:** Dr. Duncan Rollo BA,
MA, PhD
**Age range:** 9–19
**Fees:** Day £27,600–£40,100

## Emanuel School
Battersea Rise, London SW11 1HS
**Tel:** 020 8870 4171
**Headmaster:** Mr Mark Hanley-
Browne
**Age range:** 10–18
**No. of pupils:** 890
**Fees:** Day £17,574

## Francis Holland School, Sloane Square, SW1
39 Graham Terrace,
London SW1W 8JF
**Tel:** 020 7730 2971
**Head:** Mrs Lucy Elphinstone
MA(Cantab)
**Age range:** G4–18
**No. of pupils:** 520 VIth70
**Fees:** Day £17,760–£20,085

## Ibstock Place School
Clarence Lane, London SW15 5PY
**Tel:** 020 8876 9991
**Head:** Mrs Anna Sylvester-Johnson
BA(Hons), PGCE
**Age range:** 4–18
**No. of pupils:** 970
**Fees:** Day £5,220–£6,690

## King's College School
Southside, Wimbledon
Common, London SW19 4TT
**Tel:** 020 8255 5300
**Head Master:** A D Halls MA
**Age range:** B11–18 G16–18
**No. of pupils:** 967
**Fees:** Day £18,975–£20,985

## Lycée Français Charles de Gaulle
35 Cromwell Road,
London SW7 2DG
**Tel:** 020 7584 6322
**Head of School:** Mr Olivier Rauch
**Age range:** 5–19
**No. of pupils:** 4000

**MORE HOUSE SCHOOL**
*For further details see p. 62*
22-24 Pont Street, Knightsbridge,
London SW1X 0AA
**Tel:** 020 7235 2855
**Email:** office@morehouse.org.uk
**Website:**
www.morehouse.org.uk
**Co-Heads:** Mrs. Amanda Leach
& Mr. Michael Keeley
**Age range:** G11–18
**No. of pupils:** 206
**Fees:** Day £18,930

## Putney High School GDST
35 Putney Hill, London SW15 6BH
**Tel:** 020 8788 4886
**Headmistress:** Mrs Suzie Longstaff
BA, MA, PGCE
**Age range:** G4–18
**No. of pupils:** 976 VIth150

## Queen's Gate School
133 Queen's Gate, London SW7 5LE
**Tel:** 020 7589 3587
**Principal:** Mrs R M Kamaryc BA,
MSc, PGCE
**Age range:** G4–18
**No. of pupils:** 533

## St Paul's School
Lonsdale Road, Barnes,
London SW13 9JT
**Tel:** 020 8748 9162
**High Master:** Prof Mark Bailey
**Age range:** B13–18
**No. of pupils:** 897
**Fees:** Day £19,674 FB £29,466

## Streatham & Clapham
## High School GDST
42 Abbotswood Road,
London SW16 1AW
**Tel:** 020 8677 8400
**Headmaster:** Dr Millan Sachania
**Age range:** B3–5 G3–18
**No. of pupils:** 603 VIth70
**Fees:** Day £5,886–£9,810

## Swedish School
82 Lonsdale Road, London SW13 9JS
**Tel:** 020 8741 1751
**Head of School:** Ms. Annika
Simonsson Bergqvist
**Age range:** 3–18
**No. of pupils:** 300 VIth145
**Fees:** Day £8,650–£9,200–£6,900

## The Harrodian School
Lonsdale Road, London SW13 9QN
**Tel:** 020 8748 6117
**Headmaster:** James R Hooke
**Age range:** 5–18
**No. of pupils:** 890 VIth95
**Fees:** Day £10,407–£15,219

## Westminster School
Little Dean's Yard, Westminster,
London SW1P 3PF
**Tel:** 020 7963 1003
**Headmaster:** Mr Patrick Derham
**Age range:** B13–18 G16–18
**No. of pupils:** 744
**Fees:** Day £26,130–
£28,566 FB £37,740

## Wimbledon High
## School GDST
Mansel Road, Wimbledon,
London SW19 4AB
**Tel:** 020 8971 0900
**Headmistress:** Mrs Jane Lunnon
**Age range:** G4–18
**No. of pupils:** 900 VIth155
**Fees:** Day £11,445–£15,024

# West London

## Alan D Education
61-62 East Castle Street,
London W1W 8NQ
**Tel:** 020 7580 1030
**Director of Education:** Alan
Hemmings
**Fees:** Day £200 FB £12,400

## Ashbourne Middle School
17 Old Court Place,
Kensington, London W8 4PL
**Tel:** 020 7937 3858
**Principal:** M J Kirby MSc, BApSc
**Age range:** 13–16
**No. of pupils:** VIth150
**Fees:** Day £14,725 FB £21,500

## Blake College
162 New Cavendish Street,
London W1W 6YS
**Tel:** 020 7636 0658
**Course Director:** D A J Cluckie
BA, BSc
**Fees:** Day £4,720–£5,310

## David Game College
31 Jewry Street, London EC3N 2ET
**Tel:** 020 7221 6665
**Principal:** D T P Game MA, MPhil
**Age range:** 14–19
**No. of pupils:** 200 VIth150
**Fees:** Day £12,000–£13,000

## Ealing Independent
## College
83 New Broadway, Ealing,
London W5 5AL
**Tel:** 020 8579 6668
**Principal:** Dr Ian Moores
**Age range:** 13–22
**No. of pupils:** 100 VIth70
**Fees:** Day £3,865–£12,600

**International School of London (ISL) London**
139 Gunnersbury Avenue,
Ealing, London W3 8LG
**Tel:** +44 (0)20 8992 5823
**Middle & Lower School Principal:**
Andrew Mitchell
**Age range:** 3–18 years
**No. of pupils:** 480
**Fees:** Day £18,000–£24,600

**King Fahad Academy**
Bromyard Avenue, Acton,
London W3 7HD
**Tel:** 020 8743 0131
**Director General:** Dr Abdulghani
Alharbi
**Age range:** 3–19
**No. of pupils:** 550
**Fees:** Day £3,300–£4,300

**Latymer Upper School**
King Street, Hammersmith,
London W6 9LR
**Tel:** 020862 92024
**Head:** Mr D Goodhew MA(Oxon)
**Age range:** 11–18
**No. of pupils:** 1200
**Fees:** Day £18,510

**Notting Hill & Ealing High School GDST**
2 Cleveland Road, West
Ealing, London W13 8AX
**Tel:** (020) 8799 8400
**Headmistress:** Ms Lucinda Hunt
**Age range:** G4–18
**No. of pupils:** 903 VIth150
**Fees:** Day £12,849–£16,521

**Portland Place School**
56-58 Portland Place,
London W1B 1NJ
**Tel:** 0207 307 8700
**Head:** Mr Tim Cook
**Age range:** 11–18
**No. of pupils:** 300 VIth50
**Fees:** Day £12,522–£16,425

**Queen's College**
43-49 Harley Street,
London W1G 8BT
**Tel:** 020 7291 7000
**Head:** Dr F M R Ramsey MA,
DPhil(Oxon)
**Age range:** G11–18
**No. of pupils:** 360 VIth90

**Ray Cochrane Beauty School**
118 Baker Street, London W1U 6TT
**Tel:** 02033224738
**Age range:** 16–50
**No. of pupils:** 30
**Fees:** Day £2,195–£8,995

**Southbank International School – Westminster**
63-65 Portland Place,
London W1B 1QR
**Tel:** 020 7243 3803
**Interim Principal:** Siobhan McGrath
**Age range:** 11–18/19

**ST AUGUSTINE'S PRIORY**
*For further details see p. 72*
Hillcrest Road, Ealing,
London W5 2JL
**Tel:** 020 8997 2022
**Email:** office@sapriory.com
**Website:** www.sapriory.com
**Headteacher:** Mrs Sarah Raffray
M.A., N.P.Q.H
**Age range:** B3–4 G3–18
**No. of pupils:** 456
**Fees:** Day £10,656–£15,162

**ST BENEDICT'S SCHOOL**
*For further details see p. 70*
54 Eaton Rise, Ealing,
London W5 2ES
**Tel:** 020 8862 2000
**Email:** admissions@
stbenedicts.org.uk
**Website:**
www.stbenedicts.org.uk
**Headmaster:** Mr A Johnson BA
**Age range:** 3–18
**No. of pupils:** 1073 VIth219
**Fees:** Day £12,500–£16,104

**St James Senior Girls' School**
Earsby Street, London W14 8SH
**Tel:** 020 7348 1777
**Headmistress:** Mrs Sarah Labram BA
**Age range:** G11–18
**No. of pupils:** 295 VIth67
**Fees:** Day £18,330

**St Paul's Girls' School**
Brook Green, London W6 7BS
**Tel:** 020 7603 2288
**High Mistress:** Mrs Sarah Fletcher
**Age range:** G11–18 years
**No. of pupils:** 740 VIth200
**Fees:** Day £23,934–£25,731

**The Godolphin and Latymer School**
Iffley Road, Hammersmith,
London W6 0PG
**Tel:** +44 (0)20 8741 1936
**Head Mistress:** Dr Frances Ramsey
**Age range:** G11–18
**No. of pupils:** 800

# Berkshire

**Bradfield College**
Bradfield, Berkshire RG7 6AU
**Tel:** 0118 964 4516
**Headmaster:** Dr Christopher
Stevens
**Age range:** 13–18
**No. of pupils:** 790
**Fees:** Day £29,052 FB £36,315

**Brigidine School Windsor**
Queensmead, King's Road,
Windsor, Berkshire SL4 2AX
**Tel:** 01753 863779
**Headmistress:** Mrs Elizabeth
Robinson
**Age range:** B2–7 G3–18
**No. of pupils:** 300
**Fees:** Day £3,945–£11,865

**Claires Court Nursery, Girls and Sixth Form**
1 College Avenue, Maidenhead,
Berkshire SL6 6AW
**Tel:** 01628 327700
**Head of School:** Mrs M Heywood
**Age range:** B16–18 G3–18
**No. of pupils:** 495 VIth111
**Fees:** Day £5,715–£14,580

**Claires Court Senior Boys**
Ray Mill Road East, Maidenhead,
Berkshire SL6 8TE
**Tel:** 01628 327700
**Headmaster:** Mr J M Rayer BSc,
PGCE
**Age range:** B11–16
**No. of pupils:** 335 VIth112
**Fees:** Day £13,860–£14,580

**Eton College**
Windsor, Berkshire SL4 6DW
**Tel:** 01753 671249
**Head Master:** Simon Henderson MA
**Age range:** B13–18
**No. of pupils:** 1300 VIth520
**Fees:** FB £33,270

**Heathfield School**
London Road, Ascot,
Berkshire SL5 8BQ
**Tel:** 01344 898342
**Head of School:** Mrs Marina
Gardiner Legge
**Age range:** G11–18
**No. of pupils:** 200

**Leighton Park School**
Shinfield Road, Reading,
Berkshire RG2 7ED
**Tel:** +44 (0) 118 987 9600
**Head:** Nigel Williams BA(Bristol),
MA(London), PGCE
**Age range:** 11–18
**No. of pupils:** 485
**Fees:** Day £21,654 WB
£29,301 FB £34,044

**Luckley House School**
Luckley Road, Wokingham,
Berkshire RG40 3EU
**Tel:** 0118 978 4175
**Head:** Mrs Jane Tudor
**Age range:** G11–18
**No. of pupils:** 230
**Fees:** Day £15,975 WB
£25,908 FB £27,954

**LVS ASCOT**
*For further details see p. 96*
London Road, Ascot,
Berkshire SL5 8DR
**Tel:** 01344 882770
**Email:** enquiries@lvs.
ascot.sch.uk
**Website:** www.lvs.ascot.sch.uk
**Headmistress:** Mrs Christine
Cunniffe BA (Hons), MMus, MBA
**Age range:** 4–18
**No. of pupils:** 830
**Fees:** Day £9,708–£18,609
FB £24,846–£32,694

**Padworth College**
Padworth, Reading,
Berkshire RG7 4NR
**Tel:** 0118 983 2644
**Principal:** Mr John Aguilar
**Age range:** 13–19
**No. of pupils:** 116 VIth50
**Fees:** Day £14,250 FB £28,392

**PANGBOURNE COLLEGE**
*For further details see p. 94*
Pangbourne, Reading,
Berkshire RG8 8LA
**Tel:** 0118 984 2101
**Email:** registrar@
pangbourne.com
**Website:**
www.pangbourne.com
**Headmaster:** Thomas J C
Garnier
**Age range:** 11–18
**No. of pupils:** 426 VIth133
**Fees:** Day £17,055–£24,036
FB £24,021–£33,996

### Queen Anne's School
6 Henley Road, Caversham,
Reading, Berkshire RG4 6DX
**Tel:** 0118 918 7300
**Headmistress:** Mrs Julia Harrington
BA(Hons), PGCE, NPQH
**Age range:** G11–18
**No. of pupils:** 336 VIth100
**Fees:** Day £5,695 WB
£7,545–£7,975 FB £8,395

### Reading Blue Coat School
Holme Park, Sonning Lane, Sonning,
Reading, Berkshire RG4 6SU
**Tel:** 0118 944 1005
**Headmaster:** Mr Jesse Elzinga
**Age range:** B11–18 G16–18
**No. of pupils:** 710 VIth230
**Fees:** Day £16,119

### Reddam House Berkshire
Bearwood Road, Sindlesham,
Wokingham, Berkshire RG41 5BG
**Tel:** 0118 974 8300
**Principal:** Mrs Tammy Howard
**Age range:** 3 months–18 years
**No. of pupils:** 480
**Fees:** Day £9,885–£16,800 WB
£26,310–£30,330 FB £27,855–£31,875

### Redroofs School for the Performing Arts (Redroofs Theatre School)
26 Bath Road, Maidenhead,
Berkshire SL6 4JT
**Tel:** 01628 674092
**Principal:** June Rose
**Age range:** 8–18
**No. of pupils:** 100
**Fees:** Day £4,000

### St George's Ascot
Wells Lane, Ascot, Berkshire SL5 7DZ
**Tel:** 01344 629920
**Headmistress:** Mrs Liz Hewer MA
(Hons) (Cantab) PGCE
**Age range:** G11–18
**No. of pupils:** 270 VIth70
**Fees:** Day £21,900 WB
£32,460–£33,570 FB £34,350

### St Joseph's College
Upper Redlands Road,
Reading, Berkshire RG1 5JT
**Tel:** 0118 966 1000
**Headmaster:** Mr Andrew Colpus
**Age range:** 3–18
**No. of pupils:** VIth64
**Fees:** Day £6,300–£10,770

### St Mary's School Ascot
St Mary's Road, Ascot,
Berkshire SL5 9JF
**Tel:** 01344 296614
**Headmistress:** Mrs Mary Breen
BSc, MSc
**Age range:** G11–18
**No. of pupils:** 390 VIth120
**Fees:** Day £23,400 FB £32,850

### Teikyo School UK
Framewood Road, Wexham,
Slough, Berkshire SL2 4QS
**Tel:** 01753 663711
**Headmaster:** A Watanabe BA
**Age range:** 16–18

### The Abbey School
Kendrick Road, Reading,
Berkshire RG1 5DZ
**Tel:** 0118 987 2256
**Head:** Mrs Rachel S E Dent
**Age range:** G3–18
**No. of pupils:** 1100
**Fees:** Day £16,530

### The Marist Schools
King's Road, Sunninghill,
Ascot, Berkshire SL5 7PS
**Tel:** 01344 624291
**Head of Secondary School:** Mr K
McCloskey
**Age range:** G2–18
**No. of pupils:** 550 VIth60
**Fees:** Day £7,845–£10,695

### The Oratory School
Woodcote, Reading,
Berkshire RG8 0PJ
**Tel:** 01491 683500
**Head Master:** Mr A J Wyles
BSc(Hons), MEd, PGCE, FRGS
**Age range:** B11–18
**No. of pupils:** 380 VIth120
**Fees:** Day £23,250 FB
£21,540–£31,950

### Wellington College
Duke's Ride, Crowthorne,
Berkshire RG45 7PU
**Tel:** +44 (0)1344 444000
**Master:** Mr Julian Thomas
**Age range:** 13–18
**No. of pupils:** 1040
**Fees:** Day £27,930–
£32,085 FB £38,220

# Buckinghamshire

### Pipers Corner School
Pipers Lane, Great
Kingshill, High Wycombe,
Buckinghamshire HP15 6LP
**Tel:** 01494 718 255
**Headmistress:** Mrs H J Ness-Gifford
BA(Hons), PGCE
**Age range:** G4–18
**No. of pupils:** VIth72
**Fees:** Day £7,230–£14,010
WB £18,750–£222,845 FB
£18,990–£23,085

### Stowe School
Buckingham, Buckinghamshire
MK18 5EH
**Tel:** 01280 818000
**Headmaster:** Dr Anthony
Wallersteiner
**Age range:** 13–18
**No. of pupils:** 769 VIth318
**Fees:** Day £22,500 FB £30,975

### St Mary's School
94 Packhorse Road, Gerrards
Cross, Buckinghamshire SL9 8JQ
**Tel:** 01753 883370
**Headmistress:** Mrs J A Ross
BA(Hons), NPQH
**Age range:** G3–18
**No. of pupils:** 350 VIth50
**Fees:** Day £5,390–£16,115

### The Webber Independent School
Soskin Drive, Stantonbury
Fields, Milton Keynes,
Buckinghamshire MK14 6DP
**Tel:** 01908 574740
**Principal:** Mrs Hilary Marsden
**Age range:** 3–18
**No. of pupils:** 300 VIth15
**Fees:** Day £3,894–£10,371

### Wycombe Abbey
High Wycombe,
Buckinghamshire HP11 1PE
**Tel:** +44 (0)1494 897008
**Headmistress:** Mrs Rhiannon J
Wilkinson MA (Oxon) MEd
**Age range:** G11–18
**No. of pupils:** 611
**Fees:** Day £28,350 FB £37,800

# East Sussex

## Battle Abbey School
Battle, East Sussex TN33 0AD
**Tel:** 01424 772385
**Headmaster:** Mr R C Clark
BA(Hons), MA(Ed)
**Age range:** 2–18
**No. of pupils:** 286 VIth48
**Fees:** Day £6,630–£13,390 FB £23,190

## Bede's School
The Dicker, Upper Dicker,
Hailsham, East Sussex BN27 3QH
**Tel:** +44 (0)1323843252
**Head:** Dr Richard Maloney
**Age range:** 12.5–18+
**No. of pupils:** 800 VIth295
**Fees:** Day £15,450 FB £25,725

## Brighton & Hove High School GDST
Montpelier Road, Brighton,
East Sussex BN1 3AT
**Tel:** 01273 280280
**Head:** Mrs Lorna Duggleby
**Age range:** G3–18
**No. of pupils:** 680 VIth70
**Fees:** Day £5,028–£8,898

## Brighton College
Eastern Road, Brighton,
East Sussex BN2 0AL
**Tel:** 01273 704200
**Head Master:** Richard Cairns MA
**Age range:** 3–18
**No. of pupils:** 950
**Fees:** Day £9,720–£23,790
WB £32,220–£33,210 FB
£40,230–£42,420

## Buckswood School
Broomham Hall, Rye
Road, Guestling, Hastings,
East Sussex TN35 4LT
**Tel:** 01424 813 813
**Headmaster:** Mr Giles Sutton
**Age range:** 10–19
**No. of pupils:** 420

## Buckswood St George's
Westwood House, 7-9
Holmesdale Gardens, Hastings,
East Sussex TN34 1LY
**Tel:** 01424 813696
**College Director:** Ian Godfrey
**Age range:** B16–19 G16–20
**No. of pupils:** VIth50

## Eastbourne College
Old Wish Road, Eastbourne,
East Sussex BN21 4JX
**Tel:** 01323 452323 (Admissions)
**Headmaster:** Mr T Lawson
MA(Oxon)
**Age range:** 13–18
**No. of pupils:** 610 VIth274
**Fees:** Day £22,260–£22,620
FB £33,930–£34,320

## Greenfields Independent Day & Boarding School
Priory Road, Forest Row,
East Sussex RH18 5JD
**Tel:** +44 (0)1342 822189
**Executive Head:** Mr. Jeff Smith
**Age range:** 2–19

## Lewes Old Grammar School
High Street, Lewes, East
Sussex BN7 1XS
**Tel:** 01273 472634
**Headmaster:** Mr Robert Blewitt
**Age range:** 3–18
**No. of pupils:** 463 VIth50
**Fees:** Day £5,550–£10,815

## Mayfield School
The Old Palace, Mayfield,
East Sussex TN20 6PH
**Tel:** +44 (0)1435 874600
**Head:** Ms Antonia Beary MA, Mphil
(Cantab), PGCE
**Age range:** G11–18
**No. of pupils:** 365 VIth100
**Fees:** Day £19,650 FB £31,800

## Michael Hall School
Kidbrooke Park, Priory Road,
Forest Row, East Sussex RH18 5BG
**Tel:** 01342 822275
**Age range:** 3–19
**Fees:** Day £8,858–£12,180
FB £6,876–£7,876

## Moira House Girls School
Upper Carlisle Road, Eastbourne,
East Sussex BN20 7TE
**Tel:** 01323 644144
**Headmaster:** Mr James Sheridan
MA, BSc
**Age range:** G0–18
**No. of pupils:** 289

## ROEDEAN SCHOOL
*For further details see p. 97*
Roedean Way, Brighton,
East Sussex BN2 5RQ
**Tel:** 01273 667500
**Email:** info@roedean.co.uk
**Website:** www.roedean.co.uk
**Headmaster:** Mr. Oliver Bond
BA(Essex), PGCE, NPQH
**Age range:** G11–18
**No. of pupils:** 568 VIth171
**Fees:** Day £15,960–£20,865
WB £28,230–£31,470 FB
£30,930–£37,440

# Essex

## BANCROFT'S SCHOOL
*For further details see p. 79*
High Road, Woodford
Green, Essex IG8 0RF
**Tel:** 020 8505 4821
**Email:** office@bancrofts.org
**Website:** www.bancrofts.org
**Head:** Mr Simon Marshall MA,
PGCE (Cantab), MA, MPhil
(Oxon)
**Age range:** 7–18
**No. of pupils:** 1143 VIth245

## Brentwood School
Middleton Hall Lane,
Brentwood, Essex CM15 8EE
**Tel:** 01277 243243
**Headmaster:** Mr Ian Davies
**Age range:** 3–18
**No. of pupils:** 1529
**Fees:** Day £18,216 FB £35,700

## Chigwell School
High Road, Chigwell, Essex IG7 6QF
**Tel:** 020 8501 5700
**Headmaster:** Mr M E Punt MA, MSc
**Age range:** 4–18
**No. of pupils:** 915 VIth185
**Fees:** Day £10,200–£16,020
FB £26,730–£26,730

## Felsted School
Felsted, Great Dunmow,
Essex CM6 3LL
**Tel:** +44 (0)1371 822608
**Headmaster:** Mr Chris Townsend
**Age range:** 13–18
**No. of pupils:** 522 VIth426
**Fees:** Day £22,485 WB
£32,235 FB £34,275

## Gosfield School
Cut Hedge Park, Halstead Road,
Gosfield, Halstead, Essex CO9 1PF
**Tel:** 01787 474040
**Headteacher:** Mr Guy Martyn
**Age range:** 4–18
**No. of pupils:** VIth21
**Fees:** Day £4,740–£13,695 WB
£15,465–£17,310 FB £17,985–£23,130

## New Hall School
The Avenue, Boreham,
Chelmsford, Essex CM3 3HS
**Tel:** 01245 467588
**Principal:** Mrs Katherine Jeffrey MA,
BA, PGCE, MA(Ed Mg), NPQH
**Age range:** Coed 3-11,
Single 11-16, Coed 16–18
**No. of pupils:** 1180 VIth217
**Fees:** Day £9,432–£19,440 WB
£19,038–£27,813 FB £21,033–£29,847

## Park School for Girls
20 Park Avenue, Ilford, Essex IG1 4RS
**Tel:** 020 8554 2466
**Headmistress:** Mrs N O'Brien BA
**Age range:** G7–18
**No. of pupils:** 230 VIth19
**Fees:** Day £4,755–£6,285

# Hampshire

### Alton School
Anstey Lane, Alton,
Hampshire GU34 2NG
**Tel:** 01420 82070
**Head:** Graham Maher
**No. of pupils:** 502 VIth53
(£) (16)

### Bedales School
Church Road, Steep, Petersfield,
Hampshire GU32 2DG
**Tel:** 01730 711733
**Head:** Keith Budge MA
**Age range:** 13–18
**No. of pupils:** 457
**Fees:** Day £9,272 FB £11,799
(£) (16)

### Brockwood Park & Inwoods School
Brockwood Park, Bramdean,
Hampshire SO24 0LQ
**Tel:** +44 (0)1962 771744
**Co-Principals:** Mr Antonio Autor &
Dr Gopal Krishnamurthy
**Age range:** 4–19
**No. of pupils:** 112 VIth39
**Fees:** Day £5,630–£6,400
FB £21,400–£21,400
(£) (16)

### Churcher's College
Petersfield, Hampshire GU31 4AS
**Tel:** 01730 263033
**Headmaster:** Mr Simon Williams
MA, BSc
**Age range:** 3–18 years
**Fees:** Day £9,675–£14,220
(£) (16)

### Farnborough Hill
Farnborough Road, Farnborough,
Hampshire GU14 8AT
**Tel:** 01252 545197
**Headmistress:** Mrs A Neil BA, MEd,
PGCE
**Age range:** G11–18
**No. of pupils:** 550 VIth90
**Fees:** Day £14,241
(£) (16)

### Hampshire Collegiate School
Embley Park, Romsey,
Hampshire SO51 6ZE
**Tel:** 01794 512206
**Principal:** Mrs Emma-Kate Henry
**Age range:** 2–18
**No. of pupils:** 683
(£) (16)

### King Edward VI School
Wilton Road, Southampton,
Hampshire SO15 5UQ
**Tel:** 023 8070 4561
**Head Master:** Mr A J Thould
MA(Oxon)
**Age range:** 11–18
**No. of pupils:** 970
**Fees:** Day £15,510
(£) (16)

### Lord Wandsworth College
Long Sutton, Hook,
Hampshire RG29 1TB
**Tel:** 01256 862201
**Head of School:** Mr Adam Williams
**Age range:** 11–18 years
**No. of pupils:** 600
**Fees:** Day £19,650–£22,575 WB
£27,225–£30,600 FB £28,140–£32,100
(£) (16)

### Portsmouth High School GDST
Kent Road, Southsea, Portsmouth,
Hampshire PO5 3EQ
**Tel:** 023 9282 6714
**Headmistress:** Mrs Jane Prescott
BSc NPQH
**Age range:** G3–18
**No. of pupils:** 500
**Fees:** Day £2,722–£4,550
(£) (16)

### Salesian College
Reading Road, Farnborough,
Hampshire GU14 6PA
**Tel:** 01252 893000
**Headmaster:** Mr P A Wilson
BA(Hons), MA, CertEd
**Age range:** B11–18 G16–18
**No. of pupils:** 650 VIth140
**Fees:** Day £9,000
(£) (16)

### Sherfield School
Sherfield-on-Loddon, Hook,
Hampshire RG27 0HU
**Tel:** +44 (0)1256 884 800
**Headmaster:** Mr Dick Jaine
**Age range:** 3 months–18 years
**No. of pupils:** 445 VIth16
**Fees:** Day £7,350–£13,890 FB £20,946
(£) (16)

### St John's College
Grove Road South, Southsea,
Portsmouth, Hampshire PO5 3QW
**Tel:** 023 9281 5118
**Headmaster:** Mr Timothy Bayley BSc
(Hons), MA, PGCE
**Age range:** 2–18
**No. of pupils:** 560 VIth86
**Fees:** Day £8,910–£11,685
FB £25,200–£27,090
(£) (16)

### ST SWITHUN'S SCHOOL
**For further details see p. 99**
Alresford Road, Winchester,
Hampshire SO21 1HA
**Tel:** 01962 835700
**Email:** office@stswithuns.com
**Website:** www.stswithuns.com
**Head of School:** Jane Gandee
MA(Cantab)
**Age range:** G11–18
**No. of pupils:** 520
(£) (16)

### The Portsmouth Grammar School
High Street, Portsmouth,
Hampshire PO1 2LN
**Tel:** +44 (0)23 9236 0036
**Headmaster:** Mr J E Priory MA
**Age range:** 2–18
**No. of pupils:** 1556 VIth336
**Fees:** Day £9,510–£14,817
(£) (IB) (16)

### Winchester College
College Street, Winchester,
Hampshire SO23 9NA
**Tel:** 01962 621247
**Headmaster:** Dr. T R Hands
**Age range:** B13–18
**No. of pupils:** 690 VIth280
**Fees:** FB £36,678
(£) (16)

# Hertfordshire

### Aldenham School
Elstree, Hertfordshire WD6 3AJ
**Tel:** 01923 858122
**Headmaster:** Mr James C Fowler
MA
**Age range:** 3–18
**No. of pupils:** 700
**Fees:** Day £15,291–£21,414
FB £21,099–£31,384
(£) (16)

### BERKHAMSTED SCHOOL
**For further details see p. 92**
Overton House, 131 High
Street, Berkhamsted,
Hertfordshire HP4 2DJ
**Tel:** 01442 358001
**Email:** admissions@
berkhamstedschool.org
**Website:**
www.berkhamstedschool.org
**Principal:** Mr Richard Backhouse
MA(Cantab)
**Age range:** 3–18
**No. of pupils:** 1772 VIth402
**Fees:** Day £10,365–£20,250
WB £27,115 FB £32,255
(£) (16)

### Bishop's Stortford College
10 Maze Green Road, Bishop's
Stortford, Hertfordshire CM23 2PJ
**Tel:** 01279 838575
**Headmaster:** Mr Jeremy Gladwin
**Age range:** 13–18
**No. of pupils:** VIth249
**Fees:** Day £18,915–£19,086
WB £28,665–£28,839 FB
£28,950–£30,273
(£) (16)

### Champneys International College of Health & Beauty
Chesham Road, Wigginton,
Tring, Hertfordshire HP23 6HY
**Tel:** 01442 291333
**College Principal:** Ms Pam Clegg
**Age range:** 16+
**No. of pupils:** 61
**Fees:** Day £3,000–£9,050
(16) (£) (16)

### Haberdashers' Aske's School
Butterfly Lane, Elstree,
Borehamwood,
Hertfordshire WD6 3AF
**Tel:** 020 8266 1700
**Headmaster:** Mr P B Hamilton MA
**Age range:** B5–18
**No. of pupils:** 1402 VIth310
**Fees:** Day £10,641–£14,103
(16)

### Haberdashers' Aske's School for Girls
Aldenham Road,
Elstree, Borehamwood,
Hertfordshire WD6 3BT
**Tel:** 020 8266 2300
**Headmistress:** Miss Biddie A
O'Connor MA (Oxon)
**Age range:** G4–18
**No. of pupils:** 1190
**Fees:** Day £15,192–£17,433
(16)

## Haileybury
Haileybury, Hertford,
Hertfordshire SG13 7NU
**Tel:** +44 (0)1992 706200
**The Master:** Mr Martin Collier MA
BA PGCE
**Age range:** 11–18
**No. of pupils:** 804 VIth323
**Fees:** Day £16,455–£24,753
FB £20,796–£32,784

## Immanuel College
87/91 Elstree Road, Bushey,
Hertfordshire WD23 4EB
**Tel:** 020 8950 0604
**Headmaster:** Mr Philip Skelker MA
**Age range:** 11–18
**No. of pupils:** 520 VIth127
**Fees:** Day £10,995

---

**MOUNT HOUSE SCHOOL**
*For further details see p. 88*
Camlet Way, Hadley Wood,
Barnet, Hertfordshire EN4 0NJ
**Tel:** 020 8449 6889
**Email:** admissions@
mounthouse.org.uk
**Website:**
www.mounthouse.org.uk
**Headmaster:** Mr Matthew Burke
**Age range:** 11–18
**No. of pupils:** 180
**Fees:** Day £14,820

---

## Princess Helena College
Preston, Hitchin,
Hertfordshire SG4 7RT
**Tel:** 01462 443888
**Headmistress:** Mrs Sue Wallace-
Woodroffe
**Age range:** G11–18
**No. of pupils:** 194 VIth35
**Fees:** Day £15,585–£18,975
FB £22,185–£27,585

## Queenswood
Shepherd's Way, Brookmans Park,
Hatfield, Hertfordshire AL9 6NS
**Tel:** 01707 602500
**Principal:** Mrs P C Edgar BA(Hons)
London, PGCE
**Age range:** G11–18
**No. of pupils:** 400 VIth120
**Fees:** Day £19,485–£21,825
FB £26,295–£28,665

## Rudolf Steiner School
Langley Hill, Kings Langley,
Hertfordshire WD4 9HG
**Tel:** 01923 262505
**Age range:** 3–19
**No. of pupils:** 405
**Fees:** Day £2,985–£7,800

## Sherrardswood School
Lockleys, Welwyn,
Hertfordshire AL6 0BJ
**Tel:** 01438 714282
**Headmistress:** Mrs L Corry
**Age range:** 2–18
**No. of pupils:** 357
**Fees:** Day £6,720–£12,750

## St Albans High School for Girls
Townsend Avenue, St Albans,
Hertfordshire AL1 3SJ
**Tel:** 01727 853800
**Headmistress:** Mrs Jenny Brown
MA (Oxon)
**Age range:** G4–18
**No. of pupils:** 940 VIth170
**Fees:** Day £4,650–£5,910

## St Albans School
Abbey Gateway, St Albans,
Hertfordshire AL3 4HB
**Tel:** 01727 855521
**Headmaster:** Mr JWJ Gillespie
MA(Cantab), FRSA
**Age range:** B11–18 G16–18
**No. of pupils:** 870
**Fees:** Day £17,238

## St Christopher School
Barrington Road, Letchworth,
Hertfordshire SG6 3JZ
**Tel:** 01462 650 850
**Head:** Richard Palmer
**Age range:** 3–18
**No. of pupils:** 511 VIth78
**Fees:** Day £3,375–£14,505
FB £15,600–£25,470

## St Columba's College
King Harry Lane, St Albans,
Hertfordshire AL3 4AW
**Tel:** 01727 855185
**Headmaster:** David R Buxton
**Age range:** B4–18
**No. of pupils:** 860 VIth150
**Fees:** Day £8,235–£10,416

## St Edmund's College & Prep School
Old Hall Green, Nr Ware,
Hertfordshire SG11 1DS
**Tel:** 01920 824247
**Head:** Paulo Durán BA MA
**Age range:** 3–18
**No. of pupils:** 799 VIth135
**Fees:** Day £9,465–£14,955 WB
£19,830–£22,575 FB £21,855–£24,990

## St Francis' College
Broadway, Letchworth Garden
City, Hertfordshire SG6 3PJ
**Tel:** 01462 670511
**Headmistress:** Mrs B Goulding
**Age range:** G3–18
**No. of pupils:** 460 VIth75
**Fees:** Day £8,670–£13,830 WB
£19,425–£22,875 FB £24,195–£27,645

## St Margaret's School, Bushey
Merry Hill Road, Bushey,
Hertfordshire WD23 1DT
**Tel:** 020 8416 4400
**Head:** Mrs Rose Hardy MA(Oxon),
MEd, FRSA
**Age range:** G4–18 years
**No. of pupils:** 450 VIth100
**Fees:** Day £14,730 WB
£20,220–£23,670 FB £27,600

## Stanborough School
Stanborough Park, Garston,
Watford, Hertfordshire WD25 9JT
**Tel:** 01923 673268
**Head Teacher:** Ms Lorraine Dixon
**Age range:** 3–19
**No. of pupils:** 300 VIth20
**Fees:** Day £3,660–£5,500
WB £12,834–£15,846

## The Purcell School, London
Aldenham Road, Bushey,
Hertfordshire WD23 2TS
**Tel:** 01923 331100
**Headteacher:** Mr. Stephen Yeo
**Age range:** 10–18
**No. of pupils:** 180

## The Royal Masonic School for Girls
Rickmansworth Park,
Rickmansworth,
Hertfordshire WD3 4HF
**Tel:** 01923 773168
**Headmaster:** Mr Kevin Carson
M.Phil (Cambridge)
**Age range:** G4–18
**No. of pupils:** 930 VIth165
**Fees:** Day £10,455–£15,915 WB
£18,345–£25,935 FB £19,350–£28,140

## Tring Park School for the Performing Arts
Tring Park, Tring,
Hertfordshire HP23 5LX
**Tel:** 01442 824255
**Principal:** Mr Stefan Anderson MA,
ARCM, ARCT
**Age range:** 8–19
**No. of pupils:** 350 VIth263
**Fees:** Day £14,430–£22,965
FB £24,540–£34,710

# Kent

## Ashford School
East Hill, Ashford, Kent TN24 8PB
**Tel:** 01233 739030
**Head:** Mr M R Buchanan BSc(Hons),
CertEd, NPQH, CPhys
**Age range:** 3 months–18 years
**No. of pupils:** 835 VIth170
**Fees:** Day £8,400–£16,200
WB £28,500 FB £32,400

## Beckenham College
The Clockhouse Business Centre,
Unit 2, Thayers Farm Road,
Beckenham, Kent BR3 4LZ
**Tel:** 020 8650 3321
**Principal:** Mrs E Wakeling
**Age range:** 16+
**Fees:** Day £100–£3,500

## Beechwood Sacred Heart
12 Pembury Road, Tunbridge
Wells, Kent TN2 3QD
**Tel:** 01892 532747
**Headmaster:** Mr Aaron Lennon
BA(Hons)
**Age range:** 3–18
**No. of pupils:** 400 VIth70
**Fees:** Day £9,060–£15,936
WB £23,460 FB £26,460

## Benenden School
Cranbrook, Kent TN17 4AA
**Tel:** 01580 240592
**Headmistress:** Mrs S Price
**Age range:** G11–18
**No. of pupils:** 550
**Fees:** FB £35,700

## Bethany School
Curtisden Green, Goudhurst,
Cranbrook, Kent TN17 1LB
**Tel:** 01580 211273
**Headmaster:** Mr Francie Healy BSc,
HDipEd, NPQH
**Age range:** 11–18 years
**No. of pupils:** 313 VIth98
**Fees:** Day £16,245–£17,925 WB
£25,185–£27,825 FB £27,165–£30,585

## Bishop Challoner School
228 Bromley Road, Shortlands,
Bromley, Kent BR2 0BS
**Tel:** 020 8460 3546
**Headteacher:** Ms Paula Anderson
**Age range:** 3–18
**No. of pupils:** 412 VIth32
**Fees:** Day £6,441–£9,036

## BROMLEY HIGH SCHOOL GDST
*For further details see p. 80*
Blackbrook Lane, Bickley,
Bromley, Kent BR1 2TW
**Tel:** 020 8781 7000/1
**Email:** bhs@bro.gdst.net
**Website:**
www.bromleyhigh.gdst.net
**Head:** Mrs A M Drew BA(Hons),
MBA (Dunelm)
**Age range:** G4–18
**No. of pupils:** 912 VIth120
**Fees:** Day £13,356–£16,563

## Canterbury Steiner School
Garlinge Green, Chartham,
Canterbury, Kent CT4 5RU
**Tel:** 01227 738285
**Age range:** 3–18
**Fees:** Day £3,246–£4,405.50

## CATS Canterbury
68 New Dover Road,
Canterbury, Kent CT1 3LQ
**Tel:** +44 (0)1227866540
**Principal:** Mr. James Slocombe
BSc(Hons), PGCE, QTS, MA, FRSA
**Age range:** 14–18
**No. of pupils:** 400

## Cobham Hall School
Cobham, Kent DA12 3BL
**Tel:** 01474 823371
**Headmistress:** Dr Sandra Coates-
Smith BSc, PhD
**Age range:** G11–18
**No. of pupils:** 180

## Darul Uloom London
Foxbury Avenue, Perry Street,
Chislehurst, Kent BR7 6SD
**Tel:** 020 8295 0637
**Principal:** Mufti Mustafa
**Age range:** B11–18
**No. of pupils:** 160
**Fees:** FB £2,400

## Dover College
Effingham Crescent,
Dover, Kent CT17 9RH
**Tel:** 01304 205969
**Headmaster:** Mr Gareth Doodes
MA (Hons)
**Age range:** 3–18
**No. of pupils:** 301
**Fees:** Day £7,500–£15,600
WB £20,250–£24,000 FB
£24,000–£30,000

## Farringtons School
Perry Street, Chislehurst,
Kent BR7 6LR
**Tel:** 020 8467 0256
**Head:** Mrs Dorothy Nancekievill
**Age range:** 3–18
**No. of pupils:** 681 VIth94
**Fees:** Day £14,610 WB
£28,830 FB £30,600

## Kent College
Whitstable Road, Canterbury,
Kent CT2 9DT
**Tel:** 01227 763231
**Executive Head Master:** Dr David
Lamper
**Age range:** 3–18
**No. of pupils:** 704
**Fees:** Day £16,221–£17,995
FB £24,741–£33,981

## Kent College Pembury
Old Church Road, Pembury,
Tunbridge Wells, Kent TN2 4AX
**Tel:** +44 (0)1892 822006
**Headmistress:** Mrs Sally-Anne
Huang MA(Oxon), MSc, PGCE
**Age range:** G3–18
**No. of pupils:** 650 VIth102
**Fees:** Day £7,887–£17,322
FB £21,471–£27,924

## King's Rochester
Satis House, Boley Hill,
Rochester, Kent ME1 1TE
**Tel:** 01634 888555
**Principal:** Mr J Walker
**Age range:** 13–18
**No. of pupils:** 263
**Fees:** Day £18,705 FB £30,390

## Radnor House, Sevenoaks
Combe Bank Drive,
Sevenoaks, Kent TN14 6AE
**Tel:** 01959 563720
**Head:** Mr David Paton BComm
(Hons) PGCE MA
**Age range:** 2.5–18
**No. of pupils:** 250

## Rochester Independent College
Star Hill, Rochester,
Medway, Kent ME1 1XF
**Tel:** 01634 828115
**Principals:** Alistair Brownlow, Brian
Pain, Pauline Bailey
**Age range:** 11–19
**No. of pupils:** 306 VIth233
**Fees:** Day £12,000–£16,500 WB
£25,650–£27,300 FB £27,450–£29,100

## Sackville School
Tonbridge Rd, Hildenborough,
Tonbridge, Kent TN11 9HN
**Tel:** 01732 838888
**Headmaster:** Mr Justin Foster-
Gandey BSc (hons)
**Age range:** 11–18
**No. of pupils:** 160 VIth29
**Fees:** Day £14,850

## Sevenoaks School
High Street, Sevenoaks,
Kent TN13 1HU
**Tel:** +44 (0)1732 455133
**Head:** Dr Katy Ricks MA, DPhil
**Age range:** 11–18
**No. of pupils:** 1080
**Fees:** Day £22,455–£25,497
FB £35,865–£38,907

## St Edmund's School
St Thomas' Hill, Canterbury,
Kent CT2 8HU
**Tel:** 01227 475601
**Head:** Louise Moelwyn-Hughes
**Age range:** 3–18
**No. of pupils:** 535
**Fees:** Day £18,651 FB £29,781

## St Lawrence College
Ramsgate, Kent CT11 7AE
**Tel:** 01843 572931
**Principal:** Mr Antony Spencer
**Age range:** 3–18
**No. of pupils:** 640 VIth115
**Fees:** Day £7,470–£18,495
FB £26,055–£34,635

## Sutton Valence School
North Street, Sutton
Valence, Kent ME17 3HL
**Tel:** 01622 845200
**Headmaster:** Bruce Grindlay MA
Cantab, MusB, FRCO, CHM
**Age range:** 11–18
**No. of pupils:** 570

## The King's School, Canterbury
The Precincts, Canterbury,
Kent CT1 2ES
**Tel:** 01227 595501
**Head:** Mr P Roberts
**Age range:** 13–18
**No. of pupils:** 858 VIth385
**Fees:** Day £26,700 FB £35,295

## Tonbridge School
Tonbridge, Kent TN9 1JP
**Tel:** 01732 365555
**Headmaster:** T H P Haynes
**Age range:** B13–18
**No. of pupils:** 787
**Fees:** Day £29,229 FB £38,964

## Walthamstow Hall School
Sevenoaks, Kent TN13 3UL
**Tel:** 01732 451334
**Headmistress:** Mrs J Milner
MA(Oxford)
**Age range:** G2–18
**No. of pupils:** 500 VIth80
**Fees:** Day £8,070–£13,710

# Specialist schools and sixth form colleges

## Middlesex

### ACS Hillingdon International School
Hillingdon Court, 108 Vine Lane, Hillingdon, Uxbridge, Middlesex UB10 0BE
**Tel:** +44 (0) 1895 259 771
**Head of School:** Linda LaPine
**Age range:** 4–18
**No. of pupils:** 520
**Fees:** Day £17,260–£23,110

### Halliford School
Russell Road, Shepperton, Middlesex TW17 9HX
**Tel:** 01932 223593
**Headmaster:** Mr James Davies BMus
**Age range:** B11–18 G16–18
**No. of pupils:** 400
**Fees:** Day £15,285

### Hampton School
Hanworth Road, Hampton, Middlesex TW12 3HD
**Tel:** 020 8979 9273
**Headmaster:** Mr Kevin Knibbs MA (Oxon)
**Age range:** B11–18
**No. of pupils:** 1200
**Fees:** Day £6,125

### Harrow School
5 High Street, Harrow on the Hill, Middlesex HA1 3HT
**Tel:** 020 8872 8000
**Head Master:** Mr Jim Hawkins
**Age range:** B13–18
**No. of pupils:** 830 VIth320
**Fees:** FB £33,285

### Harrow Secretarial College & Computer Training Centre
68 Station Road, Harrow, Middlesex HA1 2SQ
**Tel:** 020 8424 9900
**Fees:** Day £0

---

**KEW HOUSE SCHOOL**
*For further details see p. 86*
Kew House, 6 Capital Interchange Way, London, Middlesex TW8 0EX
**Tel:** 0208 742 2038
**Email:** info@kewhouseschool.com
**Website:** www.kewhouseschool.com
**Headmaster:** Mr Mark Hudson
**Age range:** 11–18
**No. of pupils:** 450
**Fees:** Day £6,849

---

### Merchant Taylors' School
Sandy Lodge, Northwood, Middlesex HA6 2HT
**Tel:** 01923 820644
**Head:** Mr S J Everson MA (Cantab)
**Age range:** B11–18
**No. of pupils:** 865 VIth282
**Fees:** Day £16,660

### North London Collegiate School
Canons, Canons Drive, Edgware, Middlesex HA8 7RJ
**Tel:** +44 (0)20 8952 0912
**Headmistress:** Mrs Sarah Clark
**Age range:** G4–18
**No. of pupils:** 1080
**Fees:** Day £5,530–£6,545

### Northwood College for Girls GDST
Maxwell Road, Northwood, Middlesex HA6 2YE
**Tel:** 01923 825446
**Head Mistress:** Miss Jacqualyn Pain MA, MA, MBA
**Age range:** G3–18
**No. of pupils:** 840 VIth100

### Regent College
Sai House, 167 Imperial Drive, Harrow, Middlesex HA2 7HD
**Tel:** 020 8966 9900
**Principal:** Mr Selva Pankaj MBA, FCMA
**Age range:** 11–19
**No. of pupils:** 167
**Fees:** Day £2,745–£12,995

### St Catherine's School
Cross Deep, Twickenham, Middlesex TW1 4QJ
**Tel:** 020 8891 2898
**Headmistress:** Sister Paula Thomas BEd(Hons), MA
**Age range:** G3–18
**No. of pupils:** 430
**Fees:** Day £10,509–£14,517

### St Helen's School
Eastbury Road, Northwood, Middlesex HA6 3AS
**Tel:** +44 (0)1923 843210
**Headmistress:** Dr Mary Short BA, PhD
**Age range:** G3–18
**No. of pupils:** VIth165

### St John's Senior School
North Lodge, The Ridgeway, Enfield, Middlesex EN2 8BE
**Tel:** 020 8366 0035
**Headmaster:** Mr Andrew Tardios LLB(Hons), BA(Hons), CertEd
**Age range:** 11–18 years
**No. of pupils:** 309 VIth95
**Fees:** Day £13,170

### The John Lyon School
Middle Road, Harrow on the Hill, Middlesex HA2 0HN
**Tel:** 020 8515 9400
**Head:** Miss Katherine Haynes BA, MEd, NPQH
**Age range:** B11–18
**No. of pupils:** 600
**Fees:** Day £5,710–£5,928

### The Lady Eleanor Holles School
Hanworth Road, Hampton, Middlesex TW12 3HF
**Tel:** 020 8979 1601
**Head of School:** Mrs Heather Hanbury
**Age range:** G7–18
**No. of pupils:** 875
**Fees:** Day £18,945

## Surrey

### ACS Cobham International School
Heywood, Portsmouth Road, Cobham, Surrey KT11 1BL
**Tel:** +44 (0) 1932 867251
**Head of School:** Mr A Eysele
**Age range:** 2–18
**No. of pupils:** 1460
**Fees:** Day £10,690–£25,050 FB £36,810–£39,310

### ACS Egham International School
Woodlee, London Road, Egham, Surrey TW20 0HS
**Tel:** +44 (0) 1784 430 800
**Head of School:** Jeremy Lewis
**Age range:** 3–18
**Fees:** Day £7,080–£24,020

### Box Hill School
Old London Road, Mickleham, Dorking, Surrey RH5 6EA
**Tel:** 01372 373382
**Headmaster:** Mr Corydon Lowde
**Age range:** 11–18
**No. of pupils:** 425 VIth96
**Fees:** Day £16,140–£17,170 WB £24,600–£25,800 FB £29,970–£35,850

### Cambridge Tutors College
Water Tower Hill, Croydon, Surrey CR0 5SX
**Tel:** 020 8688 5284/7363
**Principal:** Mr M Eagers
**Age range:** 15–19
**No. of pupils:** 215 VIth200
**Fees:** Day £19,800

### Caterham School
Harestone Valley, Caterham, Surrey CR3 6YA
**Tel:** 01883 343028
**Head:** Mr C. W. Jones MA(Cantab)
**Age range:** 11–18
**No. of pupils:** VIth321

### Charterhouse
Godalming, Surrey GU7 2DX
**Tel:** +44 (0)1483 291501
**Headmaster:** Dr Alex Peterken
**Age range:** B13–18 G16–18
**No. of pupils:** 820

### City of London Freemen's School
Ashtead Park, Ashtead, Surrey KT21 1ET
**Tel:** 01372 277933
**Headmaster:** Mr R Martin
**Age range:** 7–18
**No. of pupils:** 877 VIth213
**Fees:** Day £10,872–£14,598 FB £23,238

### Claremont Fan Court School
Claremont Drive, Esher, Surrey KT10 9LY
**Tel:** 01372 467841
**Head of Senior School:** Mr Jonathan Insall-Reid
**Age range:** 2–18
**No. of pupils:** 780
**Fees:** Day £2,205–£17,085

## Cranleigh School
Horseshoe Lane, Cranleigh,
Surrey GU6 8QQ
**Tel:** +44 (0) 1483 273666
**Headmaster:** Mr Martin Reader MA, MPhil, MBA
**Age range:** 7–18 (including Prep School)
**No. of pupils:** 626 VIth250
**Fees:** Day £29,985 FB £36,615

## Croydon High School GDST
Old Farleigh Road, Selsdon,
South Croydon, Surrey CR2 8YB
**Tel:** 020 8260 7500
**Headmistress:** Mrs Emma Pattison
**Age range:** G3–18
**No. of pupils:** 565 VIth90

## Dunottar School
High Trees Road, Reigate,
Surrey RH2 7EL
**Tel:** 01737 761945
**Head of School:** Mr Mark Tottman
**Age range:** 11–18
**No. of pupils:** 319
**Fees:** Day £15,492

## Epsom College
Epsom, Surrey KT17 4JQ
**Tel:** 01372 821000
**Headmaster:** Mr Jay A Piggot MA
**Age range:** 13–18
**No. of pupils:** 730
**Fees:** Day £21,255 FB £31,098

## Ewell Castle School
Church Street, Ewell, Epsom,
Surrey KT17 2AW
**Tel:** 020 8393 1413
**Principal:** Mr Peter Harris
**Age range:** 3–18
**No. of pupils:** 557
**Fees:** Day £4,740–£15,975

## Frensham Heights
Rowledge, Farnham,
Surrey GU10 4EA
**Tel:** 01252 792561
**Headmaster:** Mr Andrew Fisher BA, MEd, FRSA
**Age range:** 3–18
**No. of pupils:** 497 VIth105
**Fees:** Day £5,205–£15,300 FB £19,485–£22,680

## Guildford High School
London Road, Guildford,
Surrey GU1 1SJ
**Tel:** 01483 561440
**Headmistress:** Mrs F J Boulton BSc, MA
**Age range:** G4–18
**No. of pupils:** 980 VIth160
**Fees:** Day £10,176–£16,512

## King Edward's Witley
Godalming, Surrey GU8 5SG
**Tel:** +44 (0)1428 686700
**Headmaster:** Mr John Attwater MA
**Age range:** 11–18
**No. of pupils:** 410 VIth185
**Fees:** Day £19,950 FB £30,780

## KINGSTON GRAMMAR SCHOOL
*For further details see p. 84*
70 London Rd, Kingston upon
Thames, Surrey KT2 6PY
**Tel:** 020 8456 5875
**Email:** enquiries@kgs.org.uk
**Website:** www.kgs.org.uk
**Head:** Mr Stephen Lehec
**Age range:** 11–18
**No. of pupils:** 829
**Fees:** Day £6,225

## Lingfield College
Racecourse Road, Lingfield,
Surrey RH7 6PH
**Tel:** 01342 833176
**Headmaster:** Mr R Bool
**Age range:** 2–18
**No. of pupils:** 935
**Fees:** Day £11,250–£14,600

## MARYMOUNT INTERNATIONAL SCHOOL LONDON
*For further details see p. 87*
George Road, Kingston upon
Thames, Surrey KT2 7PE
**Tel:** +44 (0)20 8949 0571
**Email:** admissions@
marymountlondon.com
**Website:**
www.marymountlondon.com
**Headmistress:** Mrs Margaret Frazier
**Age range:** G11–18
**No. of pupils:** 250
**Fees:** Day £20,015–£22,860
WB £34,365–£37,210 FB
£36,030–£38,875

## Notre Dame School
Cobham, Surrey KT11 1HA
**Tel:** 01932 869990
**Head of Seniors:** Mrs Anna King MEd, MA (Cantab), PGCE
**Age range:** 2–18
**No. of pupils:** 600

## Old Palace of John Whitgift School
Old Palace Road, Croydon,
Surrey CR0 1AX
**Tel:** 020 8686 7347
**Head:** Mrs. C Jewell
**Age range:** B3 months–4 years G3 months–19 years
**No. of pupils:** 740 VIth120
**Fees:** Day £10,086–£13,497

## Prior's Field
Priorsfield Road, Godalming,
Surrey GU7 2RH
**Tel:** 01483 810551
**Head of School:** Mrs T Kirnig
**Age range:** G11–18
**No. of pupils:** 450
**Fees:** Day £15,855 FB £25,575

## Reed's School
Sandy Lane, Cobham,
Surrey KT11 2ES
**Tel:** 01932 869001
**Headmaster:** Mr Mark Hoskins BA MA MSc
**Age range:** B11–18 G16–18
**No. of pupils:** 650 VIth230
**Fees:** Day £16,938–£21,184 FB £22,582–£28,023

## Reigate Grammar School
Reigate Road, Reigate,
Surrey RH2 0QS
**Tel:** 01737 222231
**Headmaster:** Mr Shaun Fenton MA (Oxon) MEd (Oxon)
**Age range:** 11–18
**No. of pupils:** 969 VIth262
**Fees:** Day £17,460

## Royal Grammar School, Guildford
High Street, Guildford,
Surrey GU1 3BB
**Tel:** 01483 880600
**Headmaster:** Dr J M Cox BSc, PhD
**Age range:** B11–18
**No. of pupils:** 940
**Fees:** Day £17,595

## Royal Russell School
Coombe Lane, Croydon,
Surrey CR9 5BX
**Tel:** 020 8657 3669
**Headmaster:** Christopher Hutchinson
**Age range:** 11–18
**No. of pupils:** 590 VIth180
**Fees:** Day £15,285 FB £22,365–£30,240

## Sir William Perkins's School
Guildford Road, Chertsey,
Surrey KT16 9BN
**Tel:** 01932 574900
**Head:** Mr C Muller
**Age range:** G11–18 years
**No. of pupils:** 605 VIth140
**Fees:** Day £14,163

## St Catherine's School
Bramley, Guildford, Surrey GU5 0DF
**Tel:** 01483 893363
**Headmistress:** Mrs A M Phillips MA(Cantab)
**Age range:** G4–18
**No. of pupils:** 900
**Fees:** Day £7,695–£15,660 FB £25,770

## St George's College
Weybridge Road, Addlestone,
Weybridge, Surrey KT15 2QS
**Tel:** 01932 839300
**Headmaster:** Mr Joe Peake
**Age range:** 11–18
**No. of pupils:** 909 VIth250
**Fees:** Day £15,120–£17,235

## St James Senior Boys School
Church Road, Ashford,
Surrey TW15 3DZ
**Tel:** 01784 266930
**Headmaster:** Mr David Brazier
**Age range:** B11–18
**No. of pupils:** 403 VIth65
**Fees:** Day £18,120

## St John's School
Epsom Road, Leatherhead,
Surrey KT22 8SP
**Tel:** 01372 373000
**Head of School:** Mrs Rowena Cole
**Age range:** 11–18
**No. of pupils:** 761
**Fees:** Day £23,580 WB £29,790

## St Teresa's Effingham (Senior School)
Beech Avenue, Effingham,
Surrey RH5 6ST
**Tel:** 01372 452037
**Head:** Mr Michael Farmer
**Age range:** G3–18
**No. of pupils:** 640 VIth90
**Fees:** Day £16,980–£17,595 WB £27,489–£27,795 FB £29,340–£29,955

## Surbiton High School
13-15 Surbiton Crescent, Kingston
upon Thames, Surrey KT1 2JT
**Tel:** 020 8546 5245
**Principal:** Ann Haydon BSc(Hons)
**Age range:** G4–18
**No. of pupils:** 1210 VIth186
**Fees:** Day £6,390–£10,857

## Sutton High School GDST
55 Cheam Road, Sutton,
Surrey SM1 2AX
**Tel:** 020 8642 0594
**Headmistress:** Mrs Katharine Crouch
**Age range:** G3–18
**No. of pupils:** 600 VIth60
**Fees:** Day £9,153–£15,450

## Tante Marie Culinary Academy
Woodham House, Carlton Road,
Woking, Surrey GU21 4HF
**Tel:** 01483 726957
**Principal:** Mr Andrew Maxwell
**Age range:** 16–60
**No. of pupils:** 72
**Fees:** Day £20,750

**TASIS The American School in England**
Coldharbour Lane, Thorpe,
Surrey TW20 8TE
**Tel:** +44 (0)1932 582316
**Head of School:** Mr Bryan Nixon
**Age range:** 3–18
**No. of pupils:** 700
**Fees:** Day £10,900–
£23,190 FB £41,870

**The Royal Ballet School**
White Lodge, Richmond,
Surrey TW10 5HR
**Tel:** 020 7836 8899
**Director:** Ms Gailene Stock AM
**Age range:** 11–19
**No. of pupils:** VIth80
**Fees:** Day £14,394–£18,946
FB £17,709–£25,588

**The Royal Senior School, Haslemere**
Farnham Lane, Haslemere,
Surrey GU27 1HQ
**Tel:** 01428 603052
**Principal:** Mrs Anne Lynch BA,
PGCE, FRSA
**Age range:** 11–18 years
**No. of pupils:** 243
**Fees:** Day £17,400–£17,700
WB £26,100–£26,400 FB
£29,700–£30,000

**Tormead School**
27 Cranley Road, Guildford,
Surrey GU1 2JD
**Tel:** 01483 575101
**Headmistress:** Mrs Christina Foord
**Age range:** G4–18
**No. of pupils:** 760 VIth120
**Fees:** Day £5,520–£11,565

**TRINITY SCHOOL**
*For further details see p. 89*
Shirley Park, Croydon,
Surrey CR9 7AT
**Tel:** 020 8656 9541
**Email:** admissions@trinity.
croydon.sch.uk
**Website:** www.trinity-school.org
**Head:** Alasdair Kennedy MA
(Cantab)
**Age range:** B10–18 G16–18
**No. of pupils:** 1007
**Fees:** Day £16,656

**Whitgift School**
Haling Park, South Croydon,
Surrey CR2 6YT
**Tel:** +44 (0)20 8633 9935
**Headmaster:** Mr Christopher
Ramsey
**Age range:** B10–18
**No. of pupils:** 1464
**Fees:** Day £17,340 WB
£27,924 FB £33,396

**Woldingham School**
Marden Park, Woldingham,
Surrey CR3 7YA
**Tel:** 01883 349431
**Headmistress:** Mrs Jayne Triffitt
MA(Oxon)
**Age range:** G11–18
**No. of pupils:** 530 VIth150
**Fees:** Day £23,700 FB £28,410

**Yehudi Menuhin School**
Stoke Road, Stoke d'Abernon,
Cobham, Surrey KT11 3QQ
**Tel:** 01932 864739
**Headmaster:** Dr. Richard J Hillier
MA(Cantab), PhD
**Age range:** 7–19
**No. of pupils:** 80 VIth36
**Fees:** FB £41,928

# West Berkshire

**Downe House School**
Hermitage Road, Cold Ash,
Thatcham, West Berkshire RG18 9JJ
**Tel:** 01635 200286
**Headmistress:** Mrs E McKendrick
BA(Liverpool)
**Age range:** G11–18
**No. of pupils:** VIth174
**Fees:** Day £25,440 FB £35,160

**St Gabriel's**
Sandleford Priory, Newbury,
West Berkshire RG20 9BD
**Tel:** 01635 555680
**Principal:** Mr Richard Smith MA
(Hons), MEd, PGCE
**Age range:** B6 months–11
G6 months–18
**No. of pupils:** 469 VIth40
**Fees:** Day £10,308–£16,830

# West Sussex

**Ardingly College**
College Road, Ardingly, Haywards
Heath, West Sussex RH17 6SQ
**Tel:** +44 (0)1444 893320
**Headmaster:** Mr Ben Figgis
**Age range:** 13–18
**No. of pupils:** 559
**Fees:** Day £22,380–£23,610
FB £30,480–£32,130

**Burgess Hill Girls**
Keymer Road, Burgess Hill,
West Sussex RH15 0EG
**Tel:** 01444 241050
**Head of School:** Liz Laybourn
**Age range:** B2.5–4 G2.5–18
**No. of pupils:** 550 VIth87
**Fees:** Day £7,350–£16,950
FB £27,300–£30,450

**Christ's Hospital**
Horsham, West Sussex RH13 0LJ
**Tel:** 01403 211293
**Headmaster:** Mr Simon Reid
**Age range:** 11–18
**No. of pupils:** 900
**Fees:** Day £16,950–
£21,330 FB £32,790

**Farlington School**
Strood Park, Horsham,
West Sussex RH12 3PN
**Tel:** 01403 282573
**Headmistress:** Ms Louise Higson
BSc, PGCE
**Age range:** G3–18
**No. of pupils:** 300
**Fees:** Day £5,660 WB
£9,170 FB £9,600

**Hurstpierpoint College**
College Lane, Hurstpierpoint,
West Sussex BN6 9JS
**Tel:** 01273 833636
**Headmaster:** Mr. T J Manly BA, MSc
**Age range:** 4–18
**No. of pupils:** 1156
**Fees:** Day £8,790–£22,860
WB £28,800

**Lancing College**
Lancing, West Sussex BN15 0RW
**Tel:** 01273 465805
**Head Master:** Mr Dominic T Oliver
MPhil
**Age range:** 13–18
**No. of pupils:** 550 VIth255
**Fees:** Day £7,710 FB £10,970

**Our Lady of Sion School**
Gratwicke Road, Worthing,
West Sussex BN11 4BL
**Tel:** 01903 204063
**Headmaster:** Mr M Scullion MA, BEd
**Age range:** 2–18
**No. of pupils:** 528 VIth55
**Fees:** Day £5,715–£9,150

**Seaford College**
Lavington Park, Petworth,
West Sussex GU28 0NB
**Tel:** 01798 867392
**Headmaster:** J P Green MA BA
**Age range:** 7–18
**No. of pupils:** 732 VIth194
**Fees:** Day £10,020–£20,775 WB
£20,880–£28,140 FB £32,130

**Worth School**
Paddockhurst Road, Turners Hill,
Crawley, West Sussex RH10 4SD
**Tel:** +44 (0)1342 710200
**Head Master:** Gino Carminati MA,
FRSA
**Age range:** 11–18
**No. of pupils:** 580 VIth222
**Fees:** Day £20,235 FB £27,849

# Examinations and qualifications

# Qualifications

## Common Entrance

### What is Common Entrance?

The Common Entrance examinations are used in UK independent schools (and some independent schools overseas) for transfer from junior to senior schools at the ages of 11+ and 13+. They were first introduced in 1904 and are internationally recognised as being a rigorous form of assessment following a thorough course of study. The examinations are produced by the Independent Schools Examinations Board and backed by HMC (Headmasters' and Headmistresses' Conference), GSA (Girls' Schools Association), and IAPS (Independent Association of Prep Schools) which together represent the leading independent schools in the UK, and many overseas.

Common Entrance is not a public examination as, for example, GCSE, and candidates may normally be entered only in one of the following circumstances:

   a) they have been offered a place at a senior school subject to their passing the examination, or
   b) they are entered as a 'trial run', in which case the papers are marked by the junior school concerned

Candidates normally take the examination in their own junior or preparatory schools, either in the UK or overseas.

### How does Common Entrance fit into the progression to GCSEs?

Rapid changes in education nationally and internationally have resulted in regular reviews of the syllabuses for all the Common Entrance examinations. Reviews of the National Curriculum, in particular, have brought about a number of changes, with the Board wishing to ensure that it continues to set high standards. It is also a guiding principle that Common Entrance should be part of the natural progression from 11–16, and not a diversion from it.

### Common Entrance at 11+

At 11+, the examination consists of papers in English, mathematics and science. It is designed so that it can be taken by candidates either from independent preparatory schools or by candidates from schools in the maintained sector or overseas who have had no special preparation. The examination is normally taken in January for entrance to senior schools in the following September.

### Common Entrance at 13+

At 13+, most candidates come from independent preparatory schools. The compulsory subjects are English, mathematics and science. Papers in French, geography, German, Classical Greek, history, Latin, religious studies and Spanish are also available and candidates usually offer as many subjects as they can. In most subjects, papers are available at more than one level to cater for candidates of different abilities. There are three examination sessions each year, with the majority of candidates sitting in the summer prior to entry to their senior schools in September.

### Marking and grading

The papers are set centrally but the answers are marked by the senior school for which a candidate is entered. Mark schemes are provided by the Board but senior schools are free to set their own grade boundaries. Results are available within two weeks of the examinations taking place.

### Pre-Testing and the ISEB Common Pre-Tests

A number of senior independent schools 'pre-test' pupils for entry, prior to them taking their main entrance examinations at a later date. Usually, these pre-tests take place when a pupil is in Year 6 or Year 7 of his or her junior school and will then be going on to sit Common Entrance in Year 8. The tests are designed to assess a pupil's academic potential and suitability for a particular senior school so that the child, the parents and the school know well in advance whether he/she is going to be offered a place at the school, subject to a satisfactory performance in the entrance examinations. The tests enable senior schools which are heavily oversubscribed to manage their lists and help to ensure that pupils are not entered for examinations in which they are unlikely to be successful. In short, it reduces uncertainty for all concerned.

Pre-tests may be written specifically for the senior school for which the candidate is entered but a growing number of schools are choosing to use the Common Pre-Tests provided by the Independent Schools Examinations Board. These online tests are usually taken in the candidate's own junior school and one of their main advantages is that a pupil need sit the tests only once, with the results then made available to any senior school which wishes to use them. The multiple-choice tests cover verbal reasoning, non-verbal reasoning, English and mathematics, with the results standardised according to the pupil's age when they are taken. Further information is available on the ISEB website at www.iseb.co.uk.

Parents are advised to check the entrance requirements for senior schools to see if their child will be required to sit a pre-test.

### Further information

Details of the Common Entrance examinations and how to register candidates are available on the ISEB website www.iseb.co.uk. Copies of past papers and a wide range of textbooks and other resources can be purchased from Galore Park Publishing Ltd at www.galorepark. co.uk. Support materials are also available from Hodder Education and other publishers; see the Resources section of the ISEB website for details.

Independent Schools Examinations Board Suite 3, Endeavour House,
Crow Arch Lane,
Ringwood, Hampshire BH24 1HP

Telephone: 01425 470555
Email: enquiries@iseb.co.uk
Web: www.iseb.co.uk

# 7+ Entrance Exams

### What is the 7+?

The 7+ is the descriptive name given to the entrance exams set by an increasing number of independent schools for pupils wishing to gain admission into their Year 3.

7+ entrance exams may be simply for admission into a selective preparatory school, which will then prepare the child for Common Entrance exams to gain a place at senior school. Alternatively, the 7+ can be a route into a school with both prep and senior departments, therefore often effectively bypassing the 11+ or 13+ Common Entrance exams.

The Independent Schools Examinations Board provides Common Entrance examinations and assessments for pupils seeking entry to independent senior schools at 11+ and 13+, but there is as yet no equivalent for the 7+. The testing is largely undertaken by the individual schools, although some schools might commission test from external agencies. Many schools in the incredibly competitive London area offer entrance exams at 7+ and some, such as Haberdasher's Aske's Boys' School,

share specimen papers on their website to clarify what 7+ children will face.

### Who sits the 7+?

The 7+ is sat by Year 2 children, who may be moving from a state primary school or a stand-alone pre-prep school to an independent prep school (although many prep schools now have their own pre-prep department, with a cohort of children poised to pass into Year 3 there).

Registration for 7+ entrance exams usually closes in the November of Year 2, with the exams then sat in January or February, for entry that September.

### How is the 7+ assessed?

Written exam content will be primarily English and maths based, whilst spelling, dictation, mental arithmetic and more creative skills may be assessed verbally on a one-to-one basis. Group exercises are also sometimes used to look at a child's initiative and their ability to work with others.

Schools will not only be looking for academic potential, but also good citizens and a mixture of personalities to produce a well-rounded year group. For this reason, children are often asked to attend an interview. Some schools interview all candidates, whilst others may call back a limited number with good test results. They will be looking for a child's ability to look an adult in the eye and think on their feet, but also simply to show some spark and personality. After the assessments, children will be told if they have been successful in gaining a firm place, or a place on a waiting list.

### Further Information

As the 7+ is not centrally regulated, it is best for parents to seek accurate admissions and testing information direct from the schools in which they are interested. In addition to a school's facilities and ethos, choosing a school for admission at 7+ will probably also involve whether the school has a senior department and if not, the prep school's record in gaining its students places at target senior schools.

Experienced educational consultants may be able to help parents decide which independent prep school is best suited for their child, based on their personality, senior school ambitions and academic potential. Many parents enlist the help of tutors to prepare children for the 7+, if only to reduce the fear of the unknown in these very young children. This is achieved by teaching them the required curriculum, what to expect on their test and interview days, and giving them the opportunity to practice tackling the type of assessments they will face.

# Prep School Baccalaureate

The Prep School Baccalaureate (PSB) is a framework of study for children in junior and preparatory schools that was introduced in 2012, and focuses on the active development and assessment of 6 core skills: Communication, Collaboration, Leadership, Independence, Reviewing and improving and Thinking and Learning. Member schools promote the core skills across all areas of school life, and provide guidance for pupils in progressing these skills, which are seen as essential for developing capable and balanced adults, able to make the most of the opportunities of a fast-changing world. A strong but appropriate knowledge base compliments this, with the use of focused tutoring, pastoral care and Well Being programmes.

Schools do not work to a prescribed curriculum and the emphasis is upon promoting an independent approach which works for each individual school. There are subject INSET days for PSB school staff annually and these are supported by senior school colleagues, to ensure that work done in PSB schools compliments the demands of education at higher levels.

The PSB is a whole school initiative from Early Years to either Year 6 or Year 8, at which point the certificate is awarded at the time of matriculation to senior schools. An additional PSB Year 9 framework is being developed together with international membership.

The development of skills is now recognised as essential by the Independent Schools Inspectorate (ISI), and recent ISI reports on PSB schools highlight the excellent contribution the PSB has in schools achieving excellence.

## Assessment

The PSB has a 10 point scale for all subjects studied with a compulsory spine covering: English, Maths, Science, Modern Languages, The Humanities, Art, Design Technology, Music, Sport and PE with each pupil additionally completing a cross curricular project. Optional subjects are agreed with schools but these must be supported by a scheme of work clearly identifying appropriate core skills which are assessed on a 5 point scale. There are distinction levels on both scales and the 10 point scale cross references both ISEB and National Curriculum assessment levels.

Pupils moving on to senior school do so via individual senior school pre-testing arrangements, the award of the PSB certificate, core ISEB papers or a combination of the above.

## Membership categories

Partner membership is available to schools developing the PSB with support given from existing schools and the Communications director.

Full membership entitles schools to use the PSB matriculation certificate and join the PSB committee as voting members.

Affiliated membership is for schools that have developed their own skills based approach, in line with PSB principles; staff can participate in all training opportunities and the Heads of Affiliated Schools join committee meetings as non-voting guests.

Membership of the above categories is dependent upon strong ISI reports, the development of a skills based curriculum, with skills clearly identified in schemes of work and excellent teaching.

Associate membership is for senior schools that actively support the PSB in providing staff for subject meetings, hosting meetings, conferences and committee meetings and offer a valuable perspective on the demands of GCSE, A Level and the International Baccalaureate.

## Further details

The PSB is an entirely independent charity overseen by a Board of Trustees who have expertise in both primary and secondary education. Details of the PSB can be found on the website – psbacc.org – together with contact details for the Communications Director who can provide further details on request.

# General Certificate of Secondary Education (GCSE)

### What are the GCSE qualifications?

GCSE qualifications were first introduced in 1986 and are the principal means of assessment at Key Stage 4 across a range of academic subject areas. They command respect and have status not only in the UK but worldwide.

### Main features of the GCSE

There are four unitary awarding organisations for GCSEs in England (see 'Awarding organisations and examination dates' section, p425). WJEC and CCEA also offer GCSE qualifications in Wales and Northern Ireland. Each examining group designs its own specifications but they are required to conform to set criteria. For some aspects of the qualification system, the exam boards adopt common ways of working. When the exam boards work together in this way they generally do so through the Joint Council of Qualifications (JCQ). The award of a grade is intended to indicate that a candidate has met the required level of skills, knowledge and understanding.

GCSEs are in the process of reform. New GCSEs in English literature, English language and maths were first taught in September 2015, with first results in summer 2017. Assessment in these reformed GCSEs consists primarily of formal examinations taken at the end of the student's two-year course. Other types of assessment, non-exam assessment (NEA), is used where there are skills and knowledge which cannot be assessed through exams. Ofqual have set the percentage of the total marks that will come from NEA.

Ofqual says there will be new, more demanding content, which has been developed by the government and the exam boards. Courses will be designed for two years of study (linear assessment) and no longer divided into different modules.

Exams can only be split into 'foundation tier' and 'higher tier' if one exam paper does not give all students the opportunity to show their knowledge and their abilities. Resit opportunities will only be available each November in English language and maths.

New GCSEs taught from September 2016: ancient languages, art and design, biology, chemistry, citizenship studies, computer science, combined science, dance, drama, food preparation and nutrition, history, geography, modern foreign languages (French, German, Spanish), music, physics, physical education, religious studies.

New GCSEs taught from September 2017: ancient history, astronomy, business, classical civilisation, design and technology, economics, electronics, engineering, film studies, geology, media studies, psychology, sociology, statistics, other (minority) foreign languages e.g. Italian, Polish.

### Grading

The basic principle that exam boards follow when setting grade boundaries is that if the group of students (the cohort) taking a qualification in one year is of similar ability to the cohort in the previous year then the overall results (outcomes) should be comparable.

The reformed exams taken in summer 2017 were the first to show a new grading system, with the A* to G grades being phased out.

The new grading system is 9 to 1, with 9 being the top grade. Ofqual says this allows greater differentiation between students. It expects that broadly the same proportion of students will achieve a grade 4 and above as currently achieve a grade C and above, that broadly the same proportion of students will achieve a grade 7 and above as currently achieve a grade A and above. The bottom of grade 1 will be aligned with the bottom of grade G, grade 5 will be awarded to around the top third of students gaining the equivalent of a grade C and bottom third of a grade B. Grade 9 will be set using the tailored approach formula in the first award.

Grades 2, 3, 5 and 6 will be awarded arithmetically so that the grade boundaries are equally spaced in terms of marks from neighbouring grades.

The government's definition of a 'good pass' will be set at grade 5 for reformed GCSEs. A grade 4 will continue to be a level 2 achievement. The DfE does not expect employers, colleges or universities to raise the bar to a grade 5 if a grade 4 would meet their requirements.

### Can anyone take GCSE qualifications?

GCSEs are intended mainly for 16-year-old pupils, but are open to anyone of any age, whether studying full-time or part-time at a school, college or privately. There are no formal entry requirements.

Students normally study up to ten subjects over a two-year period. Short course GCSEs are available in some subjects (including ICT and religious studies) – these include half the content of a full GCSE, so two short course GCSEs are equivalent to one full GCSE.

### The English Baccalaureate

The English Baccalaureate (EBacc) is a school

performance measure. It allows people to see how many pupils get a grade C or above (current grading) in the core academic subjects at Key Stage 4 in any government-funded school.

The DfE introduced the EBacc measure in 2010. In June 2015, it announced its intention that all pupils who start year 7 in September 2015 take the EBacc subjects when they reach their GCSEs in 2020.

## Progress 8 and Attainment 8

Progress 8 aims to capture the progress a pupil makes from the end of primary school to the end of secondary school. It is a type of value added measure, which means that pupils' results are compared to the actual achievements of other pupils with the same prior attainment.

The new performance measures are designed to encourage schools to offer a broad and balanced curriculum with a focus on an academic core at Key Stage 4, and reward schools for the teaching of all their pupils, measuring performance across 8 qualifications. Every increase in every grade a pupil achieves will attract additional points in the performance tables.

Progress 8 will be calculated for individual pupils solely in order to calculate a school's Progress 8 score, and there will be no need for schools to share individual Progress 8 scores with their pupils. Schools should continue to focus on which qualifications are most suitable for individual pupils, as the grades pupils achieve will help them reach their goals for the next stage of their education or training.

Attainment 8 will measure the achievement of a pupil across 8 qualifications including mathematics (double weighted) and English (double weighted), 3 further qualifications that count in the English Baccalaureate (EBacc) measure and 3 further qualifications that can be GCSE qualifications (including EBacc subjects) or any other non-GCSE qualification on the DfE approved list.

# General Certificate of Education (GCE) Advanced level (A level)

Typically, A level qualifications are studied over a two-year period. There are no lower or upper age limits. Schools and colleges usually expect students aged 16-18 to have obtained grades A*-C (grade 5 in the new criteria) in five subjects at GCSE level before taking an advanced level course. This requirement may vary between centres and according to which specific subjects are to be studied. Mature students may be assessed on different criteria as to their suitability to embark on the course.

## GCE Qualifications

AS level and A level qualifications are being reformed. The new subjects are being introduced gradually, with the first wave being taught from September 2015. Subjects that have not been reformed will no longer be available for teaching from September 2018.

GCE qualifications are available at two levels. The Advanced Subsidiary (AS) is the two-or three-unit General Certificate of Education (GCE). The A level is the four- or six-unit GCE. Nearly 70 titles are available, covering a wide range of subject areas, including humanities, sciences, language, business, arts, mathematics and technology.

One of the major reforms is that AS level results will no longer count towards an A level (they previously counted for 50%). The two qualifications will be linear, with AS assessments typically taking place after one year and A levels after two.

New-style AS and A levels were first taught from September 2015 for: art and design, biology, business studies, chemistry, computer studies, economics, English language, English language and literature, English literature, history, physics, psychology, and sociology.

Subjects first taught from September 2016 include: ancient languages such as Latin or Greek, dance, drama (theatre studies), geography, modern languages such as Spanish or French, music, physical education, religious studies.

Those introduced for first teaching from September 2017: accounting, design and technology, music technology, history of art, environmental science, philosophy, maths, further maths, archaeology, accounting, electronics, ancient history, law, classical civilisation, film studies, media studies, politics, geology, statistics, Chinese, Italian, Russian. In 2018 Biblical Hebrew, Modern Hebrew & languages such as Bengali, Polish and Urdu will be available for first teaching.

Some GCE AS and A levels, particularly the practical ones, contain a proportion of coursework. All GCE A levels contain in one or more of the units an assessment that tests students' understanding of the whole specification (synoptic assessment). GCE AS are graded A-E and A levels are graded A*-E.

Overall the amount of coursework at A level has been reduced in the reforms. In some subjects, such as the sciences, practical work will not contribute to the final A level but will be reported separately in a certificate of endorsement. In the sciences, students will do at least eight practical activities (16 for combined sciences), covering apparatus and techniques.

Exam questions about practical work will make up at least 15% of the total marks for the qualification and students will be assessed on their knowledge, skills and understanding of practical work.

# Cambridge International AS & A Level

Cambridge International AS & A Level is an internationally benchmarked qualification, taught in over 130 countries worldwide. It is typically for learners aged 16 to 19 years who need advanced study to prepare for university. It was created specifically for an international audience and the content has been devised to suit the wide variety of schools worldwide and avoid any cultural bias.

Cambridge International A Level is typically a two-year course, and Cambridge International AS Level is typically one year. Some subjects can be started as a Cambridge International AS Level and extended to a Cambridge International A Level. Students can either follow a broad course of study, or specialise in one particular subject area.

Learners use Cambridge International AS & A Levels to gain places at leading universities worldwide, including the UK, Ireland, USA, Canada, Australia, New Zealand, India, Singapore, Egypt, Jordan, South Africa, the Netherlands, Germany and Spain. In places such as the US and Canada, good grades in carefully chosen Cambridge International A Level subjects can result in up to one year of university course credit.

**Assessment options:**
Cambridge International AS & A Levels have a linear structure with exams at the end of the course. Students can choose from a range of assessment options:
Option 1: take Cambridge International AS Levels only. The Cambridge International AS Level syllabus content is half a Cambridge International A Level.
Option 2: staged assessment, which means taking the Cambridge International AS Level in one exam session and the Cambridge International A Level at a later session. However, this route is not possible in all subjects.
Option 3: take all Cambridge International A Level papers in the same examination session, usually at the end of the course.

**Grades and subjects**
Cambridge International A Levels are graded from A* to E. Cambridge International AS Levels are graded from A to E.

Subjects: available in 55 subjects including accounting, Afrikaans, Afrikaans – first language (AS only),

Afrikaans language (AS only), applied information and communication technology, Arabic, Arabic language (AS only), art and design, biology, business, chemistry, Chinese, Chinese language (AS only), classical studies, computing, design and technology, design and textiles, divinity, economics, English language, English literature, environmental management, food studies, French, French language (AS only), French literature (AS only), general paper, geography, German, German language (AS only), Global Perspectives & Research, Hindi, Hindi language (AS only), Hindi literature (AS only), Hinduism, history, Islamic studies, Japanese language (AS only), English language and literature (AS only), law, Marathi, Marathi language (AS only), marine science, mathematics, further mathematics, media studies, music, physical education, physical science, physics, Portuguese, Portuguese language (AS only), Portuguese literature (AS only), psychology, sociology, Spanish, Spanish first language (AS only), Spanish language (AS only), Spanish literature (AS only), Tamil, Tamil language (AS only), Telugu, Telugu language (AS only), thinking skills, travel and tourism, Urdu, Urdu language (AS only), Urdu Pakistan.
Website: www.cie.org.uk/alevel

# Cambridge International GCSE (IGCSE)

Cambridge IGCSE is the world's most popular international qualification for 14 to 16 year olds. It develops skills in creative thinking, enquiry and problem solving, in preparation for the next stage in a student's education. Cambridge IGCSE is taken in over 145 countries, and is widely recognised by employers and higher education institutions worldwide.

Cambridge IGCSE is graded from A*-G. In the UK, Cambridge IGCSE is accepted as equivalent to the GCSE. It can be used as preparation for Cambridge International A & AS Levels, UK A and AS levels, IB or AP and in some instances entry into university. Cambridge IGCSE First Language English and Cambridge IGCSE English Language qualifications are recognised by a significant number of UK universities as evidence of competence in the language for university entrance.

Subjects: available in over 70 subjects including accounting, Afrikaans – first language, Afrikaans – second language, agriculture, Arabic – first language, Arabic – foreign language, art and design, Baha Indonesia, Bangladesh studies, biology, business studies, chemistry, child development, Chinese – first language, Chinese – second language, Chinese

(Mandarin) – foreign language, computer studies, Czech – first language, design and technology, development studies, drama, Dutch – first language, Dutch – foreign language, economics, English – first language, English – literature, English – second language, enterprise, environmental management, food and nutrition, French – first language, French – foreign language, geography, German – first language, German – foreign language, global perspectives, Greek – foreign language, Hindi as a second language, Italian – foreign language, history, India studies, Indonesian – foreign language, information and communication technology, IsiZulu as a second language, Japanese – first language, Japanese – foreign language, Kazakh as a second language, Korean (first language), Latin, Malay – foreign language, mathematics, mathematics – additional, international mathematics, music, Pakistan studies, physical education, physical science, physics, Portuguese – first language, Portuguese – foreign language, religious studies, Russian – first language, science – combined, sciences – co-ordinated (double), sociology, Spanish – first language, Spanish – foreign language, Spanish – literature, Thai – first language, travel and tourism, Turkish – first language, Urdu – second language, world literature.

Website: www.cie.org.uk/igcse

# Cambridge Pre-U

Cambridge Pre-U is a post-16 qualification that equips students with the skills they need to succeed at university. Developed with universities, it was first introduced in UK schools in September 2008. It is now taught in 170 schools, including some schools outside the UK.

Cambridge Pre-U is a linear course, with exams taken at the end of two years. It encourages the development of well-informed, open and independent-minded individuals; promotes deep understanding through subject specialisation, with a depth and rigour appropriate to progression to higher education; and develops skills in independent research valued by universities.

### Assessment

Cambridge Pre-U Principal Subjects are examined at the end of two years. Cambridge Pre-U Short Courses are available in some subjects and are typically examined at the end of one year. Students can study a combination of A Levels and Principal Subjects.

In order to gain the Cambridge Pre-U Diploma, students must study at least three Cambridge Pre-U Principal Subjects (up to two A Levels can be substituted for Principal Subjects) and Cambridge Pre-U Global

Perspectives & Research (GPR). Cambridge Pre-U GPR includes an extended project in the second year, developing skills in research and critical thinking.

### Grades and subjects

Cambridge Pre-U reports achievement on a scale of nine grades, with Distinction 1 being the highest grade and Pass 3 the lowest grade.

Subjects: available in 25 subjects including art and design, biology, business and management, chemistry, drama and theatre, economics, literature in English, French, further mathematics, geography, German, global perspectives and research, classical Greek, history, Italian, art history, Latin, Mandarin Chinese, mathematics, music, philosophy and theology, physics, psychology, Russian, Spanish.

Website: www.cie.org.uk/cambridgepreu

# Edexcel International GCSEs

Pearson's Edexcel International GCSEs are academic qualifications aimed at learners aged 14 to 16. They're equivalent to a UK General Certificate of Secondary Education (GCSE), and are the main requirement for Level 3 studies, including progression to GCE AS or A levels, BTECs or employment. International GCSEs are linear qualifications, meaning that students take all of the exams at the end of the course. They are available at Level 1 (grades D-G) and Level 2 (grades A*-C). There are currently more than 100,000 learners studying Edexcel International GCSEs, in countries throughout Asia, Africa, Europe, the Middle East and Latin America. Developed by subject specialists and reviewed regularly, many of Pearson's Edexcel International GCSEs include specific international content to make them relevant to students worldwide.

Pearson's Edexcel International GCSEs were initially developed for international schools. They have since become popular among independent schools in the UK, but are not approved for use in UK state schools. If you're a UK state school, you may be interested in offering Pearson's Edexcel Level 1/Level 2 Certificates. These qualifications are based on the Edexcel International GCSE specifications but currently count towards national performance measures and are eligible for funding in UK state schools until 2016.

International GCSEs are offered in over 40 subjects. Subject areas include: Art and Design, Business & Economics, **English, Humanities**, Information and Communication Technology, **Languages, Mathematics, Sciences**. *Note that the subject areas highlighted in* *bold are also available as part of the Edexcel Certificate qualification suite.*

# Free Standing Maths Qualifications (FSMQ)

Aimed at those students wishing to acquire further qualifications in maths, specifically additional mathematics and foundations of advanced mathematics (MEI).

Further UCAS points can be earned upon completion of the advanced FSMQ in additional mathematics, whereas the higher FSMQ in foundations of advanced mathematics is designed for those not yet ready to take AS/A level GCE mathematics.

For further details see the AQA or OCR website.

# AQA Certificate in Mathematical Studies (Core Maths)

This new Level 3 qualification has been available from September 2015. It is designed for students who achieved a Grade 4 or above at GCSE and want to continue studying Maths. The qualification carries UCAS points equivalent to an AS level qualification

# Additional and Alternative

## AQA Baccalaureate

The AQA Baccalaureate is awarded to students who achieve at least three A levels (minimum grade E or 2/3), a broader study AS level subject and the EPQ, plus they must undertake a minimum of 100 hours of 'enrichment activities'.

This is a complete curriculum programme, which adds a broader range of study, and includes the Extended Project Qualification (EPQ).

This qualification is built on familiar subjects, so it can be tailored to fit in with existing curricula. It includes extracurricular activities and encourages a series of 'enrichment activities' covering personal qualities, perseverance, leadership, independence, time management, commitment and communication.

The AQA Bacc is accepted by universities; offers are based on the component parts of the diploma, with students receiving their AQA certificate alongside their A level, AS level and EPQ certificates.

## Cambridge Primary

Cambridge Primary is typically for learners aged 5 to 11 years. It develops learner skills and understanding through the primary years in English, mathematics and science. The flexible curriculum frameworks include optional assessment tools to help schools monitor learners' progress and give detailed feedback to parents. At the end of Cambridge Primary, schools can enter students for Cambridge Primary Checkpoint tests which are marked in Cambridge.
Website: www.cie.org.uk/primary

Cambridge ICT Starters introduces learners, typically aged 5 to 14 years, to the key ICT applications they need to achieve computer literacy and to understand the impact of technology on our daily lives. It can be taught and assessed in English or Spanish.

## Cambridge Secondary 1

Cambridge Secondary 1 is typically for learners aged 11 to 14 years. It develops learner skills and understanding in English, English as a second language, mathematics and science for the first three years of secondary education, and includes assessment tools. At the end of Cambridge Secondary 1, schools can enter students for Cambridge Secondary 1 Checkpoint tests which are marked in Cambridge and provide an external international benchmark for student performance.
Website: www.cie.org.uk/cambridgesecondary1

## European Baccalaureate (EB)

Not to be confused with the International Baccalaureate (IB) or the French Baccalaureate, this certificate is available in European schools and recognised in all EU countries.

To obtain the baccalaureate, a student must obtain a minimum score of 60%, which is made up from: coursework, oral participation in class and tests (40%); five written examinations (36%) – mother-tongue, first foreign language and maths are compulsory for all candidates; four oral examinations (24%) – mother tongue and first foreign language are compulsory (history or geography may also be compulsory here, dependant on whether the candidate has taken a written examination in these subjects).

Throughout the EU the syllabus and examinations necessary to achieve the EB are identical. The only exception to this rule is the syllabus for the mother tongue language. The EB has been specifically designed to meet, at the very least, the minimum qualification requirements of each member state.

Study for the EB begins at nursery stage (age 4) and progresses through primary (age six) and on into secondary school (age 12).

**Syllabus**
Languages: Bulgarian, Czech, Danish, Dutch, English, Estonian, Finnish, Finnish as a second national language, French, German, Greek, Hungarian, Irish, Italian, Latvian, Lithuanian, Maltese, Polish, Portuguese, Romanian, Slovak, Slovenian, Spanish, Swedish, Swedish for Finnish pupils.

Literary: art education, non-confessional ethics, geography, ancient Greek, history, human sciences, Latin, music, philosophy, physical education.

Sciences: biology, chemistry, economics, ICT, integrated science, mathematics, physics.
For more information, contact:
Office of the Secretary-General of the European Schools, c/o European Commission, Rue Joseph II,

30-2ème étage, B-1049 Brussels, Belgium
Tel: +32 2295 3745; Fax: +32 2298 6298
Website: www.eursc.eu

# The International Baccalaureate (IB)

The International Baccalaureate (IB) offers four challenging and high quality educational programmes for a worldwide community of schools, aiming to develop internationally minded people who, recognizing their common humanity and shared guardianship of the planet, help to create a better, more peaceful world.

The IB works with schools around the world (both state and privately funded) that share the commitment to international education to deliver these programmes.

Schools that have achieved the high standards required for authorization to offer one or more of the IB programmes are known as IB World Schools. There are over half a million students attending more than 4500 IB World Schools in 153 countries and this number is growing annually.

The Primary Years, Middle Years and Diploma Programmes share a common philosophy and common characteristics. They develop the whole student, helping students to grow intellectually, socially, aesthetically and culturally. They provide a broad and balanced education that includes science and the humanities, languages and mathematics, technology and the arts. The programmes teach students to think critically, and encourage them to draw connections between areas of knowledge and to use problem-solving techniques and concepts from many disciplines. They instil in students a sense of responsibility towards others and towards the environment. Lastly, and perhaps most importantly, the programmes give students an awareness and understanding of their own culture and of other cultures, values and ways of life.

A fourth programme called the IB Career Related Certificate (IBCC) became available to IB World Schools from September 2012. All IB programmes include:

- a written curriculum or curriculum framework;
- student assessment appropriate to the age range;
- professional development and networking opportunities for teachers;
- support, authorization and programme evaluation for the school.

### The IB Primary Years Programme

The IB Primary Years Programme (PYP), for students aged three to 12, focuses on the development of the whole child as an inquirer, both in the classroom and in the world outside. It is a framework consisting of five essential elements (concepts, knowledge, skills, attitude, action) and guided by six trans-disciplinary themes of global significance, explored using knowledge and skills derived from six subject areas (language, social studies, mathematics, science and technology, arts, and personal, social and physical education) with a powerful emphasis on inquiry-based learning.

The most significant and distinctive feature of the PYP is the six trans-disciplinary themes. These themes are about issues that have meaning for, and are important to, all of us. The programme offers a balance between learning about or through the subject areas, and learning beyond them. The six themes of global significance create a trans-disciplinary framework that allows students to 'step up' beyond the confines of learning within subject areas:

- Who we are.
- Where we are in place and time.
- How we express ourselves.
- How the world works.
- How we organize ourselves.
- Sharing the planet.

The PYP exhibition is the culminating activity of the programme. It requires students to analyse and propose solutions to real-world issues, drawing on what they have learned through the programme. Evidence of student development and records of PYP exhibitions are reviewed by the IB as part of the programme evaluation process.

Assessment is an important part of each unit of inquiry as it both enhances learning and provides opportunities for students to reflect on what they know, understand and can do. The teacher's feedback to the students provides the guidance, the tools and the incentive for them to become more competent, more skilful and better at understanding how to learn.

### The IB Middle Years Programme (MYP)

The Middle Years Programme (MYP), for students aged 11 to 16, comprises eight subject groups:

- Language acquisition
- Language and literature
- Individuals and societies
- Sciences
- Mathematics
- Arts
- Physical and health education
- Design

The MYP requires at least 50 hours of teaching time for each subject group in each year of the programme. In years 4 and 5, students have the option to take courses from six of the eight subject groups within certain limits, to provide greater flexibility in meeting local requirements and individual student learning needs.

Each year, students in the MYP also engage in at least one collaboratively planned interdisciplinary unit that involves at least two subject groups.

MYP students also complete a long-term project, where they decide what they want to learn about, identify what they already know, discovering what they will need to know to complete the project, and create a proposal or criteria for completing it

The MYP aims to help students develop their personal understanding, their emerging sense of self and their responsibility in their community.

The MYP allows schools to continue to meet state, provincial or national legal requirements for students with access needs. Schools must develop an inclusion/special educational needs (SEN) policy that explains assessment access arrangements, classroom accommodations and curriculum modification that meet individual student learning needs.

### The IB Diploma Programme (IBDP)

The IB Diploma Programme, for students aged 16 to 19, is an academically challenging and motivating curriculum of international education that prepares students for success at university and in life beyond studies.

DP students choose at least one course from six subject groups, thus ensuring depth and breadth of knowledge and experience in languages, social studies, the experimental sciences, mathematics, and the arts. With more than 35 courses to choose from, students have the flexibility to further explore and learn subjects that meet their interest. Out of the six courses required, at least three and not more than four must be taken at higher level (240 teaching hours), the others at standard level (150 teaching hours). Students can take examinations in English, French or Spanish.

In addition, three unique components of the programme – the DP core – aim to broaden students' educational experience and challenge them to apply their knowledge and skills. The DP core – the extended essay (EE), theory of knowledge (TOK) and creativity, activity, service (CAS) – are compulsory and central to the philosophy of the programme.

The IB uses both external and internal assessment to measure student performance in the DP. Student results are determined by performance against set standards, not by each student's position in the overall rank order. DP assessment is unique in the way that it measures the extent to which students have mastered advanced academic skills not what they have memorized. DP assessment also encourages an international outlook and intercultural

skills, wherever appropriate.

The IB diploma is awarded to students who gain at least 24 points out of a possible 45 points, subject to certain minimum levels of performance across the whole programme and to satisfactory participation in the creativity, activity, and service requirement.

Recognized and respected by leading universities globally, the DP encourages students to be knowledgeable, inquiring, caring and compassionate, and to develop intercultural understanding, open-mindedness and the attitudes necessary to respect and evaluate a range of viewpoints.

### The IB Career Related Programme (IBCP)

The IB Career-related Programme, for students aged 16 to 19, offers an innovative educational framework that combines academic studies with career-related learning. Through the CP, students develop the competencies they need to succeed in the 21st century. More importantly, they have the opportunity to engage with a rigorous study programme that genuinely interests them while gaining transferable and lifelong skills that prepares them to pursue higher education, apprenticeships or direct employment.

CP students complete four core components – language development, personal and professional skills, service learning and a reflective project – in order to receive the International Baccalaureate Career-related Programme Certificate. Designed to enhance critical thinking and intercultural understanding, the CP core helps students develop the communication and personal skills, as well as intellectual habits required for lifelong learning.

Schools that choose to offer the CP can create their own distinctive version of the programme and select career pathways that suit their students and local community needs. The IB works with a variety of CRS providers around the world and schools seeking to develop career pathways with professional communities can benefit from our existing collaborations. All CRS providers undergo a rigorous curriculum evaluation to ensure that their courses align with the CP pedagogy and meet IB quality standards. The flexibility to meet the needs, backgrounds and contexts of learners allows CP schools to offer an education that is relevant and meaningful to their students.

Launched in 2012, there are more than 140 CP schools in over 23 countries to date. Many schools with the IB Diploma Programme (DP) and the Middle Years Programme (MYP) have chosen the CP as an alternative IB pathway to offer students. CP schools often report that the programme has helped them raise student aspiration, increase student engagement and retention and encouraged learners to take responsibility for their own actions, helping them foster high levels of self-esteem through meaningful achievements.

For more information on IB programmes, visit: www.ibo.org

Africa, Europe, Middle East Global Centre, Churchillplein 6, The Hague, 2517JW, The Netherlands

Tel: +31 (0)70 352 6233

## Pearson Edexcel Mathematics Awards

Pearson's Edexcel Mathematics Awards are small, stand-alone qualifications designed to help students to develop and demonstrate proficiency in different areas of mathematics. These Awards enable students to focus on understanding key concepts and techniques, and are available across three subjects, including: Number and Measure (Levels 1 and 2), Algebra (Levels 2 and 3) and Statistical Methods (Levels 1, 2 and 3). The level 1 Award in Number and Measure is now also an approved stepping stone qualification for the 16-18 maths condition of funding

Designed to build students' confidence and fluency; the Awards can fit into the existing programme of delivery for mathematics in schools and colleges, prepare students for GCSE and/or GCE Mathematics, and to support further study in other subjects, training or the workplace. They offer a choice of levels to match students' abilities, with clear progression between the levels. These small, 60-70 guided learning hour qualifications are assessed through one written paper per level. Each qualification is funded and approved for pre-16 and 16-18 year old students in England and in schools and colleges in Wales.

# Projects

## Extended Project Qualification (EPQ)

AQA, OCR, Pearson and WJEC offer the Extended Project Qualification, which is a qualification aimed at developing a student's research and independent learning skills. The EPQ can be taken as a stand-alone qualification, and it is equivalent to half an A level in UCAS points (but only a third of performance points). It is also possible to take the EPQ as part of the AQA Baccalaureate.

Students complete a research based written report and may produce an artefact or a practical science experiment as part of their project

# Entry level, basic and key skills

## Entry Level Qualifications

If you want to take GCSE or NVQ level 1 but have not yet reached the standard required, then entry level qualifications are for you as they are designed to get you started on the qualifications ladder.

Entry level qualifications are available in a wide range of areas. You can take an entry level certificate in most subjects where a similar GCSE exists. There are also vocational entry level qualifications – some in specific areas like retail or catering and others where you can take units in different work-related subjects to get a taster of a number of career areas. There are also entry level certificates in life skills and the basic skills of literacy and numeracy.

Anyone can take an entry level qualification – your school or college will help you decide which qualification is right for you.

Entry level qualifications are flexible programmes so the time it takes to complete will vary according to where you study and how long you need to take the qualification.

Subjects available: art and design, computer science, english, geography, history, latin, mathematics, physical education and science

## Functional Skills

Functional Skills are qualifications in English, maths and ICT that equip learners with the basic practical skills required in everyday life, education and the workplace. They are available at Entry 1 through to Level 2. Functional Skills are identified as funded 'stepping stone' qualifications to English and maths GCSE for post-16 learners who haven't previously achieved a grade D in these subjects. There are part of apprenticeship completion requirements.

# Vocational qualifications

## AQA Technical Awards

AQA's new suite of Technical Awards are practical, vocational level 1/2 qualifications for 14-16 year olds to take alongside GCSEs. First teaching will be in September 2017.

Technical Awards provide an introduction to life and work within a range of vocational areas, equipping learners with the practical, transferable skills and core knowledge needed to progress to further general or vocational study, including level 3 qualifications, employment or apprenticeships.

There are nine individual qualifications: Children's Learning and Development, Fashion and Textiles, Food and Catering, Health and Social Care, IT, Materials Technology, Performing Arts, Sport and Visual Communication. A STEM Technical Award was introduced in September 2017.

Learners are assessed on doing rather than knowing through the project-based internal assessments, where they can apply their knowledge to practical tasks. Assignments will vary according to the subject, but activities range from designing and making a working

product or prototype; making a short film; planning and putting on a performance, or presenting to others. There are two internally assessed units worth 30% each, and an externally assessed exam worth 40%.

## AQA Tech-levels

Level 3 technical qualifications have been designed in collaboration with employers and professional bodies. They're aimed at learners aged over 16 wanting to progress into a specific sector through apprenticeships, further study or employment. There are 16 individual qualifications within IT, Engineering, Business and Entertainment Technology. These vary in size of qualification.

Transferable skills have been contextualised explicitly within each qualification and are a mandatory part of the qualification outcome.

Learners are assessed through a combination of examinations, internally and externally assessed assignments.

# AQA Applied General Level 3

Applied General qualifications are available in Business and Science and are a practical introduction to these subjects, they are a real alternative to A-level support progression to further study or employment aimed at students aged 16 to 19.

Developed together with teachers, schools, colleges and higher education institutions, they help learners to develop knowledge and skills.

A mixture of assessment types means learners can apply their knowledge in a practical way. An integrated approach creates a realistic and relevant qualification for learners.

# BTECs

### BTEC Level 2 First qualifications

ie BTEC Level 2 Diplomas, BTEC Level 2 Extended Certificates, BTEC Level 2 Certificates and BTEC Level 2 Award.

BTEC Firsts are Level 2 introductory work-related programmes covering a wide range of vocational areas including business, engineering, information technology, health and social care, media, travel and tourism, and public services.

Programmes may be taken full or part-time. They are practical programmes that provide a foundation for the knowledge and skills you will need in work. Alternatively, you can progress onto a BTEC National qualification, Applied GCE A level or equivalent.

There are no formal entry requirements and they can be studied alongside GCSEs. Subjects available: agriculture; animal care; applied science; art and design; business; children's care, learning and development; construction; countryside and the environment; engineering; fish husbandry; floristry; health and social care; horse care; horticulture; hospitality; IT; land-based technology; business; creative media production; music; performing arts; public services; sport; travel and tourism; and vehicle technology.

### BTEC Foundation Diploma in Art and Design (QCF)

For those students preparing to go on to higher education within the field of art and design. This diploma is recognised as one of the best courses of its type in the UK, and is used in preparation for degree programmes. Units offered include researching, recording and responding in art and design, media experimentation, personal

experimental studies, and a final major project.

### BTEC Nationals

ie BTEC Level 3 Extended Diplomas (QCF), BTEC Level 3 Diplomas (QCF), BTEC Level 3 Subsidiary Diplomas (QCF), BTEC Level 3 Certificates (QCF)

BTEC National programmes are long-established vocational programmes. They are practical programmes that are highly valued by employers. They enable you to gain the knowledge and skills that you will need in work, or give you the choice to progress on to a BTEC Higher National, a Foundation Degree or a degree programme.

BTEC Nationals, which hold UCAS points cover a range of vocationally specialist sectors including child care, children's play, learning and development, construction, art and design, aeronautical engineering, electrical/electronic engineering, IT, business, creative and media production, performing arts, public services, sport, sport and exercise sciences and applied science. The programmes may be taken full- or part-time, and can be taken in conjunction with NVQs and/or functional skills units at an appropriate level.

There are no formal entry requirements, but if you have any of the following you are likely to be at the right level to study a BTEC national qualification.

- a BTEC Level 2 First qualification
- GCSEs – at grades A* to C in several subjects
- Relevant work experience

There are also very specialist BTEC Nationals, such as pharmaceutical science and blacksmithing and metalworking.

### BTEC Higher Nationals

Known as HNDs and HNCs – ie BTEC Level 5 HND Diplomas (QCF) and BTEC Level 4 HNC Diplomas (QCF)

BTEC HNDs and HNCs are further and higher education qualifications that offer a balance of education and vocational training. They are available in a wide range of work-related areas such as graphic design, business, health and social care, computing and systems development, manufacturing engineering, hospitality management, and public services.

Pearson is introducing a new suite of subjects between 2016 and 2018, to match growing demand. For full information on the subjects, visit: www.ocr.org.uk/qualifications/by-type/entry-level/entry-level-2016/

BTEC higher national courses combine study with hands-on work experience during your course. Once completed, you can use the skills you learn to begin your career, or continue on to a related degree course.

HNDs are often taken as a full-time course over two years but can also be followed part-time in some cases.

HNCs are often for people who are working and take two years to complete on a part-time study basis by day release, evenings, or a combination of the two. Some HNC courses are done on a full-time basis.

There are no formal entry requirements, but if you have any of the following you are likely to be at the right academic level:

- at least one A level
- a BTEC Level 3 National qualification
- level 3 NVQ

**BTEC specialist and professional qualifications**
These qualifications are designed to prepare students for specific and specialist work activities. These are split into two distinct groups:

- Specialist qualifications (entry to level 3)
- Professional qualifications (levels 4 to 7)

# Cambridge Nationals

Cambridge Nationals, the updated version of OCR Nationals, are vocationally-related qualifications that take an engaging, practical and inspiring approach to learning and assessment.

They are industry-relevant, geared to key sector requirements and very popular with schools and colleges because they suit such a broad range of learning styles and abilities.

Cambridge Nationals are available in business, child development, engineering, health and social care, ICT, science, sport, and creative iMedia. Available as joint Level 1 and 2 qualifications, the updated Nationals are aimed at students aged 14 to 16 in full-time study.

# Cambridge Technicals

OCR's Cambridge Technicals are practical and flexible vocationally-related qualifications, offering students in-depth study in a wide range of subjects, including business, health and social care, IT, sport, art and design, digital media, science, performing arts and engineering.

Cambridge Technicals are aimed at young people aged 16 to 19 who have completed Key Stage 4 of their education and want to study in a more practical, work-related way.

Cambridge Technicals are available at Level 2 and Level 3, and carry UCAS points at Level 3.

# NVQs

NVQs reward those who demonstrate skills gained at work. They relate to particular jobs and are usefully taken while you are working. Within reason, NVQs do not have to be completed in a specified amount of time. They can be taken by full-time employees or by school and college students with a work placement or part-time job that enables them to develop the appropriate skills. There are no age limits and no special entry requirements.

NVQs are organised into levels, based on the competencies required. Levels 1-3 are the levels most applicable to learners within the 14-19 phase. Achievement of level 4 within this age group will be rare. See the OCR website for further information.

# Occupational Studies (Northern Ireland)

Targeted at learners working towards and at level 1 and 2 in Key Stage 4 within the Northern Ireland curriculum. For further information see the CCEA website.

# OCR Vocational Qualifications

These are available at different levels and different sizes. Levels 1-3 are the levels most applicable to learners within the 14-19 phase. The different sizes are indicated with the use of Award, Certificate and Diploma in the qualification title and indicate the number of hours it typically takes to complete the qualification.

Vocational Qualifications are assessed according to each individual specification, but may include practical assessments and/or marked assessments. They are designed to provide evidence of a student's relevant skills and knowledge in their chosen subject. These qualifications can be used for employment or as a path towards further education.

See the OCR website for further details.

See the OCR website for further details.

# Awarding organisations and examination dates

# Awarding organisations and examination dates

In England there are four awarding organisations, each offering GCSE, including Applied GCSEs, A level and Applied A levels (Eduqas offers only reformed qualifications in England, whereas WJEC offers in England, Wales, Northern Ireland and independent regions). There are separate awarding organisations in Wales (WJEC) and Northern Ireland (CCEA). The awarding organisation in Scotland (SQA) offers equivalent qualifications.

This information was supplied by the awarding bodies and was accurate at the time of going to press. It is intended as a general guide only for candidates in the United Kingdom. Dates are subject to variation and should be confirmed with the awarding organisation concerned.

## AQA

**Qualifications offered:**
GCSE
AS and A level
Tech-levels
FCSE
FSMQ
Entry Level Certificate (ELC)
Foundation and Higher Projects
Extended Project Qualification (EPQ)
AQA Baccalaureate
AQA Level 3 Certificates and Extended Certificates
Functional Skills
Preparation for Working Life
Tech Awards

**Other assessment schemes:**
Unit Award Scheme (UAS)
L1/L2 Tech Awards

*Examination dates for summer 2018: 7 May – 22 June*

Contact:
Email: eos@aqa.org.uk
Website: www.aqa.org.uk
Tel: 0800 197 7162 (8am–5pm Monday to Friday)
+44 161 696 5995 (Outside the UK)

Devas Street, Manchester M15 6EX
Stag Hill House, Guildford, Surrey GU2 7XJ
31-33 Windsor House, Cornwall Road, Harrogate, HG1 2PW

## CCEA – Council for the Curriculum, Examinations and Assessment

**Qualifications offered:**
GCSE
GCE AS/A2 level
Key Skills (Levels 1-4)
Entry Level Qualifications
Essential Skills (Levels 1,2 & Entry Level)
Occupational Studies (Levels 1 & 2)
QCF Qualifications
Applied GCSE, GCE and QCF Level 1 and 2 qualifications

*Examination dates for summer 2018: 1 May – 25 June*

Contact:
Email: info@ccea.org.uk
Website: www.ccea.org.uk

29 Clarendon Road, Clarendon Dock, Belfast, BT1 3BG
Tel: (028) 9026 1200

# IB – International Baccalaureate

**Qualification offered:**
IB Diploma
IB Career-related Certificate

Contact:
www.ibo.org

*Examination dates for summer 2018: 26 April – 18 May*

IB Global Centre, The Hague, Churchillplein 6, 2517 JW, The Hague, The Netherlands

Tel: +31 70 352 60 00

# OCR – Oxford Cambridge and RSA Examinations

**Qualifications offered by OCR or sister awarding organisation Cambridge International Examinations, include:**
GCSE
GCE AS/A level
IGCSE
Extended Project
Cambridge Pre-U
Cambridge Nationals
Cambridge Technicals
Functional Skills
FSMQ – Free Standing Maths Qualification
NVQ

*Examination dates for summer 2018: 14 May to 22 June*

Contact:
Website: www.ocr.org.uk (or www.cie.org.uk)

OCR Head Office, 1 Hills Road, Cambridge CB1 2EU
Tel: 01223 553998

# Pearson

**Qualifications offered:**
Pearson's qualifications are offered in the UK but are also available through their international centres across the world. They include:
DiDA, CiDA, AiDA
GCE A levels
GCSEs
Adult Literacy and Numeracy
Functional Skills
Foundation Learning
International GCSEs
Key Skills
ESOL (Skills for Life)
BTEC Customised Qualifications
BTEC Foundation Diploma in Art & Design
BTEC Nationals
BTEC Higher National Certificates and Higher National Diplomas (HNC/HND)
BTEC Firsts
BTEC Specialist qualifications
BTEC Professional qualifications
BTEC WorkSkills
NVQs
Project qualifications

*Examination dates for summer 2018: 14 May – 29 June*

Contact:
190 High Holborn, London WC1V 7BH

See website for specific contact details: www.edexcel.com

# Educational organisations

# Educational organisations

## Artsmark

Arts Council England's Artsmark was set up in 2001, schools are awarded Silver, Gold or Platinum, based on their achievements.

All schools in England can apply for an Artsmark – primary, secondary, special and pupil referral units, maintained and independent.

Artsmark provides a clear framework for teachers to plan, develop and evaluate arts, culture and creativity across the curriculum.

Artsmark, Arts Council England, Brooklands,
24 Brooklands Avenue, Cambridge CB2 8BU
Tel: 0845 300 6200 / 0161 934 4317
Email: artsmark@artscouncil.org.uk
Website: www.artsmark.org.uk

## Association for the Education and Guardianship of International Students (AEGIS)

AEGIS brings together schools and guardianship organisations to promote the welfare of international students. AEGIS provides accreditation for all reputable guardianship organisations.

AEGIS, The Wheelhouse,
Bond's Mill Estate, Bristol Road, Stonehouse,
Gloucestershire GL10 3RF
Tel/Fax: 01453 821293
Email: info@aegisuk.net
Website: www.aegisuk.net

## The Association of American Study Abroad Programmes (AASAP)

Established in 1991 to represent American study programmes in the UK.

Contact: Kalyn Franke, c/o University of Maryland in London, Connaught Hall, 36-45 Tavistock Square, London WC1H 9EX
Email: info@aasapuk.org
Website: www.aasapuk.org

## The Association of British Riding Schools (ABRS)

An independent body of proprietors and principals of riding establishments, aiming to look after their interests and those of the riding public and to raise standards of management, instruction and animal welfare.

Unit 8, Bramble Hill Farm, Five Oakes Road, Slinfold, Horsham, West Sussex RH13 0RL
Tel: 01403 790294
Email: office@abrs-info.org
Website: www.abrs-info.org

## Association of Colleges (AOC)

Created in 1996 to promote the interests of further education colleges in England, Wales, Scotland and Northern Ireland.

2-5 Stedham Place, London WC1A 1HU
Tel: 020 7034 9900
Email: enquiries@aoc.co.uk
Website: www.aoc.co.uk

# Association of Governing Bodies of Independent Schools (AGBIS)

AGBIS supports and advises governing bodies of schools in the independent sector on all aspects of governance. (Registered charity No. 1108756)
Enquiries should be addressed to: AGBIS General Secretary, Richard Harman, AGBIS, 3 Codicote Road, Welwyn, Hertfordshire AL6 9LY
Tel: 01438 840730
Fax: 0560 3432632
Email: gensec@agbis.org.uk
Website: www.agbis.org.uk

# Association of Employment and Learning Providers (AELP)

AELP's purpose is to influence the education and training agenda. They are the voice of independent learning providers throughout England.
2nd Floor, 9 Apex Court, Bradley Stoke, Bristol BS32 4JT
Tel: 0117 986 5389
Email: enquiries@aelp.org.uk
Website: www.aelp.org.uk

# The Association of School and Colleges Leaders (ASCL)

Formerly the Secondary Heads Association, the ASCL is a professional association for secondary school and college leaders.
130 Regent Road, Leicester LE1 7PG
Tel: 0116 299 1122
Fax: 0116 299 1123
Email: info@ascl.org.uk
Website: www.ascl.org.uk

# Boarding Schools' Association (BSA)

For information on the BSA see editorial on page 35

# The British Accreditation Council for Independent Further and Higher Education (BAC)

The British Accreditation Council (BAC) has now been the principal accrediting body for the independent further and higher education and training sector for nearly 30 years. There are now hundreds of BAC-accredited colleges in the UK, providing a wealth of academic programmes, including vocational and professional qualifications, foundation courses for university entry, and externally validated degree courses. Some students may also look to study outside UK at one of the institutions holding BAC international accreditation.
Ground Floor, 14 Devonshire Square, London EC2M 4YT
Tel: 0300 330 1400
Email: info@the-bac.org
Website: www.the-bac.org

# The British Association for Early Childhood Education (BAECE)

Promotes quality provision for all children from birth to eight in whatever setting they are placed. Publishes booklets and organises conferences for those interested in early years education and care.
(Registered charity No. 313082; SC039472)
136 Cavell Street, London E1 2JA
Tel: 01923 438 995
Email: office@early-education.org.uk
Website: www.early-education.org.uk

# The Choir Schools' Association (CSA)

Represents 46 schools attached to cathedrals, churches and college chapels, which educate cathedral and collegiate choristers.
CSA Information Officer, Village Farm, The Street, Market Weston, Diss, Norfolk IP22 2NZ
Tel: 01359 221333
Email: info@choirschools.org.uk
Website: www.choirschools.org.uk

# The Council for Independent Education (CIFE)

CIFE is the professional association for independent sixth form and tutorial colleges accredited by the British Accreditation Council for Independent Further and Higher Education (BAC), the Independent Schools Council or the DfE (Ofsted). Member colleges specialise in preparing students for GCSE and A level (AS and A2) in particular and university entrance in general.
The aim of the association is to provide a forum for the exchange of information and ideas, and for the promotion of best practice, and to safeguard adherence to strict standards of professional conduct and ethical propriety. Further information can be obtained from CIFE:
Tel: 020 8767 8666
Email: enquiries@cife.org.uk
Website: www.cife.org.uk

# Council of British International Schools (COBIS)

COBIS is a membership association of British schools of quality worldwide and is committed to a stringent process of quality assurance for all its member schools. COBIS is a member of the Independent Schools Council (ISC) of the United Kingdom.
55-56 Russell Square, Bloomsbury, London WC1B 4HP
Tel: 020 3826 7190
Email: pa@cobis.org.uk
Website: www.cobis.org.uk

# Council of International Schools (CIS)

CIS is a not-for-profit organisation committed to supporting its member schools and colleges in achieving and delivering the highest standards of international education. CIS provides accreditation to schools, teacher and leader recruitment and best practice development. CIS Higher Education assists member colleges and universities in recruiting a diverse profile of qualified international students.
Schipholweg 113, 2316 XC Leiden, The Netherlands.
Tel: +31 71 524 3300
Email: info@cois.org
Website: www.cois.org

# Dyslexia Action (DA)

A registered, educational charity (No. 268502), which has established teaching and assessment centres and conducts teacher-training throughout the UK. The aim of the institute is to help people with dyslexia of all ages to overcome their difficulties in learning to read, write and spell and to achieve their potential.
Centurion House, London Road,
Staines-upon-Thames TW18 4AX
Tel: 01784 222 304
Website: www.dyslexiaaction.org.uk

# European Association for International Education (EAIE)

A not-for-profit organisation aiming for internationalisation in higher education in Europe. Members share a common goal: to internationalise their institutions through collaboration, knowledge exchange and continuous professional development.
PO Box 11189, 1001 GD Amsterdam, The Netherlands
Tel: +31 20 344 5100
Fax: +31 20 344 5119
Email: info@eaie.org
Website: www.eaie.org

# European Council of International Schools (ECIS)

ECIS is a membership organisation which provides services to support professional development, good governance and leadership in international schools.
146 Buckingham Palace Road,
London SW1W 9TR
Tel: 020 7824 7040
Email: ecis@ecis.org
Website: www.ecis.org

# The Girls' Day School Trust (GDST)

The Girls' Day School Trust (GDST) is one of the largest, longest-established and most successful groups of independent schools in the UK, with 3,500 staff and 19,000 students between the ages of three and 18. As a charity that owns and runs a family of 23 schools and two academies in England and Wales, it reinvests all its income into its schools for the benefit of the pupils. With a long history of pioneering innovation in the education of girls, the GDST now also educates boys in some of its schools, and has two coeducational sixth form colleges.
(Registered charity No. 306983)
100 Rochester Row, London SWIP 1JP
Tel: 020 7393 6666
Fax: 020 7393 6789
Website: www.gdst.net

# Girls' Schools Association (GSA)

For information on the GSA see editorial on page 36

# The Headmasters' and Headmistresses' Conference (HMC)

For information on the HMC see editorial on page 36

# Human Scale Education (HSE)

An educational reform movement aiming for small education communities based on democracy, fairness and respect.
(Registered charity No. 1000400)
Email: contact@hse.org.uk
Website: www.hse.org.uk

# The Independent Association of Prep Schools (IAPS)

For further information about IAPS see editorial on page 38

# The Independent Schools Association (ISA)

For further information about ISA see editorial on page 38

# The Independent Schools' Bursars Association (ISBA)

Exists to support and advance financial and operational performance in independent schools. The ISBA is a charitable company limited by guarantee.
(Company No. 6410037; registered charity No. 1121757)
Bluett House, Unit 11-12 Manor Farm, Cliddesden, Basingstoke, Hampshire RG25 2JB
Tel: 01256 330369
Email: office@theisba.org.uk

Website: www.theisba.org.uk

# The Independent Schools Council (ISC)

The Independent Schools Council exists to promote choice, diversity and excellence in education; the development of talent at all levels of ability; and the widening of opportunity for children from all backgrounds to achieve their potential. Over 1,300 member schools educate more than 500,000 children at all levels of ability and from all socio-economic classes. Nearly a third of children in ISC schools receive help with fees. Their work is directed by a Board where individuals are nominated for appointment by each of the seven member associations.
See also page 40.

**Members:**
Association of Governing Bodies of Independent Schools (AGBIS)
Girls' Schools Association (GSA)
Headmasters' and Headmistresses' Conference (HMC)
Independent Association of Prep Schools (IAPS)
Independent Schools Association (ISA)
Independent Schools Bursars' Association (ISBA)
The Society of Heads
The council also has close relations with the BSA, COBIS and the SCIS.
First Floor, 27 Queen Anne's Gate,
London SW1H 9BU
Tel: 020 7766 7070
Fax: 020 7766 7071
Email: research@isc.co.uk

Website: www.isc.co.uk

# The Independent Schools Examinations Board (ISEB)

Details of the Common Entrance examinations are obtainable from:
Independent Schools Examinations Board,
Endeavour House, Crow Arch Lane, Ringwood BH24 1HP
Tel: 01425 470555
Email: enquiries@iseb.co.uk
Website: www.iseb.co.uk
Practice papers can be purchased from Galore Park Publishing Ltd: www.galorepark.co.uk

# The Inspiring Futures Foundation (IFF)

The IFF provides careers education and guidance to schools and students. Professional support and training is available to school staff and our Futurewise programme provides individual, web-based, support for students and their parents. Career/subject insight courses, gap-year fairs and an information service are additional elements of the service.
The Fountain Building, Howbery Park, Benson Lane, Wallingford, Oxon OX10 8BA
Tel: 01491 820381
Email: helpline@inspiringfutures.org.uk
Website: www.inspiringfutures.org.uk

# International Baccalaureate (IB)

For full information about the IB see full entry on page 186

# International Schools Theatre Association (ISTA)

International body of teachers and students of theatre, run by teachers for teachers.
(Registered charity No. 1050103)
3 Omega Offices, 14 Coinagehall St,
Helston, Cornwall TR13 8EB
Email: office@ista.co.uk

Website: www.ista.co.uk

# Maria Montessori Institute (MMI)

Authorised by the Association Montessori Internationale (AMI) to run their training course in the UK. Further information is available from:
26 Lyndhurst Gardens, Hampstead, London NW3 5NW
Tel: 020 7435 3646
Email: info@mariamontessori.org
Website: www.mariamontessori.org

# The National Association of Independent Schools & Non-Maintained Schools (NASS)

A membership organisation working with and for special schools in the voluntary and private sectors within the UK. (Registered charity No. 1083632)
PO Box 705, York YO30 6WW
Tel/Fax: 01904 624446
Email: krippon@nasschools.org.uk
Website: www.nasschools.org.uk

# National Day Nurseries Association (NDNA)

A national charity (No. 1078275) that aims to promote quality in early years.
NDNA, National Early Years Enterprise Centre, Longbow Close, Huddersfield, West Yorkshire HD2 1GQ
Tel: 01484 407070
Fax: 01484 407060
Website: www.ndna.org.uk

NDNA Cymru, Office 2, Crown House, 11 Well Street, Ruthin, Denbighshire LL15 1AE
Tel: 01824 707823
Fax: 01824 707824

NDNA Scotland, The Mansfield Traquair Centre, 15 Mansfield Place, Edinburgh EH3 6BB
Tel: 0131 516 6967

# National Foundation for Educational Research (NFER)

NFER is the UK's largest independent provider of research, assessment and information services for education, training and children's services. Its clients include UK government departments and agencies at both national and local levels. NFER is a not-for-profit organisation and a registered charity No. 313392.
Head Office, The Mere, Upton Park,
Slough, Berkshire SL1 2DQ
Tel: 01753 574123
Fax: 01753 691632
Email: enquiries@nfer.ac.uk
Website: www.nfer.ac.uk

# Potential Plus UK

Potential Plus UK is an independent charity that supports the social, emotional and learning needs of children with high learning potential of all ages and backgrounds. (Registered charity No. 313182)
Challenge House, Sherwood Drive, Bletchley,
Milton Keynes, Buckinghamshire MK3 6DP
Tel: 01908 646433
Email: amazingchildren@potentialplusuk.org
Website: www.potentialplusuk.org

# The Round Square Schools (RSIS)

An international group of schools formed in 1966 following the principles of Dr Kurt Hahn, the founder of Salem School in Germany, and Gordonstoun in Scotland. The Round Square, named after Gordonstoun's 17th century circular building in the centre of the school, now has more than 180 Member Schools and Candidates. (Registered charity No. 327117)
Swan House, Madeira Walk, Windsor SL4 1EU
Website: www.roundsquare.org

# Royal National Children's Foundation (RNCF)

The RNCF is a charity that helps children facing abuse, neglect or trauma, by enabling them to attend state and independent boarding schools.
Royal National Children's SpringBoard Foundation,
7 Grosvenor Gardens, London SW1W 0BD
Tel: 020 3405 3630
Email: admin@royalspringboard.org.uk
Website: www.rncf.org.uk

# School Fees Independent Advice (SFIA)

There are any number of advisers in the country, but few who specialise in the area of planning to meet school and university fees. SFIA is the largest organisation specialising in school fees planning in the UK.
29 High Street, Marlow, Buckinghamshire SL7 1AU
Tel: 01628 566777
Email: enquiries@sfia.co.uk
Website: www.sfia.co.uk

## Schools Music Association of Great Britain (SMA)

The SMA is a national 'voice' for music in education. It is now part of the Incorporated Society of Musicians (ISM).
(Registered charity No. 313646)
4-5 Inverness Mews, London W2 3JQ
Tel: 020 7221 3499
Email: membership@ism.org
Website: www.sim.org

## Society of Education Consultants (SEC)

The Society is a professional membership organisation that supports management consultants who specialise in education and children's services. The society's membership includes consultants who work as individuals, in partnerships or in association with larger consultancies.
Bellamy House, 13 West Street, Cromer NR27 9HZ
Tel: 0330 323 0457
Email: administration@sec.org.uk
Website: www.sec.org.uk

## The Society of Heads

For full information see editorial on page 39

## State Boarding Forum

For full information see editorial on page 35

## Steiner Waldorf Schools Fellowship (SWSF)

Representing Steiner education in the UK and Ireland, the SWSF has member schools and early years centres in addition to interest groups and other affiliated organisations. Member schools offer education for children within the normal range of ability, aged three to 18.
(Registered charity No. 295104)
Suite 1, 3rd Floor, Copthall House, 1 New Road, Stourbridge, West Midlands DY8 1PH
Tel: 01384 374116
Email: admin@steinerwaldorf.org
Website: www.steinerwaldorf.org

## Support and Training in Prep Schools (SATIPS)

SATIPS provides support and training for teachers in the independent and maintained sectors of education.
(Registered charity No. 313688)
West Routengill, Walden, West Burton,
Leyburn, North Yorkshire DL8 4LF
Website: www.satips.org

## The Tutors' Association

The Tutors' Association is the professional body for tutoring and wider supplementary education sector in the UK. Launched three years ago it now has over 500 members. Of these 150 are Corporate Members representing some 20,000 tutors throughout the UK.
Tel: 01628 890130
Fax: 01628 890131
Email: info@thetutorsassociation.org.uk
Website: www.tutor.co.uk

# UCAS (Universities and Colleges Admissions Service)

UCAS is the organisation responsible for managing applications to higher education courses in England, Scotland, Wales and Northern Ireland.
(Registered charity Nos. 1024741 and SCO38598)
Rose Hill, New Barn Lane,
Cheltenham, Gloucestershire GL52 3LZ
Customer Service: 0371 468 0 468
Website: www.ucas.com

# UKCISA – The Council for International Student Affairs

UKCISA is the UK's national advisory body serving the interests of international students and those who work with them.
(Registered charity No. 1095294)
9-17 St Albans Place, London N1 0NX
Tel:  020 7788 9214
Website: www.ukcisa.org.uk

# United World Colleges (UWC)

UWC was founded in 1962 and their philosophy is based on the ideas of Dr Kurt Hahn (see Round Square Schools).
(Registered charity No. 313690)
UWC International, Second Floor, 17-21 Emerald Street,
London WC1N 3QN
Tel: 020 7269 7800
Fax: 020 7405 4374
Email: info@uwcio.uwc.org
Website: www.uwc.org

# World-Wide Education Service of CfBT Education Trust (WES)

A leading independent service which provides home education courses worldwide.
Waverley House, Penton,
Carlisle, Cumbria CA6 5QU
Tel: 01228 577123
Email: office@weshome.com
Website: www.weshome.com

# Glossary

# Glossary

ACETS — Awards and Certificates in Education
AEA — Advanced Extension Award
AEB — Associated Examining Board for the General Certificate of Education
AEGIS — Association for the Education and Guardianship of International Students
AGBIS — Association of Governing Bodies of Independent Schools
AHIS — Association of Heads of Independent Schools
AJIS — Association of Junior Independent Schools
ALP — Association of Learning Providers
ANTC — The Association of Nursery Training Colleges
AOC — Association of Colleges
AP — Advanced Placement
ASCL — Association of School & College Leaders
ASL — Additional and Specialist Learning
ATI — The Association of Tutors Incorporated
AQA — Assessment and Qualification Alliance/ Northern Examinations and Assessment Board
BA — Bachelor of Arts
BAC — British Accreditation Council for Independent Further and Higher Education
BAECE — The British Association for Early Childhood Education
BD — Bachelor of Divinity
BEA — Boarding Educational Alliance
BEd — Bachelor of Education
BLitt — Bachelor of Letters
BPrimEd — Bachelor of Primary Education
BSA — Boarding Schools' Association
BSc — Bachelor of Science
BTEC — Range of work-related, practical programmes leading to qualifications equivalent to GCSEs and A levels awarded by Edexcel
Cantab — Cambridge University
CATSC — Catholic Association of Teachers in Schools and Colleges
CCEA — Council for the Curriculum, Examination and Assessment
CDT — Craft, Design and Technology
CE — Common Entrance Examination
CEAS — Children's Education Advisory Service
CertEd — Certificate of Education
CIE — Cambridge International Examinations
CIFE — Conference for Independent Education
CIS — Council of International Schools
CISC — Catholic Independent Schools' Conference
CLAIT — Computer Literacy and Information Technology
CNED — Centre National d'enseignement (National Centre of long distance learning)

COBIS — Council of British International )
CSA — The Choir Schools' Association
CST — The Christian Schools' Trust
DfE — Department for Education (formerly DfES and DCFS)
DipEd — Diploma of Education
DipTchng — Diploma of Teaching
EAIE — European Association for International Education
ECIS — European Council of International Schools
EdD — Doctor of Education
Edexcel — GCSE Examining group, incorporating Business and Technology Education Council (BTEC) and University of London Examinations and Assessment Council (ULEAC)
EFL — English as a Foreign Language
ELAS — Educational Law Association
EPQ — Extended Project qualification
ESL — English as a Second Language
FCoT — Fellow of the College of Teachers (TESOL)
FEFC — Further Education Funding Council
FRSA — Fellow of the Royal Society of Arts
FSMQ — Free-Standing Mathematics Qualification
GCE — General Certificate of Education
GCSE — General Certificate of Secondary Education
GDST — Girls' Day School Trust
GNVQ — General National Vocational Qualifications
GOML — Graded Objectives in Modern Languages
GSA — Girls' Schools Association
GSVQ — General Scottish Vocational Qualifications
HMC — Headmasters' and Headmistresses' Conference
HMCJ — Headmasters' and Headmistresses' Conference Junior Schools
HNC — Higher National Certificate
HND — Higher National Diploma
IAPS — Independent Association of Prep Schools
IB — International Baccalaureate
ICT — Information and Communication Technology
IFF — Inspiring Futures Foundation (formerly ISCO)
IGCSE — International General Certificate of Secondary Education
INSET — In service training
ISA — Independent Schools Association
ISBA — Independent Schools' Bursars' Association
ISCis — Independent Schools Council information service
ISC — Independent Schools Council
ISEB — Independent Schools Examination Board
ISST — International Schools Sports Tournament
ISTA — International Schools Theatre Association

| | |
|---|---|
| ITEC | International Examination Council |
| JET | Joint Educational Trust |
| LA | Local Authority |
| LISA | London International Schools Association |
| MA | Master of Arts |
| MCIL | Member of the Chartered Institute of Linguists |
| MEd | Master of Education |
| MIoD | Member of the Institute of Directors |
| MLitt | Master of Letters |
| MSc | Master of Science |
| MusD | Doctor of Music |
| MYP | Middle Years Programme |
| NABSS | National Association of British Schools in Spain |
| NAGC | National Association for Gifted Children |
| NAHT | National Association of Head Teachers |
| NAIS | National Association of Independent Schools |
| NASS | National Association of Independent Schools & Non-maintained Special Schools |
| NDNA | National Day Nurseries Association |
| NEASC | New England Association of Schools and Colleges |
| NFER | National Federation of Educational Research |
| NPA | National Progression Award |
| NQ | National Qualification |
| NQF | National Qualifications Framework |
| NQT | Newly Qualified Teacher |
| NVQ | National Vocational Qualifications |
| OCR | Oxford, Cambridge and RSA Examinations |
| OLA | Online Language Assessment for Modern Languages |
| Oxon | Oxford |
| PGCE | Post Graduate Certificate in Education |
| PhD | Doctor of Philosophy |
| PL | Principal Learning |
| PNEU | Parents' National Education Union |
| PYP | Primary Years Programme |
| QCA | Qualifications and Curriculum Authority |
| QCF | Qualifications and Credit Framework |
| RSIS | The Round Square Schools |
| SAT | Scholastic Aptitude Test |
| SATIPS | Support & Training in Prep Schools/Society of Assistant Teachers in Prep Schools |
| SBSA | State Boarding Schools Association |
| SCE | Service Children's Education |
| SCIS | Scottish Council of Independent Schools |
| SCQF | Scottish Credit and Qualifications Framework |
| SEC | The Society of Educational Consultants |
| SEN | Special Educational Needs |
| SFCF | Sixth Form Colleges' Forum |
| SFIA | School Fees Insurance Agency Limited |
| SFIAET | SFIA Educational Trust |

| | |
|---|---|
| SMA | Schools Music Association |
| SoH | The Society of Heads |
| SQA | Scottish Qualifications Authority |
| STEP | Second Term Entrance Paper (Cambridge) |
| SVQ | Scottish Vocational Qualifications |
| SWSF | Steiner Waldorf Schools Fellowship |
| TABS | The Association of Boarding Schools |
| TISCA | The Independent Schools Christian Alliance |
| TOEFL | Test of English as a Foreign Language |
| UCAS | Universities and Colleges Admissions Service for the UK |
| UCST | United Church Schools Trust |
| UKLA | UK Literacy Association |
| UKCISA | The UK Council for International Education |
| UWC | United World Colleges |
| WISC | World International Studies Committee |
| WJEC | Welsh Joint Education Committee |
| WSSA | Welsh Secondary Schools Association |

# Index

# Index

# G

# H

# M

# N

# Index

## U

## V

## W

# Y